ERNATIONAL SERIES OF MONOGRAPHS ON
PURE AND APPLIED BIOLOGY

———————

Division: **ZOOLOGY**

GENERAL EDITOR: **G. A.** KERKUT

VOLUME 19

OSMOTIC AND IONIC REGULATION IN ANIMALS

OTHER TITLES IN THE ZOOLOGY DIVISION

OTHER DIVISIONS IN THE SERIES
ON PURE AND APPLIED BIOLOGY

BIOCHEMISTRY

BOTANY

MODERN TRENDS
IN PHYSIOLOGICAL SCIENCES

PLANT PHYSIOLOGY

OSMOTIC AND IONIC REGULATION IN ANIMALS

by

W. T. W. POTTS

and

GWYNETH PARRY

A Pergamon Press Book

THE MACMILLAN COMPANY

NEW YORK

1964

THE MACMILLAN COMPANY
60 Fifth Avenue
New York 11, N.Y.

This book is distributed by
THE MACMILLAN COMPANY
pursuant to a special arrangement with
PERGAMON PRESS LIMITED
Oxford, England

Library of Congress Catalog Card Number 62-11560

Made in Great Britain

CONTENTS

v

PREFACE

The importance of homoeostatic mechanisms in a living animal cannot be over-estimated. In the field of water and electrolyte metabolism there has been a development of ideas from some sort of chemical and physical equilibrium between the animal and its environment, through a "steady state" concept in which the equilibrium resulted from the interaction of uptake and loss, ingestion and excretion, to the current picture of homoeostasis controlled by feedback mechanisms. It is now recognised that the composition and volume of the body fluids, the production of secretions, and the maintenance of cellular contents are all subject to homoeostatic control, with or without the implication of central nervous control.

The published work in the field tends to follow the same lines of development, firstly with analyses and comparison of the body fluids and tissue contents, later with evaluation of the part played by excretory organs, by swallowing, by secretion and evaporation, and finally with the investigation of the dynamics of control and of the controlling hormones or other mechanisms involved. In 1938, when Krogh published his classic work *Osmoregulation in Aquatic Animals* much of the data concerned analyses of body fluids and the external media, some information was available about excretory organs, and the first experiments dealing with rates of electrolyte exchange were included.

In the succeeding 25 years, there has been a technological revolution in this field as in others. Many new types of apparatus have become available for routine analysis on a relatively micro-scale. Such apparatus allows the accumulation of a sufficient number of data to provide estimates of mean electrolyte levels. One of the greatest advances in this field is, of course, the development of radio-isotope techniques, both in using isotopes as tracers, and in isotope dilution techniques. For the most part, Krogh was able to report on electrolyte exchanges only in stressed un-equilibrated animals, "washed-out" in distilled water, or "salt-loaded" after sojourn in high salinities. The use of isotopes has allowed the study of electrolyte fluxes through animals in equilibrium with their environments, as well as in stressed conditons, and this has lead on to the study of homoeostatic control. Naturally, many difficulties are unsolved: problems inherent in the use of isotopes such as that of "exchange diffusion" or the validity of heavy water experiments, are still matters of controversy.

The literature in the field of osmotic and ionic regulation in animals is immense. We have not intended our book as a comprehensive cover, but have preferred to present a theme of development illustrated by chosen examples from many diverse animal types. Our aim has been to clarify for the student the biophysical basis of regulation and for this reason we have included in Chapter I an elementary account of the principles involved. In the later chapters the specific responses of animals to different environments are discussed in these terms.

Since Krogh's book still stands as an invaluable source of information on the literature up to 1937, we have referred to earlier papers only when specific and detailed information was required. The recent increase in the number of papers published has made it impossible to include more than a selection of them, or even to review them right up to the date of publication. Our original manuscript was completed in mid-1961 and some additional work up to the spring of 1962 has been included. Further significant work continues to appear, but short of delaying publication, it is impossible to include it. We hope that our general approach to the subject and our selection of material will prove of sufficient merit to maintain interest, in spite of this disadvantage.

It remains for us to thank many colleagues who have assisted us by discussion or in more material ways. In particular we wish to thank J. D. Robertson for reading and commenting on the manuscript in the early stages, C. B. Cowey, R. Harden-Jones, R. Holmes, C. R. House, R. Pontin, J. Shaw, D. R. Swift and P. M. Woodhead for allowing the use of some unpublished material; S. Simmonds for Figs. II.6, II.7, and II.11, R. Pontin for Fig. II.10, A. H. Coombes, Birmingham City Analyst, for data in

Table V. 1. Many of the illustrations have been selected or adapted from the published literature (listed below) and we wish to thank the authors and publishers for permission to use these. Finally our thanks are due to the Department of Zoology and Comparative Anatomy, University of Birmingham, and to the Freshwater Fisheries Laboratory, Ministry of Agriculture, Fisheries and Food, for the facilities and opportunities offered to us during the preparation of the manuscript.

G. P.
W.T.W.P.

ACKNOWLEDGEMENTS

A number of illustrations in the text are taken from the literature. A list of the sources of these figures is printed below.

Acta physiol. scand.: Figs. VI. 3, VI. 5, VII. 6—8.

Amer. J. Physiol.: Figs. II. 2, VI. 2, VI. 4, VII. 4.

Aust. J. exp. Biol. Med. Sci. Fig. III. 2.

Biol. Bull. Woods Hole: Figs. IV. 17.

Helv. physiol. acta: Fig. II. 4, II: 5.

J. cell. comp. Physiol.: Figs. V. 11—12, VII. 9.

J. clin. Invest.: Fig, VI. 6.

J. exp. Biol.: Fig. II. 9, II. 12—13, IV. 5—9, IV. 26, V. 1—2, V. 4—8, VII. 13—15, VIII. 3.

J. gen. Physiol.: Figs. V. 9—10.

J. Mar. Biol. Ass. U. K.: Figs. IV. 19—20, IV. 24—25.

Nature, London Fig. VII. 12.

Pflüg. Arch. ges. Physiol. Fig. III. 1, IV. 12.

Physiol. comp.: Fig. IV. 21—22.

Physiol. Rev.: Figs. II. 3.

Science: Fig. III. 2.

Sci. Amer.: Figs. VII. 10—11.

Z. vergl. Physiol.: Figs. IV. 11, IV. 14—16, VII. 5, VIII. 1.

Die Binnengewässer, authors A. Remane and C. Schlieper, publ. Schweitzerbartsche, Stuttgart. Figs. IV. 13, VIII. 4.

Comparative Physiology authors C. L. Prosser *et al.,* publ. W. B. Saunders Co. Philadelphia and London. Fig. IV. 18.

Water Relations in Terrestrial Arthropods, author E. B. Edney, publ. Cambridge University Press, Cambridge and London. Fig. VI. 1.

CHAPTER I

SOME GENERAL ASPECTS OF OSMOREGULATION IN ANIMALS

Introduction

Life began in water, and most probably in sea water. The biochemical processes sustaining life, and fertilization which per-
petuates it, can take place only in water, and often in water of a
specific salt content. The simplest animals living today are small
organisms whose cells are bathed in sea water. From the surrounding sea water they take their food and oxygen, and to it
they return their waste products. In more complex animals the
tissues are no longer in direct contact with the ambient medium,
but are bathed in blood or some other extracellular fluid. These
fluids form a private pond supplying oxygen and food to
the cells and receiving their waste products. The volume of
extracellular fluid is usually much smaller than that of the cells
it surrounds, and in these crowded conditions many complex
systems have developed to regulate the composition of the
fluids. Of these regulatory processes, respiration supplies oxygen and removes carbon dioxide, digestion maintains the level
of nutrients, and osmoregulation controls the volume and
composition of the body fluids. Not only the excretory organs
osmoregulate, but also the body surface and the gut lining,
both of which may transport salt and water between the
environment and the interior of the body. Excretory systems

1

can play only a negative part in maintaining body fluid concentrations, conserving or excreting substances already present in the blood, but they are unable to add to the blood substances which are not already present. The activity of the gut and body surface, on the other hand, can play a much more positive role.

The extracellular fluids of most marine animals are in osmotic equilibrium and almost in ionic equilibrium with the surrounding sea water. The development of an internal medium, with its associated control systems, has facilitated the differentiation of freshwater and terrestrial animals which maintain internal media similar in many respects to sea water, despite very different external environments. In freshwater animals, the volume and salt content of the internal medium must be maintained in the face of the degrading effects of osmosis and diffusion, while terrestrial animals must contend with a continual desiccation. The means whereby the water and salt content of the body fluids are regulated in marine, freshwater and terrestrial animals form one of the theses of this book.

In addition to the regulation of the salt and water content of the body fluids, the salt content and sometimes the volume of each cell is actively controlled. Even in simple animals, such as the marine Protozoa, the cytoplasm is richer in potassium than the surrounding sea water. In the same way, the tissues of the Metazoa are richer in potassium and poorer in sodium than their extracellular fluids. The cell surface is thus the site of great ionic activity, excluding sodium from the cell, and usually concentrating potassium. Freshwater protozoans and coelenterates must also regulate osmotically, as well as ionically, at the cell surface, and it is possible that some metazoan cells may also regulate osmotically with respect to the body fluids (Chap. VI, pp.266, 269).

Body Fluids

The following terms are used to distinguish the body fluids.

Whole blood is the liquid collected from the circulatory vessels and includes both the suspended blood cells and the fluid surrounding them.

Plasma is the liquid which remains when blood cells and other solid particles have been removed by centrifugation or filtration.

Serum is the liquid which remains after allowing either whole blood, or plasma, to clot. It is similar to plasma in electrolyte composition, but the clotting process also removes fibrinogen, as well as the cellular elements.

Lymph is present in the vertebrates in body spaces outside the arterial capillary venous network. Like serum, it contains no red cells (erythrocytes) and less protein than the plasma, but it is more than an ultrafiltrate of the blood, although it originates in this way. It may contain a high concentration of white cells (leucocytes) and fat droplets. The protein components of the lymph are different from those of the serum.

The serum and the liquid phase of the lymph are similar to but not identical with the blood plasma in electrolyte composition. The difference in protein content may cause Donnan effects (see below, p.27), and the removal of some of the protein may remove some of the bound ions (see below, p.41). Whole blood usually differs considerably in electrolyte composition from the plasma. In particular, the potassium content of whole blood is much greater than that of the plasma because of the presence of the cells and smaller differences occur in the concentration of other ions.

Extracellular and Intracellular Fluids

In the higher Metazoa, the extracellular fluids are separated into two compartments, a primary body cavity or haemocoele, and a secondary body cavity or coelom. The fluid contents of the primary body cavity are the blood and lymph. The blood is usually circulated by the heart through a discrete system of channels, but in some animal phyla, particularly the arthropods and molluscs, the haemocoele forms large visceral sinuses. In the vertebrates, the haemocoele is further subdivided into the blood contained in a closed system of arteries, capillaries and veins, and the lymph, which is in more intimate contact with the cells. The blood occupies 2–10% of the body volume, while the lymph occupies a further 10–15% (Table I.i. Fig. I.i). Additional specialised body fluids are found in the central nervous system, the eye and the ear (Chap. VI, p.241).

The development of the coelom varies reciprocally with the extent of the haemocoele. The coelom usually receives the genital products and forms the gonoducts, and often it also receives the excretory fluids and opens to the exterior by excretory ducts. In echinoderms, vertebrates, annelids and cephalopods, the coelom forms large perivisceral spaces, but in groups with a large haemocoele such as the arthropods, and gastropod and lamellibranch molluscs, the coelom is reduced to pericardium, gonoducts and excretory system. The volume of the coelomic fluids may vary from perhaps 90% of the total body water in the echinoids, to as little as 5% in the lamellibranchs, but little quantitative data is available for many groups. The proportion of the extracellular fluid varies from 20% of the total body water in man, to 80% in the tectibranch mollusc, *Aplysia* (Table I.i). It is probably even larger, perhaps 95%, in the echinoids. In the arthropods, the volume of extracellular fluid varies with the state of the moulting cycle (Robertson, 1960).

Extracellular skeletal material is formed in the primary body cavity, and the water in it is part of the haemocoele. For example, the ionic content of mammalian connective tissue is similar to that of plasma, and sodium (as ^{24}Na) equilibrates rapidly throughout both blood and connective tissue fibres (Manery and Bale, 1941; Eichelberger and Brown, 1945; Audio, 1958; Lobeck, 1958). In cartilage, the high con-

TABLE I.1. — THE DISTRIBUTION OF BODY WATER AS A PERCENTAGE
OF THE TOTAL WATER

Animal	Cell water	Haemocoele water + coelom	Comments
Cryptochiton[1]	49.5	50.5	Coelom small
Aplysia[1]............	15	85	,, ,,
Achatina[1] .... (pulmonate)	53	47	,, ,,
Margaritifera[1] ... (lamellibranch)	45	55	Coelom moderate
Cambarus[2]	?	25% (of body volume)	Coelom small
Echinus[3]	? 3	? 97	All coelom, no haemocoele

Animal	Cell water	Blood in circulation	Plasma	Coelom + interstitial fluid	Comments
Man[4]	80	12	5.6	14	Coelom small
Octopus[1].........	66	7	—	27	Coelom moderate
Salmo[5]	80	small	—	15	,, ,,
Cyprinus[7]	78	4	2.5	19.2	
Mycteroperca[7] ...	82.5	4.5	3.2	14.2	
Squalus[6]	81	9.5	—	17.7	,, ,,
Raia binoculata[6]	82	10.2	7.9	10	
Petromyzon[7] ... in fresh water	68	11	7	25	

References: 1. Martin et al., 1958.   5. Houston, 1959.
             2. Prosser et al., 1950.   6. Thorson, 1958.
             3. Undocumented guess.   7. Thorson, 1961.
             4. Smith, 1956.

centration of chondroitin sulphate leads to reduction in chloride and an increase in cations compared with the blood (Manery, 1954). The mesogloea of coelenterates is another example of a skeletal tissue in the primary body cavity, and in composition it is anologous to an extracellular fluid.

A number of chemical methods can be used to measure the volume of the different compartments of the body. The polysaccharide, inulin, has been widely used to estimate the

2*

total volume of extracellular fluids in animals or tissues. It equilibrates rapidly throughout the extracellular fluid, but does not penetrate into the cells*. The inulin space of an animal is defined as $\dfrac{\text{concentration of inulin in the animal}}{\text{concentration of inulin in the plasma}} \times$ 100, i.e. the percentage volume of extracellular fluid in the animal, calculated on the assumption that all the inulin is uniformly distributed in the extracellular fluid. Other substances, such as sucrose or thiosulphate ions, distribute rapidly through the extracellular fluids, but in some cases these substances slowly penetrate into the cells, so that the "sucrose space" or the "thiosulphate space" may increase slowly with time, and exceed the extracellular volume. At one time, it was thought that chloride was restricted to the extracellular fluids, and "chloride spaces" were calculated as a measure of the extracellular volume. Now it is certain that many cells do contain some chloride, and a better estimate of extracellular volume is obtained using inulin.

In the vertebrates, where the haemocoele is differentiated into a closed circulatory system and a lymph system, the larger proteins are confined to the circulatory system and cannot penetrate the capillary walls into the lymph system. The volume of the plasma may be estimated by injecting such large proteins, labelled with a dye (e.g. T–1824), or a radioactive tracer. In the mammals, the blood is about half the volume of the extracellular space (as measured by inulin), while in *Octopus*, the blood is only 5% of the total body water, and the extracellular fluid is about 30%. Some estimates of the relative sizes of the water compartments in a few representative animals are given in Table I.1. The possible distribution of water in a mammal and in a crustacean are illustrated in Fig. I.1.

---

* There is some evidence that inulin does not penetrate into the interstices of connective tissue either (Krohøffer, 1946).

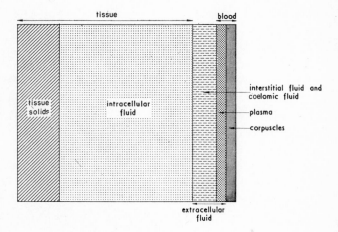

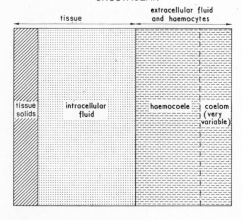

Fig. I.1. The distribution of water in a mammal and a crustacean

Definitions

Quantities and Concentrations

Quantities of solutes may be measured in terms of weight, as grams (g), milligrams (mg = 10^{-3} g), or micrograms (μg = 10^{-6} g), or as moles (M), i.e. gram-molecules, millimoles (mM = 10^{-3} M), or micromoles (μM = 10^{-6} M). Quantities of electrolytes may be expressed in terms of gram-ions or milligram-ions. In the strict sense, the term molecule cannot be applied to an ion, but for convenience, the terms moles (M) and millimoles (mM) are used as synonymous with the terms gram-ions and milligram-ions.

Quantities expressed in terms of weight are immediately comprehensible, but moles or millimoles are more convenient as they are a measure of the number of solute particles, 1 mole containing 6.025×10^{23} particles (Avogadro's number). The osmotic pressure of a solution and its other colligative properties, such as the freezing-point depression, are functions of the concentration of solute particles.

Concentrations may be expressed in terms of the quantity per unit volume of solution, or in terms of the quantity per unit weight of solvent (water). The scales commonly used are:

molar, i.e. moles of solute/litre of solution (M/l.), or millimolar (mM/l.), or micromolar (μM/l.);
molal, i.e. moles of solute/kg water (M/kg water), or millimolal (mM/kg water), or micromolal (μM/kg water).

At the level of concentration of most body fluids, millimoles are usually more convenient units than moles. The osmotic pressure of a solution and the physical properties of the solute are related more directly to the molal than to the molar concentration. In sea water and body fluids, the two scales do not differ greatly, but in body fluids of high protein content, such as mammalian plasma, they may differ by 5–10%, and in tissues by as much as 30%.

For comparison of acid-base equilibria in body fluids, the concentrations of anions and cations may be expressed as equivalents (i.e. gram-equivalent weights) in a litre or kilogram of water, i.e. E/l., or E/kg water, and as milliequivalents, mE/l. and mE/kg water.

The concentration of a solution can be calculated from one of the colligative physical properties such as the osmotic pressure. Concentrations determined in this way are often expressed in terms of osmoles, or milliosmoles, Osm/l. or mOsm/l., or Osm/kg water or mOsm/kg water. This is the equivalent concentration of a solution of an ideal non-electrolyte having the same physical characteristics. For reasons discussed subsequently, solutes do not behave exactly as ideal non-electrolytes, so the osmolal concentration of a solution is not identical with the total chemical concentration, but is generally lower. For example, sea water of a concentration of 1000 mOsm/kg water contains 1129 mM/kg water.

Tonicity and Osmoticity

One solution is isosmotic with another if it exerts the same osmotic pressure. A solution is said to be hyperosmotic to another if it exerts a greater osmotic pressure, and hypo-osmotic if it exerts a lower one.

Although many authors use the terms isotonic as synonymous with isosmotic (and similarly, hypertonic and hypotonic), the terms are not identical. Tonicity is defined in terms of the response of cells immersed in a solution. A solution is said to be isotonic with a cell (or tissue) if the cell neither swells nor shrinks when immersed in it. An isotonic solution is generally also isosmotic, but this is not necessarily so. For example, *Arbacia* (sea urchin) eggs maintain a constant volume in an isosmotic solution of sodium chloride, but swell slightly in isosmotic calcium chloride. A solution of calcium chloride isotonic with *Arbacia* eggs is therefore hyperosmotic to them (Harris, 1960, p.35). For this reason, the

terms isosmotic, hyperosmotic and hypo-osmotic are generally
to be preferred, although they may be less euphonious than
the terms isotonic, etc., which should be reserved for de-
scriptions of actual experiments.

Permeability

The permeability of a membrane to solutes or to water is
expressed in terms of the quantity passing through unit area
of surface, in unit time, for one unit of pressure, or activity
difference (see below, p.25). Solute permeabilities are usually
expressed in simple units such as the number of moles or
millimoles of solute passing through 1 cm² surface when
there is a 1 molal concentration difference between the two
sides. Permeability to water has been expressed in the literature in so many different units that some explanation of
the different terms is required.

Permeability to water will be expressed here in terms of
the total water flux, the number of cubic microns, μ^3,
passing through a $1\mu^2$ unit of surface area in 1 second. That
is to say, the water flux is in terms of $\mu^3/\mu^2/\text{sec}$, or $\mu.\sec^{-1}$,
across a membrane, when there is pure water on one side
and an infinitely concentrated solution on the other.

In the literature, permeability to water has been expressed
in terms of cm³/cm²/hr/unit activity difference (or cm. hr⁻¹)
(Shaw, 1955a); $\mu^3/\mu^2/\text{minute}$/atmosphere pressure difference
(or μ/min/atmos) (Dick, 1959); moles water/cm²/hr/molar
concentration difference (Krogh, 1938, 1939); and as day
numbers or minute numbers (Krogh, 1938, 1939).*

These diverse units may be converted into $\mu.\sec^{-1}$ as
follows: cm³/cm²/hr $\times \dfrac{10^4}{3600} = \mu^3/\mu^2/\text{sec} = \mu.\sec^{-1}$. The concentration of pure water is 55.6 molal $\left(\dfrac{1000}{18}\right)$ and a 1 molal

---

* A day number, or minute number, is the number of days, or minutes,
required for 1 cm³ of water to pass through a 1 cm² surface under a pressure
difference of 1 atmosphere.

solution exerts an osmotic pressure of 22.4 atmospheres (at 0°C). Hence,

$$\mu^3/\mu^2/\text{atm}/\text{min} \times \frac{22.4 \times 55.6}{60} = \mu^3/\mu^2/\text{sec} = \mu \cdot \text{sec}^{-1}$$

$$\text{moles}/\text{cm}^2/\text{hr}/\text{mole conc. diff.} \times \frac{18 \times 55.6 \times 10^4}{60 \times 60} = \mu^3/\mu^2/\text{sec} =$$

$$= \mu \cdot \text{sec}^{-1}.$$

$$\frac{1}{\text{day number}} = \text{water flux in } \text{cm}^3/\text{cm}^2/\text{atm}/\text{day}$$

$$\text{and} \quad \frac{1}{\text{day number}} \times \frac{10^4 \times 22.4 \times 55.6}{24 \times 60 \times 60} = \mu^3/\mu^2/\text{sec} =$$

$$= \mu \cdot \text{sec}^{-1}.$$

The Properties of Solutions and Membranes

When two solutions are separated by a barrier permeable to both solvent and solutes, solutes diffuse from the more concentrated to the less concentrated solution; the solvent passes by osmosis from the less concentrated to the more concentrated solution. This continues until the concentration differences are abolished. These two processes, diffusion and osmosis tend to degrade the organisation of the animal and must be opposed to maintain it. The opposition is achieved, in part by the development of relatively impermeable body walls, and in part by active accumulation and excretion. Almost complete impermeability has been achieved in some eggs, but some degree of permeability is characteristic of all animals, since the functions of respiration, assimilation and excretion are all impossible without some path of exchange with the environment.

Cell Membranes and Body Walls

The living cell is contained within a membrane which offers some resistance to the passage of water and has a relatively low permeability to ions and organic molecules. This barrier makes it possible for a cell to differ in composition from its environment without an impossibly large expenditure of energy.

Most of our knowledge of cell membranes has come from the intensive study of a few types of cell, in particular erythrocytes and sea urchin eggs, but the little information available suggests that the bounding membranes of other cells have similar properties. The cell wall probably consists of a layer or layers of lipid, stabilised by protein molecules lying along the surfaces. Substances may pass in or out of a cell in several different ways: oxygen and many organic molecules probably pass through by diffusion in simple solution in the lipid layer; water and ions, on the other hand, pass through more rapidly than would be expected from their solubility in lipids alone, and it is probable that they pass either through pores or in combination with lipid soluble carriers in the membrane.

Tissues and chitin are more permeable to small ions than to large ones (Table I.2; Table III.3), which suggests that most ionic movement takes place through pores. On the other hand, the ability of cell membranes to move ions against an electrochemical gradient (see below, p.27), and the phenomenon known as exchange diffusion (see below, p.21) probably depend on the existence of lipid soluble carriers in the cell wall. Discrepancies between the ionic diameter and the rate of penetration through membranes (Table I. 2) are more apparent than real, because the concept of ionic diameter is not very precise and the effective diameter depends on the degree of hydration. The outermost water molecules of a hydrated ion are almost in equilibrium between the electrostatic forces of attraction and the disruptive forces of thermal agitation, and it is probable that the number of

TABLE I. 2. — PERMEABILITY OF FROG STRIATED MUSCLE TO VARIOUS IONS
(Conway, 1956b, 1960b)

Relative rates of entry into muscle		Diameter of hydrated ion, Å		Diameter of unhydrated ion, Å
KCl	= 100	K	3.8	1.33
RbCl	38	Rb	3.6	1.49
CsCl	8	Cs	3.8	1.65
NaCl	0	Na	5.6	0.98
LiCl	0	Li	7.3	0.78
CaCl$_2$	0	Ca	9.6	1.06
MgCl$_2$	0	Mg	10.8	1.81
KCl	100	Cl	3.8	0.98
KBr	63	Br	3.6	
KNO$_3$	17	NO$_3$	1.9	
KH$_2$PO	4	HPO$_4$	8.7	
		SO$_4$	7.2	
K$_2$SO$_4$	0			
		NH$_4$	3.8	
		I	3.7	
		H$_2$O	3.0	

water molecules associated with an ion varies in different
conditions. Thus, the diameters derived from different
physical properties, e.g. ionic mobilities, rates of diffusion,
and activity coefficients, are often discordant. Even hydrostatic pressure may affect the diameter of a hydrated ion
(Podolsky, 1959). While the hydrogen ion has a high affinity
for water, this does not restrict its mobility, as the movement
of a hydrogen ion may be effectively only the transfer of a
proton from one water molecule to another.

The permeability of a sheet of cells, such as the body surface,
vertebrate capillary walls, or the glomerular wall of the
nephron, depends not only on the permeability of the constituent cells but also on the intercellular cement which binds
the cells together. Both the cell walls and the intercellular
cement are stabilised and rendered less permeable by the
presence of divalent ions, particularly calcium. In the absence

of divalent ions, the hydration of both cement and cell walls is increased and the intercellular cement may disperse, allowing the disintegration of the tissues. The differential effects of monovalent and divalent ions on the cell walls and inter-cellular cement may be analogous to the effects of the same ions on ion exchange resins. Divalent ions are taken up by the resins in preference to monovalent ions, but if the divalent ions are displaced by a large excess of monovalent ions, the osmotic pressure and the water content of the resin increases (Kitchener, 1957, p.32).

Cells and tissues exposed to the environment often develop additional protective layers outside the cell membranes. Many eggs, particularly those of freshwater animals, are surrounded by "shells" of very low permeability to both water and ions. The outer surface of many animals is similarly protected by thick layers of chitin or keratin, although in most cases more permeable windows are left in the protective covering for respiratory exchange, and most of the exchange of water and ions takes place through this respiratory surface. A thick layer of organic material such as chitin or keratin, or even of mucus, may substantially reduce the permeability of the body wall. In reptiles and mammals, the low permeability of keratin is probably related to its dense structure and low water content. In other cases, the body wall is made more imperme-able by a layer of wax (as in the insects) or of calcium carbonate or phosphate (as in many crustaceans, molluscs and fish).

Osmosis and Diffusion

Simultaneous movement of solute and solvent — It is possible to define the permeability of a membrane to solvent unambi-guously, only if there is no simultaneous movement of solutes. Similarly, it is possible to define the permeability of a mem-brane to solutes, only if there is no solvent flow. Otherwise the movement of solvent affects the movement of solute, and vice versa. Organic membranes are usually permeable to both water and solutes to some extent, and are subject to simultaneous movement of both. In these cases, it is not possible to describe the fluxes of water and solute through the membrane in terms of the permeability coefficients of the membrane to water and to solutes alone. In practice, the interactions between osmosis and diffusion are ignored, and some of the anomalies in permeability studies may be due to this. The two phenomena are discussed separately below, but for a more exact treatment see Kedem and Katchalski, 1958, 1961.

Osmosis — A membrane which is permeable to water molecules but impermeable to solute particles is said to be semipermeable. When two aqueous solutions of different concentration are separated by a semipermeable membrane, water will pass through the membrane until the molal concentrations on the two sides are the same. This movement of water is called osmosis. The hydrostatic pressure necessary to prevent any movement of water from pure water through a semipermeable membrane into a solution, is known as the osmotic pressure of the solution.

A detailed explanation of the movement of solvent into a more concentrated solution, in terms of kinetic theory, is difficult. However, it can be shown (e.g. see Dick, 1959) that the osmotic pressure of a solution of 1 gram molecule of an ideal non-electrolyte in a volume of solvent is approximately the same as the pressure exerted by 1 gram-molecule of a gas enclosed in the same volume,* so that the osmotic properties of a solution may be expressed by the ideal gas equation:

$$PV = RT$$

---

* More exactly, $P\overline{V} = -RT \ln \dfrac{n_1}{n_1 + n_2}$, where $\overline{V}$ is the partial molal volume, i.e. approximately the volume occupied by 1 gram molecule of solvent in solution, and n_1 and n_2 are the numbers of gram molecules of solvent and solute in solution. This term approximates to $PV = RT$ at low concentrations.

where P is the pressure, V the volume of solvent, and $R =$
$= .082$ litre/atm/degree/mole $= 1.987$ cal/degree/mole. $T =$
$=$ absolute temperature. If C is the molal concentration of
the solute,

$$C = \frac{1}{V}$$

and $$P = RTC.$$

The real osmotic pressure of a solution differs considerably
from that of an ideal non-electrolyte of the same molality.
The discrepancy arises from interactions between solute and
solvent particles, and between the solute particles themselves.
This discrepancy may be expressed by the osmotic coefficient,
g, the ratio of the real to the ideal osmotic pressure. This
ratio is 0.93 for a 0.1–0.2 M solution of sodium chloride,*
but $g = 1.024$ for a 0.1 molal solution of sucrose.

If the hydrostatic pressure of a solution confined within
a semipermeable membrane exceeds the osmotic pressure,
pure solvent will be expressed from the solution through
the membrane, a process known as ultrafiltration. Many biological membranes, though permeable both to water and
small ions and molecules, are impermeable to large molecules, such as proteins. In such cases, the osmotic
pressure exerted at the membrane is that due to the
large molecules alone, the colloidal osmotic pressure. While
a 1% solution of ions will exert an osmotic pressure of several
atmospheres, a 1% solution of protein exerts a colloidal
osmotic pressure of only a few centimetres of water. Ultrafiltration against a colloidal osmotic pressure produces a
solution containing salts, ions and small molecules, but free
from proteins.

The osmotic pressure of a solution is a colligative property,
i.e. it is dependent on the number of solute particles and not
on their kind. Other colligative properties of solutions are

* Assuming complete dissociation of the sodium chloride.

the depression of the vapour pressure, the elevation of the boiling point, and the depression of the freezing-point. These are all directly proportional to one another. Because the direct measurement of osmotic pressure is technically difficult and requires relatively large volumes of fluid, it is generally easier to determine the osmotic concentration of a solution by chemical estimation of the constituents, or by calculation from one of the other colligative properties. One of the most convenient of these is the depression of the freezing-point, which can be measured in minute quantities of solution (as small as 10^{-5} ml). A one molal solution of an ideal non-electrolyte in water has a freezing-point depression of $1.858°C$. Freezing-point depressions are used so frequently to determine concentrations, that the concentrations are often expressed simply in terms of this property, and the phrase "freezing-point depression" is conveniently abbreviated to Δ.

In water, electrolytes dissociate into two or more ions. Strong electrolytes are almost completely dissociated at biological concentrations, but weak electrolytes such as phosphates or magnesium salts only partially so. The osmotic coefficient is usually calculated on the assumption of complete dissociation, and while the osmotic coefficient of a strong electrolyte is close to unity, that of a weak electrolyte may be quite small. This deviation is partly the result of incomplete dissociation and partly due to the departure of the particles from ideal behaviour. Body fluids contain both strong and weak electrolytes, so it is difficult to make an accurate estimate of the osmotic pressure of a body fluid from its chemical composition. The measurement of the freezing-point depression, or one of the other colligative properties, is a more accurate way of determining osmotic pressure.

Diffusion — If, initially, a solute is unequally distributed in a solution, in time the random movements of the solute particles will produce a homogeneous solution. This process appears as a diffusion of solute from a region of high concentration to one of lower concentration.

Figure I.2 represents a cylinder of cross-section A containing a solution which decreases in concentration from left to right. Suppose that there are n particles per unit volume of solution in one plane perpendicular to the length of the cylinder, and $(n - dn)$ particles per unit volume in a plane, dx, to the right. The concentration gradient is dn/dx (neglecting signs). The rate at which the particles diffuse down the concentra-

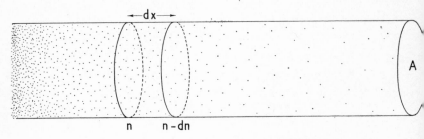

$$\leftarrow dx \rightarrow$$

$$n \qquad n - dn$$

Fig. I.2. Diffusion in a solution. For details see text.

tion gradient, dN/dt, (Fig. I.2) is proportional to the concentration gradient and the area of the cylinder. Hence,

$$\frac{dN}{dt} \propto A \frac{dn}{dx}$$

or, $$\frac{dN}{dt} = DA \frac{dn}{dx} \text{, where } D = \text{diffusion constant.}$$

If two solutions of concentration C_1 and C_2, are separated by a relatively impermeable membrane of thickness, θ, (Fig. I.3), the solute particles will diffuse much more slowly than between the two solutions in Fig. I.2. If each solution is so well mixed that the concentrations adjacent to the membrane can be regarded as constant, the concentration gradient across the membrane will be

$$\frac{C_1 - C_2}{\theta}$$

and the rate of diffusion across the membrane will be

$$\frac{dN}{dt} = DA \frac{C_1 - C_2}{\theta} = k A (C_1 - C_2),$$

where k is the permeability constant of the membrane to solute.

If solution 2 is replaced by pure solvent, particles will diffuse from left to right at a rate kAC_1, and if solution 1 is replaced by pure solvent, they will diffuse from right to left

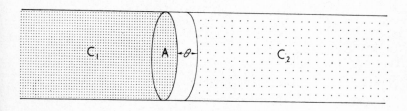

Fig. I.3. Diffusion through a membrane.
For details see text.

at a rate kAC_2. If the two solutions are labelled (e.g. with radioactive tracers), in simple cases, diffusion from left to right proceeds at a rate kAC_1, and from right to left at a rate kAC_2, and the net flux will be $kA(C_1 - C_2)$.*

If the flux from solution 1 to solution 2 is $f_{1 \to 2}$, and the reverse flux is $f_{2 \to 1}$, it follows that

$$\frac{f_{1 \to 2}}{f_{2 \to 1}} = \frac{kAC_1}{kAC_2} = \frac{C_1}{C_2}. \tag{1}$$

This equation is applicable only to simple cases.

Diffusion against a potential gradient — A potential difference (E volts) between solutions 1 and 2 will aid or hinder the

* It is important to note that the flux measured by radioactive tracers is a total flux, and not the net flux of the solute.

diffusion of ions, depending on their electrical charge. Equation 1 then becomes

$$\frac{f_{1 \to 2}}{f_{2 \to 1}} = \frac{C_1}{C_2} \cdot \exp\left(\pm \frac{zEF}{RT}\right) \tag{2}$$

where z is the valency of the ion.

If potassium is ten times as concentrated inside a cell, as in the plasma, but the cell is 58 mV negative to the plasma, then

$$\frac{f_{1 \to 2}}{f_{2 \to 1}} = \frac{1}{10} \cdot \exp\left(\frac{.058F}{RT}\right) = \frac{1}{1}$$

and the efflux and influx will be equal.

Diffusion through pores — Equation 1 is true only if diffusion takes place through an extensive surface where influx and efflux do not mutually interfere. If diffusion takes place through narrow pores, the fluxes may mutually interfere. The number of particles entering a pore at *a* from a solution (Fig. I.4), at a concentration C_1, will be proportional to C_1, while the number leaving the pore at *a* will be proportional

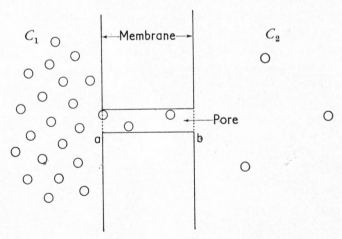

Fig. I.4. Diffusion through a narrow pore.
For details see text.

to C_2, a lower concentration. Similarly at b, the number of particles entering will be proportional to C_2 and the number leaving to C_1. If the pore is so narrow that the particles cannot pass one another, and if C_1 and C_2 are both so large that the pore is always occupied by several particles, then the particles will rarely penetrate from C_2 to C_1. Each particle entering a from C_1 has a probability $\dfrac{C_2}{C_1}$ of returning to C_1, and a probability $\dfrac{C_1 - C_2}{C_1}$ of progressing along the pore. Particles can only progress from the lower concentration C_2 to the higher concentration C_1 by a series of improbable events. If the number of particles in the pore at any time is large, diffusion from C_1 to C_2 will cease altogether, and the total flux from C_1 to C_2 will then be the same as the net flux.

This is an extreme condition, but if any significant part of a flux takes place through narrow pores, there will be interference between the influx and efflux and Equation 1 will not be applicable. (E.g., see Hodgkin and Keynes, 1955 a and b.)

Exchange diffusion — Another exchange process which cannot be described by Equation 1 is exchange diffusion (Ussing, 1947; Levi and Ussing, 1948). If the membrane separating two solutions is impermeable to ions but contains carrier units of ion exchange material which are free to diffuse between the boundaries of the membrane, ions may cross the membrane in combination with the carrier. If the carrier has a high affinity for the ions it will always be saturated, but a 1 : 1 exchange of ions between carrier and solution may take place at either surface, so that the total flux in both directions will be the same, even if the concentrations on the two sides of the membrane are unequal (Fig. I. 5). Labelled ions will be able to cross the membrane in either direction, but there need be no net transfer of ions.

Exchange diffusion can take place only if there is a significant concentration of ions on both sides of the membrane.

3*

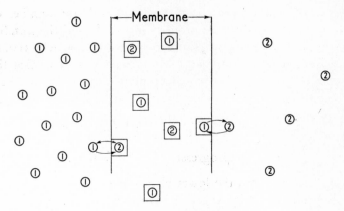

Fig. I.5. Illustration of exchange diffusion.
For details see text.

If solution 1 is replaced by pure solvent, the flux, $f_{1\rightarrow2}$, ceases, and therefore flux $f_{2\rightarrow1}$ also stops. In simple cases of diffusion where Equation 1 is applicable, the flux $f_{2\rightarrow1}$ continues unchanged if solution 1 is replaced by pure solvent. This is an important distinction between exchange diffusion (Chap. VII, p.318) and simple diffusion (Equation 1).

Permeability to Heavy Water

The permeability of a membrane to water may be measured, and defined, either in terms of the rate of flow of water through the membrane under the influence of an osmotic concentration difference, or in terms of the rate of diffusion of heavy water across the membrane. The two processes may be reduced to comparable terms (see p.10) but the permeabilities determined in these ways are rarely identical. The movement of water by osmosis occurs as the result of a difference of concentration (or more exactly, of the mole fractions*) of water in the two solutions. If two solutions, C_1 and C_2, are separated by a

---

* The mole-fraction of water in a solution is the ratio of the number of water molecules to the total number of particles.

permeable membrane, the net water flux in unit time, w, will be proportional to the area of the membrane, A, and the difference between the mole-fractions of the water on the two sides of the membrane, q_1 and q_2.

$$w = d_p A(q_1 - q_2),$$

where d_p is the permeability constant of the membrane to water. This net flux can be measured by any volume method.

The net movement of water arises from the differences between the passage of water in opposite directions. The flux of water in unit time from solution 1 to solution 2, $w_{1 \to 2} = d_p A q_1$, and the reverse flux, $w_{2 \to 1} = d_p A q_2$. If solution 1 is labelled, for example with heavy water, D_2O, the flux measured will be the total flux from solution 1 to solution 2, $w_{1 \to 2} = d_p A q_1$. Thus,

$$\frac{w_{1 \to 2}}{w_{2 \to 1}} = \frac{q_1}{q_2},$$

and the net flux is related to the total flux:

$$\frac{w}{w_{1 \to 2}} = \frac{q_1 - q_2}{q_1},$$

The mole fraction of water in a 1 molal aqueous solution is $\dfrac{55.6}{55.6 + 1}$,* so the net flux of water due to the osmotic pressure difference will be only a small fraction of the total water flux measured by heavy water.

In practice, the permeability constant derived from the rate of diffusion of heavy water, the diffusion permeability constant, is generally smaller than that derived from the rate of flow of water caused by osmotic pressure differences, the filtration permeability constant. Koefoed-Johnsen and Ussing (1953) have suggested that the discrepancy arises from the bulk flow of solution through pores in the membrane, under

---

* One kg of water contains $\dfrac{1000}{18}$ or 55.6 moles of water.

the influence of the osmotic pressure. Using Poiseuilles' equation (which governs the rate of flow through capillaries) and assuming that bulk flow takes place, it is possible to calculate the total area and diameter of the pores from the ratio of the permeability diffusion constant, d_p, and the filtration diffusion constant, d_f.

$$r^2 = 14.3 \times 10^{-16} \times \left(\frac{d_f}{d_p} - 1 \right) \quad \text{(Solomon, 1959)},$$

where r is the pore diameter (centimetres). A large discrepancy between d_f and d_p implies a pore of wide diameter, but for pores less than 10 Å the two constants are almost the same (Kedem and Katchalsky, 1961).

Pore diameters calculated on the Koefoed-Johnsen-Ussing theory from heavy water fluxes vary from 60–120 Å in capillary walls, gastric mucosa and ileum epithelium, to 11 Å in mammalian erythrocytes and 4 Å in *Amoeba* and in frog body cavity eggs. The apparent pore size is altered by the concentration of ions such as calcium and by some hormones (Whittembury, Sugino and Solomon, 1960; Chap. VIII, p.347).

Activity Coefficients

It has been assumed that the properties of electrolytes in solution are simple functions of their concentrations, i.e. that they behave as "ideal" solutions. However, their properties differ significantly from those of ideal solutions except at very low concentrations. The activity, a, of an ion is its effective concentration, calculated on the basis of ideal behaviour. It is related to the concentration by the activity coefficient, j, which is the ratio of the activity to the concentration. Hence, $a = j \times$ concentration, and j is always less than unity, but approaches it at infinite dilution. To a first approximation, the activity coefficient of an ion is given by the equation

$$-\ln j = 0.51 \ z^2 \mu,$$

where z is the valency of the ion and μ is the ionic strength
of the solution;

$$\mu = \tfrac{1}{2}[C_1 z_1^2 + C_2 z_2^2 + \ldots C_n z_n^2]$$

where C_1, C_2 etc. are the molalities of each of the ionic species.
The mean activity coefficient of sodium and chloride ions
in a 0.1 molal solution is about 0.8, and falls to about 0.7 in
0.5 molal solutions. Direct measurements have shown that
the activity of sodium and potassium in squid giant axons is
about 0.6 (Hinke, 1961).

In biological equilibria, we are not concerned with the
absolute activities of ions in solution, but only with the ratio
of the activities of any ion in two different solutions on either
side of a membrane. As the activity coefficients change only
slowly with concentration, the ratio of the activities is similar
to that of the two concentrations, and the difference is often
ignored. While this is a valid simplification for monovalent
ions, it can lead to significant errors with divalent ions. For
example, the activity coefficient for magnesium ions is 0.045
in sea water and 0.16 in teleost blood, so that in this instance,
the ratio of the activities of the ions is very different from its
concentration ratio.

It is important to distinguish between the activity of a
solute and that of a solvent. The osmotic coefficient, g,
(see above, p. 17) is related to the activity coefficient of the
solvent, and the colligative properties of a solution depend on
the solvent activity. The activity coefficient of water does
not differ significantly from unity at most biological concentrations, so that the activity of the water in biological solutions
is proportional to its concentration, or more exactly to its
mole-fraction.

The Energy Required to Move Solvents and Solutes Against Concentration Gradients

Energy is liberated when water moves by osmosis from a less concentrated to a more concentrated solution, or when solutes diffuse down a concentration gradient. Conversely, energy is required to move water and solutes against concentration gradients.

If P is the osmotic pressure to be overcome W, the work done in producing a volume V of solute by ultrafiltration, then

$$W = PV. \tag{3}$$

Conversely, this will be the energy dissipated when a volume, V, of a solute passes by osmosis into a solution of osmotic pressure, P.

The work, W', which must be done to move 1 mole of a solute from a solution of osmotic pressure, P_1, to a solution of higher osmotic pressure, P_2, is given by the equation

$$W' = RT \ln \frac{P_1}{P_2},$$

and as the osmotic pressure is proportional to the concentration (ignoring the activity coefficient)

$$W' = RT \ln \frac{C_1}{C_2} \tag{4}$$

where C_1 and C_2 are the molal concentrations of the two solutions.

If an electrical potential difference exists between the two solutions, W' will depend both on the electrical potential and on the ratio of concentrations of an ion in the two solutions. The energy required to move 1 mole of an ion against an electrical potential of E volts is zEF, where z is the valency of the ion, and F the Faraday (96,450 coulombs/gram equivalent). Hence,

$$W' = RT \ln \frac{C_1}{C_2} + zEF \tag{5} \text{ (cf. Equation 2).}$$

The direction in which an ion will move depends on the electrical potential E, and on what may be called the chemical potential $\dfrac{RT}{zF} \ln \dfrac{C_2}{C_1}$. The sum of these two is known as the electrochemical potential

$$= \frac{RT}{zF} \ln \frac{C_2}{C_1} + E.$$

An ion will tend to diffuse from a higher to a lower electrochemical potential and will be in equilibrium only when the electrochemical potential is zero.

Donnan Equilibria

Biological membranes are usually differentially permeable and small ions such as potassium generally penetrate a membrane more readily than larger ones such as calcium or magnesium. If two solutions are separated by a membrane which is impermeable to one of the ion species, diffusion cannot distribute all the ions equally on the two sides of the membrane, and only a special type of equilibrium can be achieved. This kind of situation is illustrated in Fig. I.6, where a solution

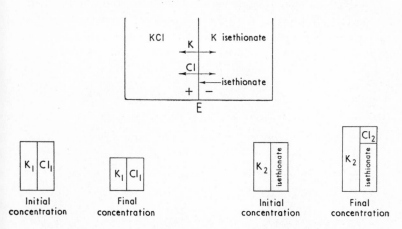

Fig. I.6. Illustration of a simple Donnan equilibrium.

of potassium chloride is separated from a solution of potassium isethionate ($K^+C_2H_5SO_4$) by a membrane which is permeable to potassium and chloride ions but not to the large isethionate ions. Chloride will diffuse down the concentration gradient into the isethionate compartment, but no isethionate can diffuse the other way. As the chloride ions move into the right hand compartment, the isethionate compartment will acquire a negative charge which will attract the potassium ions into the compartment as well. While the chloride ions diffuse down the concentration gradient into this compartment, the potassium ions are diffusing up the gradient. As the process continues, the chloride concentration gradient declines, but the potassium gradient increases. Equilibrium is attained when the tendency for chloride ions to diffuse into the right hand compartment is balanced by the tendency of the potassium to diffuse back into the left hand compartment; that is, when the energy liberated by the chloride ions diffusing down the chloride concentration gradient just balances the energy required to pull an equal number of potassium ions up the potassium concentration gradient.

If the potential difference across the membrane is E volts, the energy required to move 1 equivalent from one compartment to another will be that required to move ions across the electrochemical gradient (Eq.5).* The energy required to move 1 gram equivalent of potassium into compartment 2, up the concentration gradient but down the potential gradient, is:

$$W'' = RT \ln \frac{K_2^+}{K_1^+} - FE \qquad (5)$$

and the energy liberated when 1 gram equivalent of chloride ions moves down the concentration gradient, but up the potential gradient, is:

$$W'' = RT \ln \frac{Cl_1^-}{Cl_2^-} - FE.$$

* This assumes that the system in Fig. I.6 is so large that the movement of 1 gram equivalent of ions does not effectively change the concentrations on either side, or the potential on the membrane.

At equilibrium, these will be equal, so that

$$\frac{K^+_2}{K^+_1} = \frac{Cl^-_1}{Cl^-_2}.$$

Such an equilibrium is known as a Donnan equilibrium.

If the diffusing ions are polyvalent, A^x and B^y, the energy required to move 1 gram equivalent of cations across the membrane would be

$$W'' = \frac{RT}{x} \ln \frac{A_2}{A_1} - FE$$

and the energy liberated by the movement of 1 gram equivalent of anions

$$W'' = \frac{RT}{y} \ln \frac{B_1}{B_2} - FE.$$

Hence, at equilibrium,

$$\frac{1}{x} \ln \frac{A_2}{A_1} = \frac{1}{y} \ln \frac{B_1}{B_2} \quad \text{or} \quad \left(\frac{A_2}{A_1}\right)^{\frac{1}{x}} = \left(\frac{B_1}{B_2}\right)^{\frac{1}{y}}$$

For example, if the ions involved in the equilibrium are the divalent calcium and monovalent chloride, the Donnan ratio will be

$$\sqrt{\frac{Ca^{++}_2}{Ca^{++}_1}} = \frac{Cl^-_1}{Cl^-_2}.$$

When ionic equilibrium has been reached, the two sides are no longer in osmotic equilibrium. If the two compartments were initially in osmotic equilibrium,

$$K^+_1 + Cl^-_1 = K^+_2 + \text{isethionate}^-,$$

there will have been a net transfer of both potassium and chloride ions into the right hand compartment, so that

$$K^+_1 + Cl^-_1 \rightarrow K^+_2 + Cl^-_2 + \text{isethionate}^-.$$

If the left hand compartment is initially hyperosmotic to the right hand one, the conditions will be reversed in the final equilibrium, because in this case the potassium will be diffusing down the concentration gradient until its concentration on the two sides is the same. A Donnan equilibrium will then develop.

A special case of a Donnan equilibrium in osmotic balance is found in striated muscle and nerve cells. These cells are freely permeable to potassium and chloride ions, but contain large amounts of indiffusible anions, mainly phosphate compounds and amino acids. So far, the situation is similar to that in Fig. I.6, with compartment 2 representing the cells.

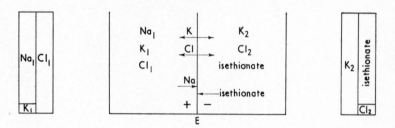

Equilibrium condition   Equilibrium condition

Fig. 1.7. Illustration of a double Donnan equilibrium.

However, the body fluids with which the cells are in equilibrium contain a large concentration of sodium ions which are excluded from the cells. This is represented in Fig. I.7. and

$$\frac{K^+_{plasma}}{K^+_{cells}} = \frac{Cl^-_{cells}}{Cl^-_{plasma}}.$$

The presence of the sodium ions in the plasma balances the excess concentration of ions in the cells due to the Donnan equilibrium, and the osmotic pressure of the plasma is the same as that of the cytoplasm. Many other constituents are present, but approximately,

$$Na_{plasma} + K_{plasma} + Cl_{plasma} = Na_{cells} + K_{cells} + C_{cells} +$$

organic constituents (Fig. I.6), and the sum of the anions

balances the sum of the cations in both the plasma and the cells. So, approximately,

$$Na^+{}_{plasma} + K^+{}_{plasma} = Cl^-{}_{plasma}$$

and

$$Na^+{}_{cells} + K^+{}_{cells} = Cl^-{}_{cells} + organic\ anions.$$

(Fig. I.7)

This complex equilibrium has been called a "Double Donnan Equilibrium" to distinguish it from the simpler anisosmotic condition. It can be maintained, provided that any sodium ions which enter the cells are extruded again. In many tissues this active extrusion of sodium is accompanied by, or linked with, the active uptake of potassium ions, so that potassium is accumulated in the cells in excess of the Donnan equilibrium concentration, that is:

$$\frac{K^+{}_{cells}}{K^+{}_{plasma}} > \frac{Cl^-{}_{plasma}}{Cl^-{}_{cells}}.$$

A link between sodium extrusion and potassium uptake has been demonstrated in frog muscle (Keynes, 1954), in *Sepia* (cuttlefish) nerve axons (Hodgkin and Keynes, 1955 a) and in erythrocytes (Harris and Maizels, 1951). For a recent review see Glynn, 1959. In general, striated muscle and nerves deviate only slightly from a Donnan equilibrium, but in other tissues such as erythrocytes, smooth muscle and kidney cortex, the deviations are considerable.

In the Donnan equilibrium of the cell discussed above (Fig. I.5), the electrochemical potential of the potassium on the two sides of the membrane would be the same, so that

$$E = \frac{RT}{F} \ln \frac{K^+_2}{K^+_1} \qquad (6)$$

and conversely for the chloride ion,

$$E = \frac{RT}{F} \ln \frac{Cl^-_1}{Cl^-_2}.$$

Hence, the electrical potential associated with a Donnan equilibrium can be accurately defined by the conditions of the equilibrium; a ten-fold concentration difference of a monovalent ion is associated with a potential difference of about 58 mV (see above, p.20).

The existence of a potential difference between the two compartments in Fig. I.6, when equilibrium has been reached, shows that the number of chloride ions that migrated into compartment 2 was slightly greater than the number of potassium ions. Thus, the sum of the cations in compartment 2 is not exactly the same as the sum of the anions, and the same is true of the cell in Fig. I.7. However, the difference is so small that it cannot be detected by chemical means. The electrical charge on the membrane depends on the potential difference and on the capacity of the membrane, but it is always so small that, in practice, it can be neglected in the summation of cations and anions.

Active Transport of Ions

The differentiation and organisation of fluids and cells can occur only if substances are moved against electrochemical gradients. All the diffusible substances in permeable systems move down electrochemical gradients and organisation is lost unless some materials are moved against the gradients to maintain the differences. The movement of a substance against an electrochemical potential is called active transport and requires a supply of energy. When a substance is moved against a gradient, energy is required equivalent to the product of the electrochemical gradient and the amount of substance moved.

In complex systems, such as those involving Donnan equilibria, detailed information about the electrochemical potentials of the system is necessary before it is possible to decide which ions are moved by active transport and which are moving down gradients. It is important to note that movement against a concentration gradient alone, as in the case of potassium in Fig. I.5, is not evidence of active transport.*

A number of hypothetical systems have been devised to illustrate how active transport may take place. Most of these hypotheses suggest that the transported ions are temporarily bound in some complex which acts as a carrier, operating in a cyclical manner so that on one side of a membrane the carrier combines with an ion, and on the other, releases it. To maintain electrical neutrality, the transported ion must be accompanied by another of opposite charge, or be exchanged for another ion of the same charge. The combination of ion and carrier is imagined as occurring spontaneously, while the release of an ion is accompanied by the simultaneous supply of the necessary energy. The carrier itself is probably fat soluble, since it must function within the lipid layer at the cell surface, but it must also be able to combine with strong electrolytes. Minute quantities of a lipid soluble compound which has a high affinity for ions, have been isolated from blood (Solomon, Lionetti, and Cuman, 1956), from yeast (Conway, 1956 a) and from kidney (Rhodes and Vanatta, 1958). Recently, Hokin and Hokin (1959, 1961) have been able to show that the turnover of phosphatidic acid in the avian salt gland (Chap. VII, p.303) increases when the gland is stimulated to secrete salt. Phosphatidic acid is a fat derivative, in which one of the three fatty acids attached to glycerol has been replaced by phosphate. It is fat soluble, but at the same time, it has a high affinity for cations. Thus, it fulfils some of the requirements of a carrier. In a sheet of cells, a net flux of sodium can result if the sodium pump is restricted to one side of the layer. This was first suggested for frog skin (Koefoed-Johnsen and Ussing, 1958), but, with modifications, the model has since been used to explain transport of sodium in *Necturus* kidney tubules (Giebisch, 1960).

*In certain circumstances active transport can take place down an electrochemical gradient. This is sometimes distinguished as facilitated diffusion (cf. *Nereis*, Chap. IV, p.153).

Shaw (1959 a and b, 1961a) and Shaw and Sutcliffe (1961) have shown, in a variety of crustaceans, that while the active influx of ions at high concentrations is independent of the external medium, at low concentrations, it is approximately proportional (Chap. IV, Fig.8, p.134; Chap. V, Fig. 2, p.191). They suggest that the transport mechanism becomes saturated at high external concentrations, but at lower concentrations the active influx is limited by the availability of ions. The relation between active influx and external concentration may be described by the equation

$$f = f_{max} \left(\frac{M}{S+M} \right) \qquad (7)$$

where f is the influx at an external concentration M, f_{max}, the influx at high external concentrations when the transport system is saturated, and S is a constant which is a measure of the affinity of the system for the ion transported.

Shaw's equation is analogous to the Michaelis-Menten equation:

$$v = v_{max} \left(\frac{M_s}{S' + M_s} \right)$$

which describes the relation between the velocity of an enzymic reaction and the concentration of the substrate, M_s. In the Michaelis–Menten equation, S' is a constant which is a measure of the affinity of an enzyme for its substrate and is equivalent to the substrate concentration at which the reaction proceeds at half the maximum velocity.* In the same way, what may be called "Shaw's constant" is equivalent to the external concentration at which the influx is half of the maximum influx. The characteristics of this kind of transport system may be described in terms of f_{max} and S.

The link between oxidative metabolism and transport systems cannot yet be defined in precise terms. Two principal

---

* See standard textbooks, e.g. Baylis, 1959, Vol I, p.311. The Michaelisen-Menten equation was applied to the problem of ion-uptake by plant roots by Epstein and Hagen (1952).

theories now current are the "redox pump" theory supported by Conway (1958) and Lundegårdh (1954), and the theory that adenosine triphosphate activates the carrier system (Ussing, 1958; Caldwell, 1960).

Redox pump theory — Oxidation and reduction can be regarded as essentially a process of transfer of electrons from the reductant to the oxidant. The uptake of a hydrogen atom may be interpreted as the uptake of a hydrogen ion subsequent to the gain of an electron. All the energy used by a cell comes directly or indirectly from such oxidation-reduction, or redox, reactions. The transfer of electrons between two redox systems is associated with a potential difference between them which is a measure of the available energy of the reaction.

The principle of the redox pump may be illustrated by Conway's theory of gastric secretion (Conway, 1953). He suggests that the hydrogen ions secreted are derived from the dehydrogenation of metabolites. During the final stages of oxidation, the hydrogen, in combination with "hydrogen carriers" (pyridine nucleotides), is transferred to oxidised cytochrome, forming reduced cytochrome and water. The cytochrome is then reoxidised by free oxygen.

In terms of electron transfer, the process may be described as follows. The reduced hydrogen carrier loses electrons to the oxidised cytochrome, forming oxidised carrier and hydrogen ions. If we write "carrier 2H" for the reduced hydrogen carrier, the reaction may be expressed:

$$\text{carrier } 2H \rightarrow \text{carrier} + 2e + 2H^{+}.$$

The electrons are ultimately transferred to the oxidised cytochrome to form cytochrome and reduced oxygen. The reduced oxygen combines with the hydrogen ions to form water. If we write "cytochrome O_2" for oxidised cytochrome, the reaction may be expressed:

$$\tfrac{1}{2} \text{ cytochrome } O_2 + 2e \rightarrow \tfrac{1}{2} \text{ cytochrome} + O^{--}.$$

The following reactions may then occur:

either, $O^{--} + H^+ \rightarrow OH^-$ and $OH^- + H^+ \rightarrow H_2O$

or, $O^{--} + H_2O \rightarrow 2OH^{--}$ and $2OH^{--} + 2H^+ \rightarrow 2H_2O$.

Typically, the end-product of the reaction is water, but the dehydrogenating and cytochrome systems are distinct and could be spatially separated. If they were linked to a system able to transfer electrons, the separation could be considerable. In this case, the hydrogen and hydroxyl ions could be produced on opposite sides of a membrane impermeable to both, and the separation of acid and base would have been achieved. If the hydrogen ions could not reach the reduced oxygen, the reaction would follow the first half of the second alternative route above. With a slight modification, sodium ions could be substituted for hydrogen ions, or the theory made applicable generally to other forms of ion transport. The potential differences between biological redox systems are quite adequate to transport ions against the very large concentration differences which are maintained across gastric mucosa or frog skin.

The ratio of the number of ions transported, to the number of oxygen molecules used in the oxidative process, has been a source of controversy. In the simple case outlined above, where oxygen is the final electron acceptor, four hydrogen ions could be produced for each molecule of oxygen consumed. Conway (1958) has claimed that it is significant that the ratio is four or less in the gastric mucosa of several animals. However, the situation is complex, because at any time, only a part of the gastric mucosa is involved in acid secretion. On the other hand, in frog skin it is quite clear that when allowance is made for the basic oxygen consumption, each incremental oxygen metabolised is associated with the transport of 18 sodium ions (Zerahn, 1956 b; Leaf and Renshaw, 1956, 1957). Recent work on kidney cortex tissue has shown that 29 sodium ions are transported for each molecule of oxygen (Larsen, Munck and Thaysen, 1961). These higher ratios are incompatible with the simple redox pump theory. Conway has countered this by suggesting that the cyclic use of adenosine triphosphate would enable the redox pump to run at a higher gear, so that it could give higher ratios of ions transported to oxygen consumed, in particular circumstances.

Adenosine triphosphate theory — The hypothesis that ion transport involves adenosine triphosphate has been put forward by several workers (for example, Ussing 1958; Caldwell, 1960; Whittam, 1961). In a number of tissues it has been shown that ion transport is dependent on the presence of adenosine triphosphate (Ussing, 1958; Caldwell, 1960). The link between active transport and metabolism is so close that the inhibition of active transport by non-respiratory poisons, or the absence of the transported ion, causes a concomitant reduction in the respiratory rate. For example, in rabbit brain tissue, a $5 \mu M$ solution of ouabain, which inhibits sodium extrusion, causes a 50% reduction in the respiratory rate. If the sodium in the bathing medium is replaced by choline, there is a similar reduction, but the addition of ouabain causes no further reduction. Cellular respiration is governed by the concentration of adenosine diphosphate, which in turn is controlled by the rate of hydrolysis of adenosine triphosphate. Any reduction in the rate of active transport may therefore affect the rate of respiration. In a number of tissues, red cells, kidney, brain, and crab nerve, no less than 50% of the respiration appears to be directly linked with active transport.

Some of the observed characteristics of active transport systems are difficult to explain in terms of the redox theory. For example, dinitrophenol inhibits sodium transport in frog skin, but stimulates oxygen consumption, suggesting that it is not oxidative processes *per se* which are involved in ion transport. Again, the oxygen consumption of frog skin adjusts to a new transport rate only after some delay, suggesting that there is some intracellular biochemical energy store. The ion transport rate of frog skin may be altered by changes in external con-

4*

centration or by the application of an electrical potential across the skin (Chap. V, p. 210). Direct evidence of the importance of adenosine triphosphate has been produced recently by Caldwell and Keynes (1957) and by Caldwell, Hodgkin, Keynes and Shaw (1960), who showed that microinjections of adenosine triphosphate would restore sodium extrusion from squid axons previously poisoned by dinitrophenol or cyanide. Conway has pointed out, however, that dinitrophenol does not inhibit sodium extrusion from frog sartorius muscle (Conway, 1958), but perhaps this is because it does not inhibit glycolytic formation of adenosine triphosphate.

According to Zerahn (1956 a) and Leaf and Renshaw (1957), a linear relation exists between oxygen consumption and ion transport in some tissues. The oxygen consumption is independent of the electrochemical gradient against which transport takes place, over a moderate range of concentrations, but transport is not possible against a potential of more than 140 mV (Chap. V, p.212). The free energy liberated by the reactions involved will be proportional to the oxygen consumed. This free energy must be sufficient to transport ions against the maximum electrochemical potential. If the ratio of the ions transported to oxygen consumed is constant at all concentration gradients at which transport can take place, it follows that the energy required will be independent of the concentration gradient, and the efficiency of the system will be inversely related to the demands made upon it. Thus, at the maximum electrochemical potential, the transport system will function at maximum efficiency, perhaps approaching 100%, but at lower potentials, the efficiency will be reduced, unless the ratio of ions transported to oxygen consumed can be changed. It is not certain from the experiments whether the ratio remains constant.* If frog skin can take up ions from a solution containing less than 0.01 mM NaCl/l. (Krogh, 1939 p.159; Chap. V, p.212), this would imply a maximum efficiency

* Zerahn did not use sodium ratios across the membrane greater than 1:10.

of at least 80%. This is an improbably high figure and it is possible that the transport systems can adjust to different demands either by "changing gear" at each transport site, or by having a variety of sites of different capacity.

A high overall efficiency within the animal could be maintained by adapting the "gear ratios" to their circumstances. This may explain why, in frog muscle, each extra molecule of oxygen is associated with about 4 sodium ions transported (Conway, 1960 a), while in mammalian kidney, where much of the transport is between almost isosmotic solutions, the ratio is one molecule of oxygen to 29 sodium ions (Thaysen, Larsen and Munck, 1961). Within the kidney, it is possible that the ratio is higher in the proximal tubule and loop of Henle where the concentration gradients are low, than in the collecting duct and distal convoluted tubule where transport may be taking place against high concentration gradients.

Animals such as the brackish water crab, *Carcinus*, living in a variable environment, will have to transport ions at less than maximum efficiency for much of the time, if the ratio is constant. Even a freshwater animal will be faced with some problems. If the threshold below which active uptake is impossible is set too low, the transport system will be inefficient in fresh water of higher salt content, but if the threshold is too high, the animal will not be able to survive in very soft water. It is notable that a transport system of the kind described for the freshwater crayfish, *Astacus*, for the brackish water *Carcinus* and for the freshwater *Gammarus* (Shaw and Sutcliffe, 1961) appears to have no threshold, and Shaw's equation implies that some transport will take place at any finite concentration. If this is the case, the transport ratio must change. On the other hand, further investigations may disclose a limiting concentration below which transport is impossible. Shaw's equation would not then hold at low concentrations, and the relation between influx and external concentration (Chap. IV, Fig. 8; Chap. V, Fig. 2) would be different. (For a recent review of the efficiency of transporting systems, see Croghan, 1961.)

Active Transport of Water

Although the net result of ion and water movements may suggest active water transport, a closer investigation usually shows that the water is moving passively. For example, the production of the concentrated solution of urea in mammalian kidney tubules is brought about by the active movement of ions and the water only moves passively down an osmotic gradient (Chap. II, p.97). Similarly, water enters the marine teleosts down a concentration gradient, as the result of the abstraction of ions from the gut (Chap. VII, p.288). In these and in many other cases, water movement is the indirect result of the active transport of ions, even in circumstances where the active transport of water, were it possible, would seem to be more advantageous.

In the vertebrate gut, water generally moves down a concentration gradient (Chap. VI, p.260), but in some circumstances water uptake from the gut occurs while the gut lumen is hyperosmotic to the plasma (Chap. VI, p.260). The surface of the gut is exceedingly complex, with many deep folds, some possibly continuous with the endoplasmic reticulum of the cells, and it is possible either that ion transport produces local osmotic gradients within the cells, sufficient to remove water from the gut lumen, or reduces the concentration of fluid within the folds until it is less than that of the plasma. This would allow water to move into the cells down the concentration gradient, even though the fluid in the gut lumen as a whole is hyperosmotic. In the same way, it is possible to explain the apparent uptake of water against an osmotic gradient in *Artemia* gut (Chap. VII, p.315) or in some crabs (Chap. IV, p.122) without postulating the active uptake of water.

However, there remain some few cases where active water transport is indicated. The rectal fluid of an insect becomes more concentrated while its volume becomes reduced (Chap. II, p.86) and proportionately more water is abstracted than salt. In this case, water transport must be taking place, unless salt is resorbed together with the water at one site, while the salt is returned to the rectal contents at another site. The production of a hypo-osmotic fluid by the malpighian tube, and by the contractile vacuole (Chap. II, p.83 and p.79) may also involve active transport of water, although alternative explanations can be devised, involving secretion followed by resorption on a minute scale.

Another force may be involved in water movement. If an electrical potential difference is maintained between two compartments containing water, separated by a capillary or porous membrane, water will flow through the membrane, usually towards the negative compartment. Generally, the interface between a liquid and a solid is electrically charged. In this case, the interface between the membrane and the water contained in its pores or capillaries develops an electrical double layer, two sheets of electrical charges of opposite sign. Most solids become negatively charged with respect to water, but some become positively charged and the charge on an adsorbed layer of protein may be reversed by a change in pH. If an electrical field is applied to such a system, the two phases tend to move in opposite directions. If the solid is free to move, the movement is called electrophoresis, but if the aqueous phase is free while the solid phase is immobile (as when two solutions are separated by a porous membrane), the water movement is called electrosmosis.

Electrosmosis is frequently invoked to explain water movements in biological systems where no other explanation seems adequate, but its importance is uncertain.

Ion Binding by Proteins and Other Ion Complexes

Many organic substances, including proteins, creatine phosphate and adenosine triphosphate are able to combine with both monovalent and polyvalent ions, but particularly the latter. It has sometimes been suggested that a large fraction of the intracellular ions is not in free solution. Direct measurements of potassium in squid giant axon show that the activity coefficient is only slightly less than that of the potassium in an organic solution of the same concentration (see above, p.25). In many tissues, practically all the sodium, potassium and chloride is freely exchangeable with these ions in the extracellular fluid, and in several tissues, the intracellular ions can be shown to be in a Donnan equilibrium with the ions outside. Recently, it has been calculated that, in frog muscle, the adenosine, myosin and creatine phosphate together hold 13% of monovalent cations, 64% of the calcium, and 70% of the magnesium in undissociated complexes (Nanninga, 1961). The complexed ions are in equilibrium with the free ions and are freely exchangeable. More stable complexes of ions with proteins, in which the bound ions are not freely exchangeable with the free ions, are known. There is some evidence that proteins can bind small quantities even of monovalent ions. Albumen combines about 10 chloride ions to each albumen molecule (Dick, 1959), a quarter of the potassium in *Nephrops* muscle may be bound (Robertson, 1961) and about a quarter of the sodium in squid giant axon (Hinke, 1961). It has been argued that the kinetics of sodium and potassium exchange in muscle imply that a significant proportion of these ions are bound (Harris, 1957; Botzler and Levine, 1958), but the data are open to other interpretations.* The possibility of several phases or compartments within the cell should not be forgotten (Harris and Sjodin, 1961). Mitochondria are able to accumulate sodium, potassium and chloride, although it does not follow that these ions are bound within the mitochondria (Robertson, Wilkins and Hope, 1955; Harris, 1960). Probably some form of ion binding occurs temporarily during active transport of ions, but at any time the proportion of ions bound in this way will be very small.

Although the binding of monovalent ions is uncommon, there is good evidence for the binding of both calcium and

* For recent reviews, see Glynn, 1959 and Robinson, 1960.

magnesium ions in blood. Robertson's dialysis experiments (Chap. III, p.107) show that a significant fraction of the plasma calcium is bound to protein in the crustaceans and molluscs, although magnesium binding does not seem to be significant. The binding of calcium in molluscan blood has also been demonstrated by tracer techniques (Chap. V, p.168). In mammalian plasma about a third of the magnesium is bound (Carr and Woods, 1955).

Inside the cells, the proportion of calcium and magnesium bound to proteins is much greater. Frog muscle has been estimated to contain about 1.5 mM Ca/kg water and 1.5 mM Mg/kg water bound intracellularly, and a further 0.25 mM Ca and 0.35 mM Mg are adsorbed on the cell surface (Gilbert and Fenn, 1956; Gilbert, 1960).

There is little evidence to support the view that any considerable proportion of intracellular water is bound although this suggestion has been made. According to recent work, protein in the cell may bind about 3 g of water for 100 g of protein (Robinson, 1960); in this case, only about 1% of the intracellular water will be bound in most tissues.

CHAPTER II

EXCRETORY ORGANS

Introduction to the Different Types

Excretory organs of one kind or another are found in all the metazoans, with the exceptions of the tunicates, echinoderms and coelenterates. In spite of their great variety of form, excretory organs can be grouped into four functional types, viz. ultrafiltration systems, malpighian tubes, contractile vacuoles, and flame cells and solenocytes.

In the molluscs, the crustaceans, the vertebrates,* and possibly those annelids which possess open nephridia, urine is produced initially by ultrafiltration from the blood into a coelomic space. While some of the invertebrate structures may not present all the criteria for ultrafiltration, this is at present the simplest explanation of their function. It is probable that the coxal glands of the arachnids also work in this way. A wide variety of animals and many larvae produce excretory fluids by a system of flame cells or solenocytes. These are characteristic of primitive animals which lack a high blood pressure, such as the platyhelminths and rotifers. When flame cells occur in larvae, as in the molluscan trochophore, they are generally replaced by ultrafiltration systems when the heart develops. In the insects, and in some other terrestrial arthropods, the excretory organs are malpighian tubes. These work in intimate association with the hind gut, which forms an essential part of

---

* With the exception of some teleosts, see p.53 below.

44

the excretory system. Some primitive insects still retain maxillary glands homologous with crustacean excretory organs, and many terrestrial arachnids have coxal glands like their marine relative, *Limulus*, but malpighian tubes appear to have replaced ultrafiltration systems in most terrestrial arthropods. Malpighian tubes have several advantages over ultrafiltration systems. They open into the gut and this allows subsequent water absorption in the rectum; they do not require a high blood pressure, absent in terrestrial arthropods breathing by tracheal systems; and finally, the ultrafiltration systems of arthropods open on to the limbs, mouthparts or legs, which could be inconvenient for a terrestrial animal.

Contractile vacuoles are found only in the freshwater protozoans and sponges and in marine ciliates. In the latter group, they are probably an inheritance from freshwater ancestors.

The principles of urine production are only understood in ultrafiltration systems. The forces which result in the accumulation of urine in the lumen of the malpighian tube, the flame cell or the contractile vacuole, are not known.

Ultrafiltration Systems

General

An ultrafiltrate is similar in electrolyte composition to the blood but differs in two ways, in that the ions in it are in a Donnan equilibrium with those in the blood, and ions bound to proteins in the blood are absent from the ultrafiltrate. These factors result in minor differences between the ionic content of blood and ultrafiltrate. In general, the ratio of the concentration of any substance of low molecular weight in the primary excretory fluid to its concentration in the blood (U/B ratio) will be close to unity. After the ultrafiltrate has been formed, it may be modified by absorption or secretion. In most animals, especially terrestrial forms, some degree of water resorption takes place. This increases the U/B ratio of any substance not simultaneously resorbed. In this way, waste products become highly concentrated in the urine without any secretory process. Some substances, notably the polysaccharide inulin, are neither secreted nor absorbed, so that the increase in the U/B ratio of these substances is a measure of the degree of water resorption, and the total quantity of inulin excreted is a measure of the filtration rate. The volume of blood which must be filtered in unit time to provide the inulin excreted, is the inulin clearance rate.

Glucose, amino acids and many ions are salvaged from the urine by resorption. The final U/B ratio for any solute will depend on the relative amounts of water and solute resorbed. Some poisons can prevent the resorption of solutes without stopping ultrafiltration; for example, phlorizin inhibits glucose resorption, leading to a U/B ratio for glucose the same as that for inulin.

Some substances, such as the dye phenol red, in addition to passing through the glomerular wall in the ultrafiltrate, are actively secreted by the kidney tubules after the ultrafiltrate has formed. When secretion occurs, the U/B ratio of these substances will be higher than that of inulin, but in the presence of a poison, 2-4-dinitrophenol, secretion of phenol red stops, and the U/B ratio returns to that of inulin. These general characteristics of ultrafiltration systems are modified in different classes of animals, and are discussed in greater detail in the following pages.

Vertebrates

The functional unit of the vertebrate kidney is the nephron. This consists of a knot of capillaries lying in a narrow coelomic space which is drained by a long convoluted tubule (Fig. II.1.). A single kidney may contain hundreds or thousands of such units. Ultrafiltration takes place from the capillaries into the coelomic space of the glomerulus and the ultrafiltrate is

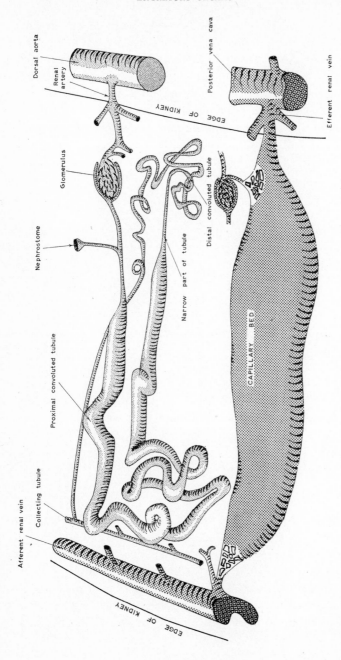

Fig. II.1. The structure of a single nephron

modified by resorption and secretion as it passes down the tubules. The convoluted tubule is usually divided into proximal and distal portions and additional segments are often present (Figs. II.1 and II.3). The glomeruli are supplied with blood from the renal arteries at high pressure. A renal portal system and the efferent vessels from the glomeruli supply the tubules in most fishes, amphibians and reptiles. In mammals and birds, the renal portal system has been lost but the supply from the efferent vessels is retained. Physiological studies of the amphibian kidney have been facilitated by the ease with which the two blood supplies can be separated.

Amphibia — The functioning of the frog's kidney, which represents an unspecialised type, is known in some detail. The average blood pressure in the glomerular capillaries is about 20 cm water, while the colloidal osmotic pressure of the blood is only 10 cm water (Hayman, 1927). Analyses of the blood and glomerular urine of the urodele *Necturus* showed that the concentrations of chloride, urea, inorganic phosphate and creatine, and the total osmotic pressure of the two fluids were the same, confirming that the urine is an ultrafiltrate of the blood (Westfall, Findlay and Richards, 1934; Richards, 1935). The glomerulus is permeable to small protein molecules such as haemoglobin, but haemoglobin does not appear in normal urine since it is confined within the erythrocytes.

During the passage of the ultrafiltrate down the proximal convoluted tubule, most of the glucose is resorbed (Fig. II.2a), while inulin and phenol red increase by about 30% as the result of the isosmotic resorption of water and salt (Walker and Hudson, 1937). In the presence of phlorizin, glucose resorption is stopped, and the concentration of glucose then also increases as urine passes along the proximal tubule. In the distal tubule, most of the remaining salt (Fig. II.2b) and some water is resorbed, so that the definitive urine is hypo-osmotic to the blood and almost salt free, but contains a fairly high concentration of nitrogenous waste (Walker, Hudson,

Findlay and Richards, 1937). In the presence of phlorizin, the glucose content of the urine rises to two and a half times that of the plasma in *Necturus*, and to three times that of the plasma in the frog, showing that considerable water resorption takes place (Walker and Hudson, 1937). The volume of the definitive

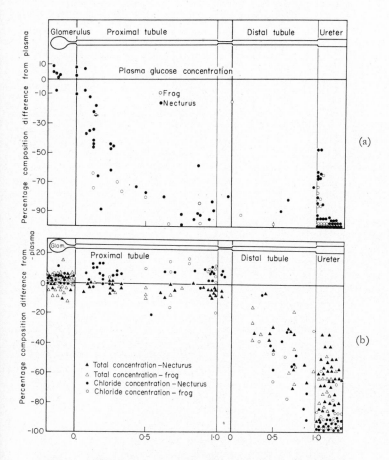

Fig. II.2. The glucose (2a) and chloride (2b) concentrations in the renal tubules of the frog and *Necturus*. The concentrations are expressed in terms of percentage deviation from the concentration in the plasma. From Walker, Hudson, Findlay and Richards, 1937; Walker and Hudson, 1937.

urine is controlled by the filtration rate, and/or by the proportion resorbed (see Chap. VI, p.236; Chap. XI, p.348). Recent measurements of the electrical potential differences across the wall of *Necturus* nephrons show that the sodium is extracted by a sodium pump in the outer wall of the tubule cells. Chloride moves passively down the electrical gradient created by the sodium flux (Giebisch, 1960).

The structure of the nephron in freshwater fish is similar to that of the amphibians and probably this represents a primitive type of vertebrate kidney. A number of modifications occur in those vertebrates which have returned to the sea or have become completely terrestrial.

Cyclostomes — The marine hagfishes retain a metamerically segmented kidney, each segment possessing a glomerulus and tubule, but there is no distal convoluted tubule (Fig. II.3). The absence of the distal convoluted tubule, which is usually associated with salt resorption and thus is an adaptation to fresh water, may here be a primitive feature; it should be noted, however, that it is secondarily absent in some marine teleosts. Both the blood and urine in marine hagfishes are isosmotic with sea water, and the high concentration is due almost entirely to salts (Robertson, 1954). The hagfishes may be primitively marine, unlike other vertebrates which have a low salt concentration in the blood and are descended from freshwater ancestors (Robertson, 1957).

The freshwater cyclostomes have a low blood concentration of only 274 mOsm/kg water (Sawyer, M. 1955). The urine flow of 160-360 ml/kg/day is large (Wikgren, 1953; Sawyer, M. 1955) although the filtration surface is relatively small. The urine chloride is low; 0.7 mM/l. in *Lampetra* (Wikgren, 1953), 4.7 mM/l. in *Petromyzon* (Sawyer, M. 1955) as a result of salt resorption which probably takes place in the distal tubule.

Elasmobranchs— Elasmobranchs, although ultimately of fresh water origin, are a marine group with a few secondary freshwater species (Romer and Grove, 1935; Robertson, 1957). They have glomerular kidneys with elaborate proximal tubules, and

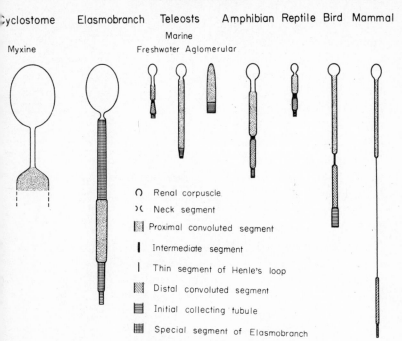

Cyclostome   Elasmobranch   Teleosts   Amphibian Reptile Bird Mammal

Marine

Myxine   Freshwater Aglomerular

Ω   Renal corpuscle

)(Neck segment

▓   Proximal convoluted segment

| Intermediate segment

| Thin segment of Henle's loop

▨   Distal convoluted segment

☰   Initial collecting tubule

▤   Special segment of Elasmobranch

Fig. II.3. Comparative structure of some vertebrate nephrons. From Marshall, 1934.

the urine is usually a little hypo-osmotic to the blood. A relic of their freshwater origin is the low salt concentration of the blood, although the total osmotic concentration is greater than that of sea water, because of the presence of a high concentration of urea. Urea is filtered by the glomeruli, but it is largely resorbed during the passage of the urine through the proximal convoluted tubules. Special segments are present at either end of the proximal tubule (Fig. II.3) but urea resorption does not appear to be localised in these parts. The unresorbed urea varies directly with the rate of ultrafiltration and inversely with the resorption of water (Kempton, 1953). The urine flow in marine elasmobranchs is very low (2–24 ml/kg/day) (Smith, 1931 a), even though the rate of filtration is much higher (80–90 ml/kg/day) (Clarke, 1936).

5

Freshwater elasmobranchs still retain a high blood urea concentration. Osmotic inflow of water through the gills is considerable and this dilutes the blood and increases urine flow, therefore increasing urea excretion and reducing the blood urea. In turn, this reduces the urine flow and starts a new cycle of urea retention; the blood concentration thus varies cyclically (Smith, 1953).

Teleosts — In freshwater teleosts, the structure of the nephron is the typical vertebrate one, but in marine forms, the distal tubule is often absent and some marine fish are aglomerular (Edwards, 1928). One freshwater pipefish, *Microphis boaja*, probably a recent immigrant from the sea, is also aglomerular. In freshwater fishes, the urine is hypo-osmotic to the blood (ca. 13 mOsm/kg water, Black, 1957) as a result of salt resorption. In marine teleosts with a glomerular kidney, the neck segment between the glomerulus and the tubule is often restricted and the kidney may be functionally aglomerular. The proximal tubule is divided into two parts, of which the second is homologous with the tubule of the aglomerular kidney (Fig. II.3). Most endogenous nitrogen is lost through the gills, but some nitrogen end products are concentrated in the urine, even in the aglomerular *Lophius* (the angler fish) (Brull, Nizet and Verney, 1953).

Since marine teleosts suffer from a chronic water shortage (Chap. VII, p.287), filtration is low and water is resorbed in the kidney tubule (Marshall and Grafflin, 1932) so that urine flow is reduced to a minimum. For example, *Myoxocephalus*, the sculpin, filters 14 ml/kg/day, but excretes only about a fifth of this (Clarke, 1934). The urine is nearly isosmotic with the blood, but contains less sodium and chloride, more magnesium, sulphate and nitrogenous waste. A comparison of the clearance rates and of magnesium and sulphate concentrations show that magnesium and sulphate are secreted into the urine after filtration (Marshall, 1934). Secretion in the kidney tubules of the flounder *Pseudopleuronectes* is dependent on the presence of potassium, and is inhibited by cold and drugs. It may be dependent on the activity of alkaline phosphatase present in the tubule cells (Forster, 1948; Forster and Taggart, 1950; Taggart and Forster, 1950; Forster, Sperber and Taggart, 1954).

The presence or absence of glomeruli in the kidneys of marine fish seems to be as much a species characteristic reflecting the phylogenetic relationships of the fish as a response to environment. Aglomerular and glomerular kidneys are not sharply separated and both forms may occur even within a single genus. The relative roles played by filtration and secretion in the formation of the urine may change with variable conditions. For example, the sculpin, *Myoxocephalus*, usually filters less than 15 ml/kg/day, but during diuresis caused by handling, filtration may increase to 188 ml/kg/day. When the fish is in dilute sea water, the U/B ratio of inulin may fall to 0.67, indicating that water may be secreted as well as filtered (Forster, 1953) (cf. the rainbow trout, below).

The aglomerular marine teleosts must produce urine solely by secretion. The blood supply is a renal portal system at a very low pressure, but urine formation in *Lophius* kidney is independent of the blood pressure and rate of blood flow above a critical level, but at very low levels or in the presence of metabolic poisons such as cyanide or fluoride, it is reduced or stopped (Brull, Nizet and Verney, 1953; Brull and Cuypers, 1954 a, 1954 b). Inulin does not appear in the urine from the blood, nor does exogenous or endogenous sugar (Forster, 1953).

In the aglomerular teleosts, as in the glomerular ones, the urine is slightly hypo-osmotic to the blood and contains much less sodium and chloride, and more non-protein nitrogen and magnesium (Table VII.5). In *Lophius*, magnesium may be concentrated up to a hundred times in the urine, the degree of concentration being independent of the plasma magnesium above a threshold of 2mM Mg/l. (Brull and Cuypers, 1954). If blood is perfused continuously through an isolated kidney, magnesium secretion continues until all detectable magnesium has been removed from the blood. During laboratory diuresis, the urine of *Lophius* becomes almost isosmotic with the blood, and its chloride concentration may even exceed that of the blood (Forster, 1953).

Many teleosts are able to move from one salinity to another with little change in blood concentration. Part of the accommodation to a new salinity is achieved by altering the urine flow (Hickman, 1959; Holmes, R., 1961). The rainbow trout, *Salmo gairdnerii*, in fresh water produces a large volume (75–90 ml/kg/day) of dilute urine (5–12 mM Cl/l.) but in sea water a small volume (1–0.5 ml/kg/day) of isosmotic urine (200–220 mM Cl/l.). The reduction in urine flow after transfer to sea water is first achieved both by an increase in tubular resorption and by a reduction in filtration rate. Later, the filtration rate returns to normal, but tubular resorption continues at a high level (Holmes, R., 1961, and pers. comm.).

As a general rule, the urine of marine fish is acid (Smith, 1929a). Chloride is excreted principally by the gills, but magnesium and phosphate by the kidney. Magnesium excretion can be achieved only at a low pH of 6 or less, otherwise magnesium hydroxide will precipitate out. Magnesium phosphate is excreted as a supersaturated solution (Pitts, 1934).

Reptiles — The reptiles are primitively a terrestrial group and many species live in dry habitats, yet the kidney is morphologically and physiologically similar to that of the amphibians or freshwater fishes, although the renal portal blood supply is less important. Nitrogenous waste is mostly converted to insoluble uric acid, so the osmotic pressure of the urine is not raised by high concentrations of nitrogenous material, and the volume of urine can be reduced to conserve water. A further resorption of water may take place in the cloaca, and the urine form a semi-solid paste there, but however concentrated, the urine is never hyperosmotic to the blood.

Even in the aquatic alligator, considerable resorption takes place after filtration. The glomerular filtrate is 1.5–3.4 ml/kg/hr, but the urine flow is only 0.4–1.2 ml/kg/hr (Marshall, 1934). The urine is approximately isosmotic with the blood, but the greater part of its osmotic pressure is due to ammonium and bicarbonate ions (Coulson and Hernandez, 1959). Marine reptiles have extrarenal organs of salt excretion which enable them to remove salt but conserve water (Chap. VII, p.303) and these organs must be regarded as a corollary of the primitive structure of the reptile kidney.

Birds and mammals — In both the birds and the mammals, the kidneys produce a urine which may be hyperosmotic to the blood. In the birds, this is not very marked, but in the mammals, a concentration as high as 2150 mOsm./l. has been reported for seal urine (Smith, 1936b), and 3,600 mM urea/l. has been reported in the kangaroo rat, *Dipodomys* (Schmidt-Nielsen, 1951). In both birds and mammals, the salt concentration of the urine may exceed that of the blood. Korr (1939) found that urine of the domestic hen could contain up to 190 mM NaCl/l. when the blood contained only 161 mM*; urine chlorides as high as 900 mM/l. have been reported for the kangaroo rat (Schmidt-Nielsen, Schmidt-Nielsen and Schneiderman, 1948).

The morphological equivalent of the ability to produce a hyperosmotic urine is the loop of Henle, a thin portion of duct intercalated between the proximal and distal tubules (Figs. II.3 & II.4). In mammals, where the loop of Henle is best developed, the glomeruli and the proximal and distal tubules are confined to the outer portion or cortex of the kidney, while the loops of Henle run down into the medulla (Fig. II.3), although only a small proportion extend into the papilla.

Glucose resorption takes place in the proximal convoluted tubule and there is a considerable isosmotic resorption of

* The North American Savannah sparrow, *Passerculus sandwichensis beldingi* can produce urine containing 960 mM Cl/l, more than five times the plasma concentration, and can maintain a constant weight when confined to drinking 0.7 M NaCl. It does not secrete hyperosmotic salt solutions extrarenally (Paulson and Bartholomew, 1962).

salts and water so that urea may be concentrated by the
time the urine reaches the loop of Henle, although at this
stage the urea is still only a small component of the total
osmotic pressure. Further resorption of salt and water occurs

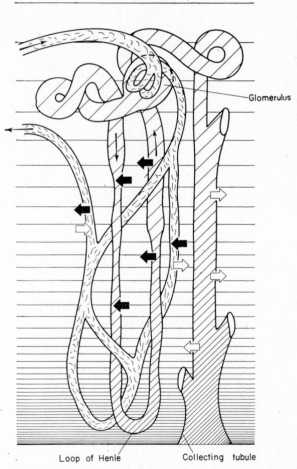

Fig. II.4. The mammalian nephron and blood vessels. The density
of the shading corresponds to the osmotic concentration. The
open arrows indicate water movement, the solid arrows indicate
salt movement. From Wirz, 1953.

in the distal convoluted tubule so that the urea may be concentrated again when the urine reaches the collecting tubule, where further water resorption takes place.

Hargitay, Kuhn and Wirz (1951) have shown that the contents of the proximal convoluted tubule are isosmotic with the blood, but the urine becomes concentrated as it descends the loop of Henle and then diluted again in the ascending limb of the loop (Figs. II.4 and II.5). In the first part of the distal tubule, the urine is slightly hypo-osmotic to the blood (Wirz, 1956) but becomes isosmotic again by the middle of the distal tubule, and as the urine descends the collecting tubule it becomes concentrated once more. In any section of the medulla concentric with the kidney surface, the contents of the two limbs of the loop of Henle and the collecting tubules are thus all approximately isosmotic (Fig. II.5).

At first sight it seems extraordinary that the urine, initially isosmotic, should become concentrated, then diluted and finally concentrated for a second time, while flowing through the nephron. Hargitay et al. (1951) have provided an ingenious hypothesis to account for this. They suggest that the contents of the loop of Henle become concentrated by a "hairpin counter current" mechanism. If solutes are transferred from the ascending limb to the descending limb as the urine flows through the loop of Henle, the urine in the loop will become concentrated. The solute transfer need not take place between the two parts of the same limb but a general transfer from ascending to descending limbs is envisaged. The site of active transport has not been localised; it probably takes place between the ascending limbs and the peritubular fluid, and solutes pass to the descending limb by diffusion. As a result of these movements, the urine in the descending limb will receive continuous increments of salt and so will become increasingly concentrated until it enters the ascending limb where an equivalent quantity of salt will be lost. It is important to note that in an ideal system of this sort, no energy will be required to maintain the system once it has been established, because any two adjacent ascending and descending limbs are isosmotic at all points. Hargitay

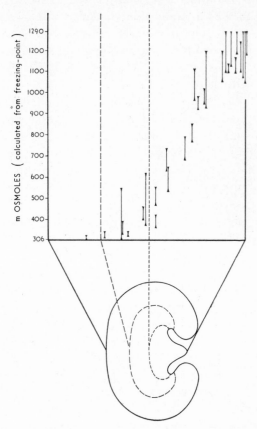

Fig. II.5. The total osmotic concentration in the lumen of the tubules of the kidney of the rat. From Hargitay, Kuhn and Wirz, 1951.

et al. go on to suggest that the concentrated salt solution in the loop of Henle then concentrates the urine in the collecting tubule by exosmosis, so that the urine leaving the kidney may be isosmotic with the liquid in the head of the loop of Henle.

Recent micropuncture studies (Lassiter, Gottschalk and Mylle, 1961) show that there is a net loss of solute from the ascending, and water from the descending limb. The results are compatible with an active transport of salt and a passive movement of water and urea.

As the result of resorption in the distal convoluted tubule, the flow of liquid in the collecting tubule may be only a fraction of the flow of liquid in the loop of Henle, so the influx of water back into the loop from the collecting tubules would not seriously disturb the concentration gradients established in the loop. However, the influx and the active resorption of sodium chloride from the ascending limb would slightly reduce the concentration in the loop of Henle so that the urine leaving the loop is slightly hypo-osmotic to the blood. Much of the active work of the kidney must be performed in transferring salt across the small concentration difference between the two limbs (Fig. II.4). The concentration of the urine cannot exceed the maximum concentration in the loops of Henle. When concentrated urine is being produced (antidiuresis), the concentrations of salt and urea vary inversely. The final concentration of salt depends on the degree of salt resorption in the distal convoluted tubules and collecting ducts (Schmidt-Nielsen, O'Dell and Osaki, 1961). This complex mechanism may be advantageous in two ways. First, although it ultimately produces a very concentrated urine, there are no steep concentration gradients within the kidney and the large concentration differences are produced by compounding small ones along considerable lengths of tubule. Steep concentration gradients, such as would be produced by the direct excretion of the urea from the blood into the urine, would require very powerful transport mechanisms and would suffer from considerable back diffusion of solutes and water down the concentration gradients. Secondly, the concentration is produced by the active transport of ions and not of urea. Although selachians can apparently transport urea, it is generally not subject to active transport. Ion transport, however, is a universal property of cells and it may be that ions can be more easily and efficiently transported.

The blood vessels in the medulla, the vasa recta, are also U-shaped, and their contents in each zone are isosmotic with the contents of the loops of Henle (Wirz, 1953; Gottschalk, 1960). It is probable that the "hairpin counter current" system operates here as well. In this way, the medulla may be supplied with blood without upsetting the osmotic gradient. Berliner, Levinsky, Davidson and Eden (1960) have recently criticised the hairpin counter current hypothesis on the grounds that, in order to establish the gradient, it is necessary for there to be a small osmotic concentration difference at each point between the limbs of the loops of Henle, and this requires that the limbs shall be impermeable to water. On the other hand, the resorption of water from the collecting tubules requires that the limbs shall be freely permeable to water. These authors argued that the hypothesis is therefore self-contradictory. However, the concentration differences within the loop are generally much smaller than those between the loop and the collecting tubule, so a significant uptake could be achieved from the latter while the osmotic movements between the former, although wasteful of energy, would not be sufficient to upset the gradient.

Although the mammalian kidney appears to be finely adapted to producing a hyperosmotic urine, it is still capable of producing a hypo-osmotic urine. When the rat is heavily loaded with water, the urine remains hypo-osmotic to the blood from the distal convoluted tubule right through to the ureter, and the resorption of water which normally occurs in the distal tubule and the collecting tubule is inhibited although salt resorption continues (Wirz, 1956). In diuresis, the distal convoluted tubule is relatively impermeable to water, but salt resorption is unaffected. The counter current system still operates but the concentrating effect is reduced by the large influx of water from the collecting ducts and the osmolar concentration in the papilla is low (Kill and Aukland, 1960). Wirz suggests that the antidiuretic hormone acts by increasing the permeability of the walls of the distal tubule and collecting tubule, facilitating the osmotic withdrawal of water from the urine. In this way, the amount of water excreted can be independent of the urea excretion, which depends on the filtration rate.

The amounts of the individual ions in the urine are also independent of the rates of water and urea excretion. In general, sodium and potassium are resorbed passively as the result of the active uptake of chloride (Koch, Brazeau and Gilman, 1956) and the kidney does not distinguish between these two ions. Potassium in the ultrafiltrate is small, because it is derived from the blood, but when there is an excess of potassium in the body, active potassium secretion and sodium absorption by exchange occurs in the distal tubule (Berliner, Kennedy and Hilton, 1950).

Although the resorption of sodium and potassium is linked with that of chloride, the acid-base balance of the urine can be altered by the synthesis and secretion of ammonia and by the secretion of hydrogen ions in exchange for sodium in the distal tubule. The high phosphate content of the urine buffers it against acid and alkali secretion, but even so, the pH of human urine may fluctuate between 4.8 and 7.8.

The mammalian kidney is capable of secreting a very large number of different substances into the urine, but there are relatively few secretory mechanisms, each dealing with a variety of substances. As a result, substances which are secreted fall into a number of groups. For example, one such group includes phenol red, p-aminohippuric acid, penicillin and diodrast. In moderate amounts, each of these substances mutually inhibits the excretion of the other members of the same group, which suggests that they all compete for the same mechanism. Any poison, such as probenecid, which blocks the excretion of one member of the group, blocks them all. Another group includes a number of organic bases, such as tetraethylammonium and N-methylnicotinamide. Again, members of this group mutually inhibit one another but they do not interact with members of the other group, and the excretion of the substances of this group is prevented by minute quantities of the dye cyanine, which has no effect on the excretion of the phenol red group.

The final volume of urine in the mammals is largely controlled by the degree of resorption, and the filtration rate is relatively constant. Desert mammals have thicker medullary zones than related non-desert animals, and desert rodents have remarkably long papillae extending down into the ureters (Sperber, 1944). This may be a specialisation to allow for greater resorption and the development of a more concentrated urine.

Bird kidneys probably function in a similar fashion to mammalian kidneys but the final volume of urine depends to a greater degree on the filtration rate (Korr, 1959). The main nitrogen excretory product is uric acid, not urea. Since water is resorbed from the collecting tubules, uric acid is precipitated and may form a thick soup or sludge within the kidney. In order to facilitate the removal of this viscous urine, the ureters are peristaltic and branch to meet the collecting ducts (there being no pelvis as in the mammal). As the maximum osmotic pressure of the urine is not very high, the maximum salt content is probably much lower than in the mammal. Unlike the reptiles they appear to have no cloacal resorption.

The kidneys of the lower vertebrates are known to resemble the mammalian kidney in many respects, such as in their ability to respond to the antidiuretic hormone, to adjust the acid-base balance of the urine, and to secrete substances into the urine after filtration, but such information is scattered and incomplete compared with our knowledge of the mammalian kidney.

Invertebrates

Molluscs: Lamellibranchs, Gastropods, Pulmonates, and Cephalopods — In the lamellibranchs, ultrafiltration probably takes place through the walls of the heart into the pericardium and the urine passes to the exterior through a pair of excretory ducts variously referred to as kidneys, nephridia, renal organs, or the organs of Bojanus. The excretory ducts are U-shaped. The glandular proximal limb drains the pericardium through the reno-pericardial opening and then runs ventral to the distal limb which forms a thin-walled bladder (Fig. II.6).

Experimental evidence of the function of the excretory system is confined to the freshwater species which produce a copious urine, but it is probable that the marine species produce urine in the same way, as they are anatomically similar.

In the freshwater *Anodonta*, Picken (1937) has shown that the mean hydrostatic pressure in the ventricle (6.0 cm water) is greater than the colloidal osmotic pressure of the blood (2.8 cm water) which is an essential condition for ultrafiltration.* The pericardial fluid has the composition of an ultrafiltrate of the blood; its colloidal osmotic pressure is very low indeed but its total osmotic pressure is the same as that of the blood (Picken, 1937), while the chloride, calcium and phosphate contents are almost identical(Florkin and Duchâteau, 1948). The calcium concentration is anomalous because about 29% of the calcium appears to be bound to protein (Fredericq, Bacq and Florkin, 1951).

The rate of inulin clearance in *Anodonta* varies from 2.0 ml/kg/hr at 0°C, to 12 ml/kg/hr at 18°C, and the rate of urine flow appears to be similar (Potts, 1954 b†), although Picken

* The colloidal osmotic pressure of the blood was calculated from the protein content, on the rather doubtful assumption that the average molecular weight of the proteins was the same as in human blood. Some direct measurements of the colloidal osmotic pressure of the blood would be valuable.

† Weight here refers to an animal without shell.

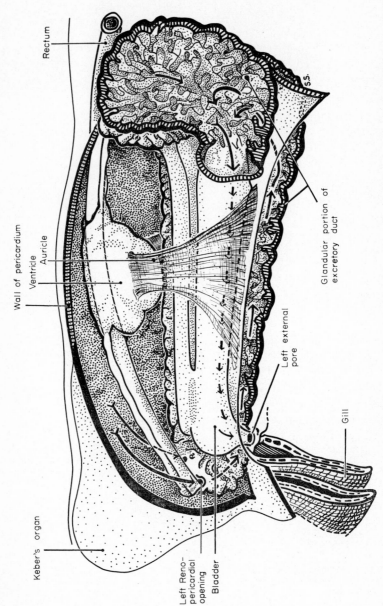

Rectum

S.S.

Wall of pericardium

Ventricle

Auricle

Glandular portion of excretory duct

Left external pore

Keber's organ

Gill

Left Reno-pericardial opening

Bladder

Fig. II.6. Diagram to illustrate the structure and relations of the excretory system of a lamellibranch, *Anodonta*.

(1937) found that when the pericardium was opened, fluid accumulated at an average rate of 200 ml/kg/hr at 17°C. It can be calculated that the rate of inulin clearance in the American freshwater lamellibranch, *Margaritifera*, was equivalent to 8.1% of body water/hr (temperature and weight unspecified), whereas in the marine species, *Mytilus californianus*, the rate of inulin clearance was equivalent to only 1.1% of the body water/hr (Martin, Harrison, Huston and Stewart, 1958).

Before it is voided, the composition of the urine is modified by the activity of the excretory duct. In *Anodonta*, the bladder urine has only 60% of the osmotic concentration of the blood (Picken, 1937) and the chloride has fallen to 55% (Florkin and Duchâteau, 1948). No data are available for the composition of the urines of marine lamellibranchs, but it is to be expected that some degree of ionic regulation occurs.

In the lamellibranchs, the pericardial wall is usually thickened to form pericardial glands. They are particularly well developed in the Unionidae and are known as Keber's organs (Fig. II.6). These glands will absorb dyes such as ammonium carmine, but their function in normal conditions is not known.

The excretory system of the lower gastropods consists of two renal organs draining the pericardium, and pericardial glands which lie over the auricles, but in higher gastropods the right post-tortional organ is no longer excretory.* In the pulmonates, the renal organ opens to the exterior by a long narrow duct In the freshwater pulmonate *Lymnaea peregra*, the pericardial fluid is approximately isosmotic with the blood (Picken, 1937), but the final urine has only 70% of the blood concentration.

As in the lamellibranchs, the hydrostatic pressure of the

---

* A recent study of the primitive gastropod, *Haliotis*, indicates that both right and left kidneys filter inulin, whereas phenolsulphonphthalein and *p*-amino-hippuric acid are secreted by the right kidney, and glucose is resorbed by the left kidney (Harrison, 1962).

blood in the heart of *Lymnaea stagnalis* (8 cm water) exceeds the colloidal osmotic pressure (2.5 cm water) and the pericardial fluid contains much less protein than the blood and so is probably an ultrafiltrate. The rate of filtration in *Lymnaea* is unknown, but it can be calculated (from the figures of Martin *et al.*, 1958), that the inulin clearance rate in the marine species, *Aplysia californicus*, is 1.4% of the body water/hr.

Land pulmonates usually conserve water. Nitrogen waste is converted to uric acid and accumulates in the cells lining the lumen of the renal organ and is excreted in the urine. In the large African snail *Achatina*, ultrafiltration appears to take place, not from the heart, but from the renal artery, into the lumen of the renal organ (Martin, Stewart and Harrison, 1954). When a free flow of urine was allowed, the ultrafiltration rate was 50 ml/kg/hr and the U/B ratio of inulin was approximately unity. In the presence of suitable poisons, the U/B ratios of glucose and phenol red were also approximately unity, but in the absence of these poisons, glucose was resorbed and the dye secreted into the urine. U/B ratios for phenol red as high as 90 were recorded. When the urine flow was impeded, a back pressure was created and the U/B ratio for inulin rose, indicating water resorption, but the dye was still secreted into the urine. The duct is provided with sphincters which could aid water conservation by raising pressure within the renal organ. It is not clear if water absorption takes place in the duct as well as in the renal organ. Under normal conditions the pressure within the renal organ will reduce the filtration rate, but the rate of filtration is doubtless much greater than the rate of urine production. During aestivation or hibernation, the urine flow may cease altogether. The inulin clearance rate of the slug, *Arion*, is 5.4% body water/hr (from the data of Martin *et al.*, 1958), but again, it is probable that most of this filtrate is resorbed.

In the cephalopods, the renal organs form a pair of thin-walled coelomic sacs surrounding the afferent branchial veins.

The branchial and systemic hearts are so muscular that ultrafiltration through the hearts is unlikely. Martin (1957) suggested that ultrafiltration took place through a network of fine veins, the renal appendages, which cover the afferent branchial veins as they run through the renal sacs. The afferent branchial veins and the vessels of the renal appendages are peristaltic so that local pressure would be available for ultrafiltration. However, recent work (Martin and Harrison, pers. comm.) indicates that filtration occurs in the pericardial glands which form large organs adjacent to the branchial hearts. The lumen of these glands communicates with the lumen of the branchial hearts and with that of the renal sacs. The renal sacs are probably the site of resorption.

In *Octopus*, urine appears to be formed by ultrafiltration and modified by resorption and secretion. The U/B ratio for inulin is about unity, showing that water resorption does not occur. When the renal sacs of *Octopus honkongensis* were catheterised, the inulin clearance rate was *ca.* 4 ml/kg/hr (Martin *et al.*, 1958), but when the sacs were ligated, it was only 2.6 ml/kg/hr (Martin, 1957), presumably because the increased pressure in the renal sacs reduced the ultrafiltration rate. In *Sepia*, the sucrose clearance rate was at least 18 ml/kg/hr (Robertson, 1953).

Ammonia is highly concentrated in the urine, most probably by diffusing in as ammonia and being trapped as the larger and less diffusible ammonium ion. Robertson (1954) found that *Sepia* excretory fluid contained 146 mM NH_4/kg water; Denton, Shaw and Gilpin-Brown (1958) found that some squid contained 480 mM NH_4/kg water in the coelomic fluid (Chap. III, p.97). Although the ammonia content of *Octopus* blood is very low, it excretes large quantities (Delaunay, 1931). In the bathyscaphoid squids, the coelomic fluid was very acid (pH 5.2), and so the concentration of unionised ammonia will be lower than in the blood (Denton *et al.*, 1958). A reduction of 2 pH units would lower the concentration of free ammonia a hundred-fold.

6

Crustaceans — The renal organs of crustaceans are maxillary (shell) glands and antennal (green) glands. These pairs of glands are said to be the remnants of a segmental excretory system and traces of a complete segmental arrangement can be seen in the cephalocaridan, *Hutchinsoniella* (Waterman, 1960). In general, the glands have three principal parts, an internal end-sac, an excretory tubule, and an exit duct sometimes enlarged into a bladder. These parts may be modified in different species, sections being absent in some, and extra segments appearing in others.

In some ways, the structure of the antennal gland is analogous to a single vertebrate nephron, but whether it functions in the same way is still a matter of controversy. A capillary blood system has not yet been demonstrated in the crustacean end-sac, but there is a relatively direct arterial blood supply to the whole organ, splitting into numerous fine vessels in the region of the end-sac (Balss, 1944; Parry, G., 1955; Burger, 1957) (Fig. II.7). The end-sac is said to be held open by strands of connective tissue running to adjacent structures (Goodrich, 1946).

The end-sac leads into the excretory tubule (labyrinth), which modifies the fluid passing through it. The labyrinth is very variable in its development within the group, being completely absent in some marine forms such as the shrimp, *Crangon*, while an additional segment, probably concerned with the production of the hypo-osmotic urine, is present in some freshwater forms such as the crayfishes and gammarids (Peters, 1935; Schwabe, 1933). The labyrinth leads to the excretory duct, which in some species, especially in the hermit crabs, ramifies into an extensive bladder.

Whether a sufficient hydrostatic pressure for ultrafiltration is present is much debated. The relatively direct arterial blood supply to the end-sac should provide a considerable pressure, at least at systole. In the freshwater crayfish, *Astacus*, the hydrostatic pressure in the first leg is about 37 cm water and the colloid osmotic pressure 27 cm water, while that

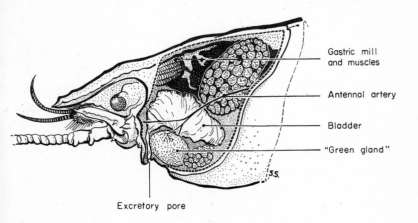

Gastric mill
and muscles

Antennal artery

Bladder

"Green gland"

Excretory pore

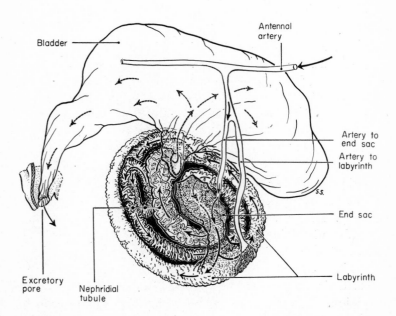

Bladder

Antennal
artery

Artery to
end sac

Artery to
labyrinth

End sac

Labyrinth

Excretory
pore

Nephridial
tubule

Fig. II.7. The structure and relations of the renal organ in the
crayfish *Astacus pallipes*.

of the urine is only 4 cm water (Picken, 1936). In the marine lobster, *Homarus*, the hydrostatic pressure in the heart was only 9 cm water greater than in the haemocoele (Burger and Smythe, 1953), but the lobster produces only a very small volume of urine and has been shown to be anuric for long periods (Burger, 1957). Changes in the salinity of the medium can change the rate of urine flow in the brackish water prawn, *Palaemonetes varians* (Parry G., 1955, 1957) (Chap. VIII. p.320). The crab, *Cancer pagurus*, kept in 50% sea water showed a rise in the hydrostatic pressure of the blood, which increased still further if the excretory ducts were blocked (Huf, 1936). Urine formation in lobsters ceased when the blood became concentrated after they had been desiccated (Burger, 1957), and this was associated with high blood protein levels. Although Burger does not interpret his data in terms of ultrafiltration, this could provide a mechanism for altering colloid osmotic pressures to regulate the rate of urine flow.

In the lobster, the U/B ratio of inulin is close to unity in all media. Magnesium has a U/B ratio greater than unity in sea water, but less in diluted sea water, indicating that it is secreted in sea water but resorbed in diluted sea water. Glucose and phosphate are resorbed, and as in the vertebrates, phlorizin inhibits glucose resorption and the U/B ratio drops to unity. As in the vertebrates, *p*-aminohippuric acid and phenol red are secreted into the urine and their U/B ratios are greater than unity, but if the plasma concentrations of these substances are very high, their U/B ratios approach unity. That is to say, the secretory system is easily saturated, and at high plasma levels, the fraction filtered greatly exceeds the fraction secreted (Burger, 1957).

If the common shore crab, *Carcinus*, is kept in water saturated air, the U/B ratio for inulin rises steadily over a 4 day period. At the same time, the ratio for sodium declines to about 0.5, those for chloride and potassium remain relatively steady at about unity, while those for calcium and especially for magnesium rise. This has been interpreted as evidence for water resorption from the urine after primary filtration from the blood. Even in crabs in sea water aquaria, the U/B ratios for inulin are about 2, so water resorption probably also takes place in normal conditions. The concurrence of the rising U/B ratio for inulin, and the falling one for sodium, suggests that the withdrawal of sodium and water are linked. Magnesium in the urine rises to such high concentrations that it seems most probable that this ion is secreted (Riegel and Lockwood, 1961).

Crustacean urine is isosmotic with the blood except in some freshwater species such as the crayfishes, e.g. *Cambarus* (Lienemann, 1938) and *Astacus* (Bryan, 1960 a), and the gammarids, e.g. *Gammarus duebeni* and *G. pulex* (Lockwood, 1961). In these forms an additional segment is intercalated between the nephridial tubule and the bladder. Analyses of chloride in the end-sac fluid of *Astacus* showed it to be present there in almost the same concentration as in the blood, even though chloride in the definitive urine is very low. The reduction in chloride concentration takes place during the passage of the urine along the nephridial canal (Fig. II.8). In the freshwater crayfishes, *Procambarus clarkii* and *Orconectes viridis*, both producing a hypo-osmotic urine, the usual inulin U/B ratios are between 2 and 3, indicating some water loss (Riegel, 1961). Other freshwater crustaceans produce urine almost isosmotic with the blood, e.g. *Palaemonetes antennarius* (blood 403 mOsm/kg water; urine 360 mOsm/kg water) (Parry, G., 1957), *Eriocheir sinensis* (blood 318 mOsm, urine 330 mOsm) (Scholles, 1933) and *Potamon edule* (blood and urine 630 mOsm/kg water) (Duval, 1925). These forms lack the additional nephridial segment. *Artemia* living in a very saline medium is said to produce a hyperosmotic urine (blood 376 mOsm/kg water, urine 1480 mOsm/kg water) (Medwedewa, 1927) but this requires confirmation and other mechanisms could account for its osmoregulatory activity (Chap. VII, p.315).

Analyses of individual ions in the urine of the marine decapods indicate that monovalent ions are relatively similar to
their concentrations in the blood; while the divalent ions, calcium, magnesium and sulphate, are altered in concentration.
This can be interpreted adequately in terms of an ultrafiltration

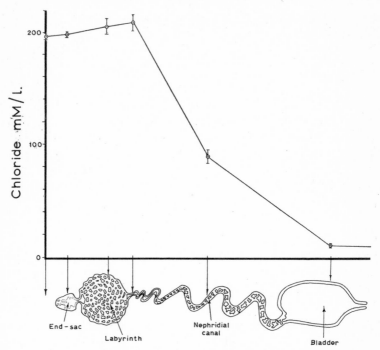

Fig. II.8. The concentration of chloride in the renal duct of the
crayfish, *Astacus fluviatilis*. From Peters, 1935.

of the blood in the end-sac, followed by resorption of calcium
and secretion of magnesium and sulphate in the excretory
tubule. In freshwater decapods, resorption of monovalent
ions also takes place.

As a result of his experiments with the American freshwater
crayfish, *Procambarus (Cambarus)*, Maluf (1939, 1941 a and b) did
not interpret his data in terms of filtration, but believed that

all the components of the urine were secreted. He found U/B rations for inulin greater than two, and sometimes as high as five. Although Maluf explained his data in terms of secretion, the concentration of these substances in the urine could also result from water resorption following filtration. Some recent experiments with this species, using both chemical and radio-active methods, have demonstrated that U/B ratios greater than unity could be brought about by water resorption (Riegel and Kirschner, 1960). These authors have reinterpreted Maluf's data and shown that their explanation is adequate to interpret his results.

The behaviour of injected dyes gives some indication of the functioning of the glands. Some dyes appear to be eliminated by the end-sac, some by the excretory tubule, while some are dealt with by both parts of the gland. Their behaviour seems to depend on molecular size, and is not incompatible with the theory of filtration followed by secretion in the tubular part of the kidney.

Nitrogen excretion in crustaceans (principally ammonia with some urea, and a very little uric acid) is not usually the concern of the antennal glands. The greater part of the nitrogenous waste is lost directly by diffusion, most probably through the thin epithelium of the gills. Uric acid is sometimes stored in "nephrocytes", or is utilised in the white chromatophores (Mollitor, 1937). In some terrestrial crustaceans, e.g. woodlice, it is deposited in the integument and cast with the moult (Dresel and Moyle, 1950) and even in the freshwater *Asellus*, uric acid is deposited in Zenker's organ (Lockwood, 1959b).

The semi-terrestrial crab, *Uca*, which is immersed in water only for short periods, is unusual in excreting a high concentration of ammonium ions in the urine (75 mM NH_4/l.) and the blood concentration is also very high (20 mM NH_4/l.) (Green, Harsch, Barr and Prosser, 1959). The ammonia may be concentrated in the urine by filtration and the resorption of water, but the urine is more acid than the blood so the ammonium may enter by diffusion as ammonia and be trapped as ammonium ions.

Arachnids — Little is known about the function of arachnid coxal glands. In the scorpion, the coxal gland consists of a central medulla (possible equivalent to an end-sac) and a tubular cortex. The cellular structure of the cortex is similar to that of mammalian proximal tubule (Rasmont, Vandermeersche and Castiaux, 1958). The blood-sucking mite, *Ornithodorus*, after a meal, produces a large volume of urine hyperosmotic to the blood (Boné, 1944).

Annelids — Primitive annelids have closed nephridia fed by numerous solenocytes, but in many species, the nephridia open into the coelom by a ciliated funnel, or nephrostome. In species with open nephridia, the relations between blood, coelom and nephridia are such that it would be possible for ultrafiltration to take place from the blood into the coelom, and for a modified coelomic fluid to appear as urine. In this case, the whole of the coelom would be equivalent to the arthropod end-sac (Ramsay, 1954 b). The evidence available neither denies nor confirms this hypothesis.

In the earthworm, *Lumbricus terrestris*, Ramsay (1949 a) found that the coelomic fluid was generally slightly hyperosmotic to the blood. This difference was not abolished when the worms were desiccated or when desiccated worms were returned to water. If the coelomic fluid is not isosmotic with the blood, it cannot be a simple ultrafiltrate. This concentration difference could withdraw osmotic water from the blood and provide a substitute for, or aid to, ultrafiltration. The hydrostatic blood pressure in *Lumbricus* may not be sufficient to overcome the colloidal osmotic pressure which may be high because of a high concentration of haemoglobin dissolved in the blood. Such an osmotic system could be maintained if salt were transferred from the blood to the coelom at some point, and returned to the blood or coelom from the nephridia.

On its passage to the exterior, the urine becomes hypoosmotic to the blood in the region of the wide tubule of the nephridium, and has lost 4/5th of its solutes by the time it reaches the bladder (Fig. II.9). Initially, the fluid at the inner end of the nephridium is isosmotic with the coelomic fluid and it seems probable that the definitive urine is a modification of the coelomic fluid. However, Bahl (1947) suggests that some ultrafiltration may take place from the blood directly into the nephridium. Wolf (1940) found that in *Lumbricus* the urine was produced at a rate of 25 ml/kg/hr.

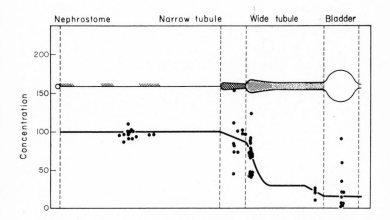

Fig. II.9. The osmotic pressure of the urine in different levels in the nephridium of the earthworm. The osmotic pressure of the Ringer surrounding the nephridium has been equated to 100. From Ramsay, 1949 a.

The observations of Bahl (1947) on the earthworm *Pheretima* raise a number of problems. He reports that as in *Lumbricus*, the sodium and chloride contents of the coelomic fluid of *Pheretima* are greater than those of the blood and that the urine has a much lower concentration than either, but that the total osmotic concentration of the blood is much higher than that of the coelomic fluid. This would imply that the blood contains a very large quantity of some non-electrolyte. This solute has not been identified, and until information is available it is difficult to relate Bahl's account of the physiology of *Pheretima* to that of other animals. If ultrafiltration does occur in the annelids, it is most likely to be found in marine species with open nephridia where the coelomic fluid is probably isosmotic with the blood.

Protonephridia

Many of those animals which lack a high pressure blood system, and which therefore cannot produce urine by direct ultra-filtration from the blood, possess protonephridia. A proto-nephridium is a narrow duct or a number of confluent ducts which end blindly in a flame bulb or solenocyte. A flame bulb bears a tuft of cilia which project into the lumen of the duct; a solenocyte bears only a single flagellum which usually extends far down the narrow duct. The cilia or the flagellum maintain a ceaseless movement and have something of the appearance of a flickering candle flame (Fig. II.10). Protonephridia are found in platyhelminths, nemertines, rotifers, gastrotrichs, endoproct polyzoans, cephalochordates and some annelids. They also occur in the trochophore larvae of the annelids and molluscs but are replaced in the molluscs and most annelids when the contractile blood vessels and adult excretory organs develop.

Although protonephridia are so widely distributed, little is known of their function. They are so minute that no one has yet succeeded in collecting and analysing their contents. There is not even much direct evidence that they are excretory organs, but Herfs (1922) showed that in an unnamed freshwater cer-caria, which possesses a regularly contracting bladder, the rate of urine production varied inversely with the concentration of the medium. This indicates that the protonephridia which feed the bladder, can function as osmoregulatory organs. In the rotifer, *Asplanchna*, the nephridia open into rhythmically con-tracting bladders and the flame beat and the urine flow de-crease with the osmotic gradient (Pontin, pers. comm.) The pro-tonephridia can excrete the equivalent of the body volume in about 11 hours at 16°C. In the euryhaline platyhelminth, *Gyratrix hermaphroditus*, the duct of the nephridium is longest and most elaborate in freshwater specimens, and simplest in marine ones (cf. crustaceans) (Kromhaut, 1943).

A number of workers (Bahl, 1945; Pantin, 1947; Martin, 1957) have suggested that the activity of the cilia or flagellum gives rise to a negative pressure inside the lumen of the proto-

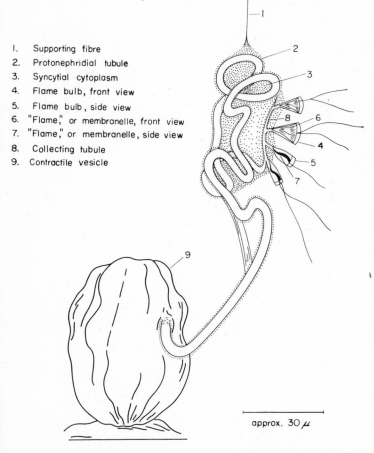

1. Supporting fibre
2. Protonephridial tubule
3. Syncytial cytoplasm
4. Flame bulb, front view
5. Flame bulb, side view
6. "Flame," or membranelle, front view
7. "Flame," or membranelle, side view
8. Collecting tubule
9. Contractile vesicle

approx. 30 μ

Fig. II.10. The structure of the protonephridium of the rotifer *Asplanchna priodonta*. From Pontin (unpublished).

nephridium and that urine is formed by ultrafiltration. This is supported by the observation that the rate of ciliary beat is proportional to the rate of urine production from the bladder (Pantin, unpublished). It is difficult to suggest any other function for the cilia, since a mere stirring of the contents of the duct would seem unnecessary in such a minute system, where diffusion would rapidly eliminate any concentration differences. However, it is difficult to imagine that the activity of a single flagellum or a small group of cilia could produce a pressure sufficient to produce ultrafiltration through the whole thickness of the flame bulb or solenocyte. To test this hypothesis, it should be possible to calculate from the dimensions of the system and the frequency of the "flame", the order of magnitude of the pressure produced.

Alkaline phosphatase, associated with actively secreting or absorbing cells, was not found in the flame bulbs of a planarian and a nemertine, although it was abundant lower down the duct in both animals (Danielli and Pantin, 1950). The distribution of this enzyme is not incompatible with the ultrafiltration theory and implies that the ultrafiltrate is modified by further secretion or resorption lower down the duct. In rotifers, the duct is long and histologically differentiated, suggesting that urine is modified during its passage along it.

Contractile Vacuoles

A contractile vacuole is a small vacuole which fills rhythmically with a clear liquid until it reaches a certain volume, when it empties its contents to the exterior. Contractile vacuoles are found in most freshwater protozoans and at least some freshwater sponges; they are also found in marine ciliates and some freshwater protozoans.

Recent studies by electron microscopy have confirmed that the contractile vacuole is bounded by a discrete layer of dense material and is surrounded by a zone of mitochondria which

presumably provide the energy required to differentiate its
contents (Fig. II.11). The contractile vacuole grows, at least
in part, by the addition of minute droplets, but perhaps also
by direct secretion into the vacuole. In *Paramecium*, the
droplets are fed into the contractile vacuole along a series
of radial ducts, but in *Amoeba*, no ducts can be seen (Fig.

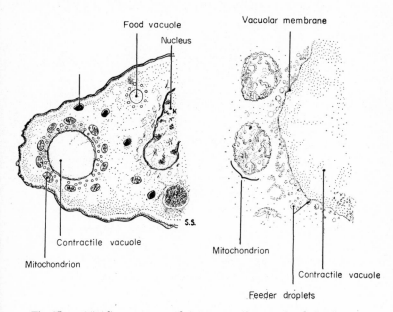

Fig. II.11. The fine structure of the contractile vacuole of *Amoeba
proteus*. Adapted from Mercer, 1959.

II.11). Electron micrographs show that these small feeder
droplets are also bounded by a distinct membrane similar
to that surrounding the main vacuole (Mercer, 1959). It has
been suggested that the vacuoles are differentiated by a
process of coacervation (e.g. Frey-Wyssling, 1948, p. 11), that is,
the separation of a complex solution into two phases as the
result of a change in the concentration of a component, but the
presence of a discrete bounding membrane does not support
this hypothesis. Experiments by Kitching (1954) suggest that

the contraction of the vacuole is unrelated to the turgor of the cytoplasm but is brought about by the vacuolar membrane.

The general distribution of contractile vacuoles suggests that they are mainly osmoregulatory organs and this is confirmed by the numerous experiments, with many species, which have shown that the vacuolar output is highest in fresh water and varies inversely with the concentration of the medium. Kitching (1934, 1938) has shown that when the activity of the contractile vacuoles is inhibited by very dilute cyanide, there is a marked increase in the body volumes of both freshwater ciliates and of marine ciliates in dilute sea water. This strongly suggests that the function of the vacuole is to bale out water entering by osmosis, and that this requires energy derived from oxidative processes.

The occurrence of contractile vacuoles in marine ciliates is not inconsistent with this idea, since in the marine peritrich ciliates the rate of vacuolar output is very low, and of the same order as the rate of water uptake by food vacuoles (Kitching, 1939). The ciliates are better represented in fresh water than in the sea and it is probable that the group is originally a freshwater one. The marine forms may have retained the contractile vacuoles for the secondary purpose of eliminating water taken in with the food.

It has often been suggested, by analogy with the excretory organs of the vertebrates, that the contractile vacuole functions as an organ of nitrogen excretion. However, physical considerations suggest that diffusion would be quite adequate for the removal of ammonia from protozoans in normal circumstances. Kitching (1956) and Weatherby (1929) showed that most of the urea produced by *Spirostomum* was not eliminated by the contractile vacuole. Experiments by Koehring (1930) showed that protozoans which had been kept in a dilute solution of neutral red did not excrete it by the contractile vacuoles, although it was accumulated in the food vacuoles.

Excretion in Insects: Malpighian Tubes

The excretory system of insects consists of the malpighian tubes and the hind-gut. The malpighian tubes produce a copious flow of a potassium-rich solution into the hind gut. Potassium, sodium and probably phosphate ions are secreted into the tubes against electrochemical gradients; chloride, amino acids, and sugars probably enter by diffusion. In the hind-gut, most of the water and solutes are resorbed, and uric acid, surplus water and salts are eliminated (Fig II.12).

The greater part of the solution produced by the malpighian tubes is resorbed in the hind-gut, just as in the mammalian kidney most of the ultrafiltrate from the glomerulus is resorbed by the proximal and distal tubules. The malpighian tube differs from the vertebrate kidney in that the urine is produced by a process of secretion, not ultrafiltration (Ramsay and Riegel, 1961).

The malpighian tube is also found in other air-breathing arthropods such as the centipedes and millipedes, in *Peripatus* and in some of the arachnids. In the insects, the malpighian tubes consist of a number of thin tubular glands which lie in the haemocoele and drain into the intestine near the junction of the mid- and hind-guts. In many insects, the blind proximal ends of some of the tubes are reflected back and lie along the rectum. The tubes vary in number from 2 to 150; when fewer in number they are generally longer, so that the total surface area is always considerable. In *Periplaneta*, for example, their surface area is said to be equivalent to about 400 mm^2/mg animal (Schindler, 1878, in Wigglesworth, 1953, p.367).

A malpighian tube consists of an elastic tubular membrane covered with longitudinal and circular muscles and lined with a layer of cells with a well developed brush border, a feature often associated with secretion or absorption. The hind-gut is lined with a thin water-permeable cuticle, and the cells of its epithelium are often arranged into six longitudinal rows. In many groups, such as the Orthoptera and the Diptera, these

longitudinal folds form discrete rectal glands of large colum-
nar cells. The narrower anterior portion of the hind-gut,
lacking these folds or rectal glands, is often distinguished as
the ileum.

The insects are a class of specialists and vary so greatly in

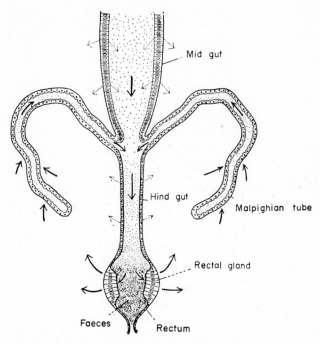

Fig. II.12. The insect excretory system. The arrows indicate the
direction of water movement. From Wigglesworth, 1931.

habit and physiology that no insect can be regarded as typical;
Carausius (=*Dixippus*) (examined in detail by Ramsay) is as
representative as any other.

The blood of *Carausius* has a fairly high osmotic pressure
(320 mOsm/l.), but only a small part of this is due to sodium
and chloride ions. The malpighian tubes produce urine (*ca.*
4–6 ml/g/hr) which is almost isosmotic with the blood, but

TABLE II. 1. — THE COMPOSITION OF THE SERUM, URINE AND RECTAL FLUID OF THE STICK INSECT *Carausius morosus*. MM/L. (Ramsay, 1955a, 1956)

Ion, etc.	Serum*	Urine	Rectal fluid
Sodium	11	5	19
Potassium	18	145	320
Calcium	3.5	1	
Magnesium	54	9	
Chloride	87	65	
Phosphate	39	51	
Uric acid	0.27	2.6	
pH	6.6	6.8—7.5	3.5—4.5
Total, mOsm/l.	≐ 320	≐ 317	≐ 735

* Protein — free serum prepared by heating the plasma
** = $H_2PO_4^-$ + $HPO_4^=$ in this pH range.

differing from it in containing a very high concentration of potassium (145 mM K/l.) (Ramsay, 1954 a).

Simultaneous measurements of the osmotic pressure of urine and serum showed that the urine was slightly but significantly hypo-osmotic (Ramsay, 1954 a) by an average of 3 mOsm/l. A further series of experiments showed that the tubes from which the distal part had been removed, and in which only the proximal part was immersed in serum, could produce urine as much as 40 mOsmoles hypo-osmotic to the serum. It is therefore improbable that the urine is initially osmotic with the serum and it is concluded that water is secreted into the tubes. It may be noted that the tubes continue to secrete against a hydrostatic pressure of up to 20 cm water.

The potassium concentration of the urine is five to ten times that of the serum (Table II.1) and experiments with isolated pieces of tube showed that all parts excrete a potassium rich fluid. The contents of the tubes are 10–20 mV positive to the serum (Ramsay, 1953 b). The potassium is therefore secreted against both electrical and concentration gradients; the elctrical potential may be the consequence of the active secretion of potassium. Although the sodium content of the urine is less

7

than that of the serum, it is greater than its equilibrium concentration, so sodium is also secreted against the electrochemical gradient. This is confirmed by experiments which showed that in conditions of very low serum potassium, the sodium content of the urine could exceed that of the serum (Ramsay, 1955 b).

Although water seems to be excreted against an osmotic gradient, the rate of water secretion is intimately related to the rate of potassium secretion, perhaps because potassium provides the bulk of the cations in the urine and the water secretion mechanism cannot function against a high osmotic gradient. The rates of potassium secretion and of urine production are proportional to the concentration of potassium in the serum. On the other hand, the rate of urine production is almost independent of the serum sodium (Fig. II.13).

The concentration of chloride in the urine is less than in the serum. The urine/serum ratio varies from 0.9 when the serum chloride is 120 mM/l. to 0.4 when the serum chloride is 35 mM/l. As the inside of the tube is positive with respect to the serum, the chloride is probably entering by diffusion down the electrochemical gradient.

Phosphate is more concentrated in the urine than in the serum. The urine/serum ratio varies from 4 when the serum phosphate is 6 mM/l. to 1.5 when the serum phosphate is 88 mM/l. (Ramsay, 1956). The positive potential would tend to concentrate phosphate inside the tube, but the phosphate is concentrated to a relatively greater degree than chloride whereas organic membranes generally are more easily penetrated by chloride than by phosphate ions, so it is probable that the phosphate is actively secreted. The rate of urine production is related to the rate of phosphate secretion and hence to the concentration of phosphate in the serum; just as in the case of potassium, a high serum phosphate favours a high rate of urine production.

Calcium and magnesium are only about one tenth as concentrated in the urine as in the plasma, and probably enter the

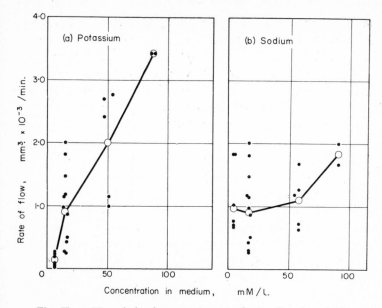

Fig. II.13. The relation between the rate of urine flow in a single malpighian tube of the stick insect, *Carausius morosus*, and the concentration of sodium and potassium in the medium. From Ramsay, 1955 b.

urine by diffusion down the electrochemical gradient. The urine/serum ratios of a number of sugars and amino acids vary between 0.2 and 0.8 and for any of these substances, are almost independent of concentration, but the ratios fall as the rate of urine production increases. This suggests that such substances accumulate by simple diffusion. Urea, which is a very freely diffusible substance, has a urine/serum ratio of almost unity. Uric acid is concentrated ten-fold in the tubular urine and the degree of concentration is such that uric acid must be moved against the electrochemical gradient. Phenol red and some other dyes are also actively secreted into the urine.

Most of the urine secreted into the malpighian tubes is re-sorbed in the hind gut. From a consideration of the rates of flow and from analyses of the faeces, Ramsay (1955 b) concluded that 95% of the sodium and 80% of the potassium secreted in

7*

the tubes was resorbed in the hind gut. The flux of materials is so great that the tubes secrete the equivalent of all the body water each day and all the body potassium every three hours. These fluxes continue almost unabated in the starved animal. The reflection of some of the malpighian tubes along the rectum probably helps to facilitate this cycle of solutes and water.

Observations of injected phenol red (Ramsay, 1955 a) show that most of the water resorption takes place in the hind gut. The mean osmotic concentration of the rectal fluid of *Carausius* is equivalent to 735 mOsm./l. This is two or three times the osmotic concentration of the blood or malpighian tube fluid, and it is probable that in the rectum, as in the malpighian tube, the movement of water is against the osmotic gradient. The contents of the rectum are relatively acid (pH 3.5–4.5), a condition which will favour uric acid precipitation, while the tubular urine is generally more alkaline than the serum.

The stick insect is a terrestrial herbivore, and like most herbivorous insects, it has a high plasma potassium and a fairly low protein intake. Nevertheless, its excretory system seems to be fairly typical. A survey of a wide variety of insects including *Locusta* (Orthoptera), *Pieris* (Lepidoptera), *Tenebrio*, *Dytiscus* (Coleoptera), *Rhodnius* (Hemiptera) and *Aedes* (Diptera) showed that in all these animals, the urine is much richer in potassium than is the plasma, even in forms in which the blood sodium is high (Ramsay, 1953 a). Except for *Locusta* and *Rhodnius*, the inside of the malpighian tubes is electrically positive and in all cases the potassium must be secreted against an electro-chemical gradient. Water resorption generally occurs in the rectum, as Wigglesworth (1932) and later authors have shown.

In the bug, *Rhodnius*, water resorption takes place in the lower part of the malpighian tube. This was noted by Wigglesworth (1931) and led him to suggest that potassium urates are secreted into the upper alkaline portion of the tube and potassium resorbed and uric acid precipitated in the lower acid portion. However, the division of the tube into well defined upper and lower portions is a peculiarity of *Rhodnius*, and in

Carausius, (and probably in most other insects) the whole of the
tube is secretory, and resorption and acid conditions are confined to the hind gut. Ramsay suggests that the peculiar conditions of *Rhodnius* are an adaptation to the blood-sucking
habit, which lays a very heavy temporary burden on the excretory system. Wigglesworth suggested that potassium secretion took place because the potassium salts of uric acid are more
soluble than the sodium ones. However, the flux of potassium
through the malpighian tube is so much greater than the flux
of uric acid (the urine containing 140 mM/l. of potassium and
only 2.4 mM/l. of uric acid) that it is probable that the high
potassium content is not directly linked with the problem of
uric acid elimination, but is somehow related to the water flow.

As in mammals, the quantity of water and solutes ultimately
eliminated is only a small part of the material passing through
the excretory system. The very high rate of flow through the
excretory organ should allow the animal to maintain a delicate
control of the composition of the blood, and to eliminate
rapidly any surplus material. However, when the level of
sodium in the blood of *Carausius* is artificially raised by the
injection of sodium chloride, it remains high for several days,
and an increase in the blood potassium level requires 24 hours
for its correction (Ramsay, 1955 b). In both cases, the rate of
excretion by the malpighian tubes is increased, but so is the
rate of resorption in the rectum.

Carausius never normally meets such a sudden influx of
sodium or potassium ions, and the excretory system is probably geared to deal only with a slow influx of these ions from
the food. Other insects, such as the blood-sucking bug, *Rhodnius*, or the mosquito larva, *Aedes*, which lives in a variable
environment, are able to adjust the rates of excretion and resorption much more effectively. The mosquito, *Aedes detritus*,
can maintain a remarkably constant blood composition whether it is living in distilled water or in solutions of sodium or
potassium chloride (Table II.2). In each environment, the
malpighian tubes excrete a fluid much richer in potassium than

TABLE II.2: — THE COMPOSITION OF THE HAEMOLYMPH, URINE AND RECTAL FLUID OF THE LARVA OF THE MOSQUITO, *Aedes detritus*, IN VARIOUS MEDIA. mM/L. (Ramsay, 1953, a and b)

Body Fluid	Distilled water		KCl 85 mM/l.		NaCl 85 mM/l.	
	Na	K	Na	K	Na	K
Haemolymph	87	3	87	5.7	113	3
Urine*	24	88	23	138	71	90
Rectal Fluid	4	25	14	90	100	18

* The urine was collected in the intestine but is derived mainly from the malpighian tubes.

sodium, but the degree of resorption in the rectum is so adjusted that surplus ions are eliminated and those in short supply are conserved. This suggests that the resorptive mechanisms in the rectum are closely linked with the level of electrolytes in the bood. It also illustrates how vital is the role played by the rectum, which forms a most essential part of the excretory system.

CHAPTER III

IONIC REGULATION
IN MARINE ANIMALS

Introduction

Sea water provides the most constant environment for animals. Even in widely separated oceans, the composition of sea water varies only slightly, and the relative concentrations of the principal ions are almost constant. It has long been established (Dittmar, 1884) that the ratios of the concentrations of these ions are almost unaffected by land drainage, and independent of the total salt content. This constancy allows the composition of sea water to be deduced from the concentration of a single component. In practice, the component most usually estimated is chloride, and tables are available for the calculation of the concentration of other electrolytes from the chloride content (Table III.1).

Dilutions or concentrations of sea water are described by reference to a standard "Normal Copenhagen Sea Water" (*ca.* 19.1‰). The concentration may be expressed very approximately as a percentage of full strength sea water (i.e. 50% etc.), or more precisely defined in terms of salinity (S ‰) or chlorinity (Cl ‰) (on a weight for weight basis), or in terms of one or other of the electrolytes when a specific ion equilibrium is being discussed. Salinity and chlorinity are related by an empirical relation:

$$S\text{‰} = 0.03 + 1.805 \times Cl\text{‰}.$$

TABLE III. 1. — CONCENTRATION OF PRINCIPAL INORGANIC IONS IN SEA
WATER, CHLORINITY* 19‰, SALINITY 34. 33‰, AT 20°C
(From Barnes, 1954)

Ion	1 kg sea water		1 litre sea water		1 kg water	
	grams	mM	grams	mM	grams	mM
Chloride	18.980	535.3	19.440	548.3	19.658	554.4
Sulphate	26.49	27.58	2.713	28.25	2.744	28.56
Bicarbonate	01.40	2.29	0.143	2.34	0.145	2.37
Calcium	04.00	9.98	0.410	10.23	0.414	10.34
Magnesium	12.72	52.30	1.303	53.57	1.317	54.17
Potassium	0.380	9.72	0.389	9.96	0.394	10.07
Sodium	10.556	459.0	10.813	470.2	10.933	475.4

* Chlorinity is obtained from a silver nitrate titration and includes other halides, estimated as chloride.

This equation implies that water of very low chlorinity still contains other anions (e.g. carbonate and sulphate) but the ratios of the major constituents are a function of the chlorinity. Equations for calcium, magnesium, carbonate and sulphate and total salts can be derived from this relationship. Other ions are in a constant ratio to chlorinity (Lyman and Fleming, 1940).

To some extent, the composition of sea water is reflected in the composition of the extracellular fluids of animals. Macallum's hypothesis (1926) postulates that changes in the composition of sea water within geological time are of biological significance. The origin and possible evolution of sea water are of interest in this context.

The cations in sea water have been leached from the earth's crust. Sedimentary rocks contain significantly less sodium than igneous rocks, but the quantities of sodium, potassium, calcium and magnesium in the sea are only a small part of the amounts of these ions that have been exposed to weathering; it is the availability of soluble anions, particularly chloride, sulphate and bicarbonate, that has limited the amounts of salt in the sea. Sea water is approximately neutral; probably this has always been so, because a large excess of cations is available (as aluminium silicates) to neutralise any excess of anions, while bicarbonates provide a more delicate buffering system. Chlorides and sulphates are rare in igneous rocks and the ultimate source of these ions in sea water is probably hydrochloric acid and sulphur oxides of volcanic origin (Rubey, 1951). These volatile compounds are still reaching the earth's surface at a significant rate. Sulphate is produced also by the oxidation of sulphides, but this can only have begun when oxygen accumulated in the atmosphere following photosynthesis.

Carbonate and bicarbonate in sea water are in equilibrium with the carbon dioxide in the atmosphere. The partial pressure of carbon dioxide is very close to the equilibrium pressure of the reactions:

$$MgSiO_3 + CO_2 \rightleftharpoons MgCO_3 + SiO_2$$
$$CaSiO_3 + CO_2 \rightleftharpoons CaCO_3 + SiO_2.$$

Magnesium and calcium silicates are amongst the most abundant minerals and it has been suggested that these reactions control the amount of carbon dioxide in the atmosphere (Urey, 1952, p.148). If this is so, the quantity of carbon dioxide in the atmosphere has remained fairly constant, although vast quantities have been removed by plants to produce coal, oil and oxygen. Alternatively, the atmosphere may have originally contained carbon dioxide at least equivalent to the present quantity of oxygen, and the present low level of carbon dioxide is due to photosynthesis.

Calcium in solution in sea water is limited by the solubility product of calcium carbonate. If atmospheric carbon dioxide has remained constant, then the calcium content of the sea has also been invariable. If the carbon dioxide level were higher in the past, the sea must then have contained greater concentrations of bicarbonates, it would have been slightly more acid, and it would have contained a higher concentration of calcium ions.

The quantity of potassium in igneous rocks is almost the same as that of sodium, but in sea water there is relatively less potassium. Probably, potassium is removed from sea water by adsorption on to clay minerals, which have a higher affinity for potassium than for sodium, because the potassium ion fits more easily into the crystal lattice of the clays (Hutchinson, 1944). As a result, argillaceous rocks have a higher potassium/sodium ratio than igneous rocks, from which they are ultimately derived. Conway(1943) suggested that the formation of glauconite by biological action is the main process removing potassium from the sea, and he concluded that the primeval ocean was richer in potassium than the present one. It is tempting to correlate the generally high concentration of potassium in cells with this early potassium-rich sea, but the quantities of glauconite in rocks seem quite insufficient to account for the dearth of potassium in the sea (Hutchinson, 1944).

Salt is continuously removed from the sea as spray, and at times, large quantities have been removed to form salt deposits by the evaporation of isolated arms of the sea. Sulphates are removed continuously by conversion to sulphides in oxygen-deficient mud, and calcium is continuously removed by inorganic precipitation and by biological deposition; but these processes are reversed when the deposits are exposed to erosion. Most of the salt carried by rivers to the sea today is being recycled in these ways, but it is probable that some hydrochloric acid is being added continuously by volcanic action. Whether the total concentration of the oceans has remained constant depends on whether the relative rates of accretion of anions, mainly chloride, and of water, have remained constant. Some at least of the volcanic steam reaching the surface may be juvenile water and de Turville (1961) has suggested that hydrogen emitted from the sun and intercepted by the earth has been the main source of the earth's water. If this is so, the oceans must have been growing continuously since the earth was formed, and the concentration of salts has probably remained fairly constant.

The body fluids of most marine animals are almost in osmotic equilibrium with sea water and have a similar salt content.

The osmotic equilibrium was first shown clearly by the cryoscopic measurements of Botazzi (1897, 1908) and has been confirmed many times since. However, there are a number of important exceptions to this generalisation. Among the vertebrates, only the hagfishes have a similar salt content to sea water, and among the invertebrates, some crustaceans are hypo-osmotic to sea water (Chap. VII.). It is possible that many crustaceans are hyperosmotic to sea water in the premoult stage (e.g. *Carcinus*, the shore crab, Robertson, 1960) (see below, p.112). The rest of the marine fauna is more or less isosmotic with sea water.

Many analyses of the body fluids of marine animals have been published (e.g. Prosser, Green, Jahn and Wolff, 1950, Table 9) but most can be accepted only with reservations because of the limitations of the methods employed. The ionic ratios of sea water calculated from the analyses of some workers differ considerably from the established ratios (Robertson, 1949), and the discrepancies between analyses of the same species by different workers are often too large to be attributed to individual variation in the animals. The ions most subject to analytical errors are calcium, magnesium and sulphate, while measurements of chloride concentration are probably the most reliable. Although the number of animals analysed is only a minute fraction of the marine fauna, some generalisations are possible.

1. Many animals differ significantly in ionic composition from sea water, even when they are isosmotic with it.
2. There is a very considerable variation in the ionic regulation; each of the major ions in sea water is concentrated by some animals, and maintained at a low concentration by others.
3. In spite of this great variation, related animals usually show similarities in ionic regulation.

The data given in Table III.2 have been chosen to represent a wide range of animals. All the data in this table have been calculated in terms of a standard sea water concentration, on the assumption that the concentration of each ion in the body fluid is proportional to its concentration in sea water. This assumption may be incorrect, but the error introduced is not likely to be large.

Survey

The characteristics of ionic regulation in the more common phyla are discussed below.

Crustaceans

Most of the larger species of crustaceans are decapods, and for this reason most of the available information about regulation in these animals relates to this single group. Little is known about the smaller forms. With the exception of some prawns, crabs and isopods (Chap. VII), the marine crustaceans are more or less isosmotic with their medium, but although isosmotic, they show a considerable degree of ionic regulation. Sodium is usually a very little higher in the blood than in sea water (Table III.2), and this may be the result of low concentrations of other cations. For example, where the magnesium concentration is particularly low, as in the lobster *Homarus* (14% of the sea water concentration) the sodium is considerably higher (111% of sea water). Chloride is always very similar to the concentration in sea water, but potassium is generally more concentrated. An interesting exception to this is *Nephrops*, the Norway lobster (Table III. 2).

Calcium in the blood is often considerably higher than in sea water. In the isopod *Ligia*, for instance, the analysed calcium is three times as great as that of sea water, but some of this is probably bound to proteins (Numanoi, 1934). The concentrations of this ion in crustacean blood varies with the phase in the moulting cycle. In *Carcinus*, the intermoult crabs have a calcium content of 130% of the sea water concentration and in

TABLE III. 2. — CONCENTRATION OF COMMON IONS (mM/kg water) IN SOME MARINE ANIMALS

	Sodium	Potassium	Calcium	Magnesium	Chloride	Sulphate	Protein mg/ml
Sea Water Standard*	478.3	10.13	10.48	54.5	558.4	28.77	—
Aurelia[1] mesogloeal fluid	474	10.72	10.03	53.0	580	15.77	0.7
Aphrodite[1] coelomic fluid	476	10.50	10.45	54.6	557	26.50	0.2
Echinus[1] coelomic fluid ...	474	10.13	10.62	53.5	557	28.70	0.3
Mytilus[2] blood	474	12.00	11.90	52.6	553	28.90	1.6
Loligo[1] blood	456	22.20	10.60	55.4	578	8.14	149.7
Ligia[4] blood.................	566	13.30	34.90	20.2	629	4.03	—
Maia[1] blood.................	488	12.37	13.56	44.1	554	14.50	—
Carcinus[3] blood.............	531	12.26	13.32	19.5	557	16.46	60
Nephrops[1] blood	541	7.81	11.95	9.28	552	19.8	33
Myxine[1] blood	537	9.12	5 87	18.0	542	6.33	67

* Figues are recalculated from the literature in proportion to this sea water standard

1. Robertson, 1949, 1953, 1954
2. Potts, 1954 a
3. Webb, 1940
4. Parry, 1953

the premoult crabs it rises to 163%. This increase is associated with a resorption of salts from the old exoskeleton (Robertson, 1957). Immediately after the moult, the calcium content drops to 120% of sea water, probably because of the dilution of the blood when the crab drinks sea water. After another two days, the calcium drops to 88% of sea water while it is being deposited in the exoskeleton.

Magnesium and sulphate are often considerably lower in the blood than in sea water (Table III.2): magnesium varies from about 90% of sea water in the spider crab, *Maia*, to only 17% in *Nephrops*.

Arachnids

Analyses of the blood of the marine arachnid, *Limulus*, have been published by Cole (1940), who quotes a further analysis by Smith. Although the results are not very consistent, they both agree that potassium is concentrated with respect to sea water and magnesium and sulphate are reduced, as in the majority of the crustaceans.

Molluscs

Most molluscs concentrate potassium to some extent, up to 219% of sea water in the squid, *Loligo*, and most concentrate calcium. Generally, the concentration of sulphate in the blood is less than the concentration in sea water, but the mussel, *Mytilus galloprovincialis*, is peculiar in concentrating this ion to 120% of the sea water concentration. In marked contrast to the crustaceans, the molluscs do not lower the magnesium concentration to any great extent. The lowest concentration of magnesium recorded is 96.5% of sea water in the blood of *M. galloprovincialis* while the majority, e. g. *Ostrea, Archidoris, Neptunea, Buccinum, Eledone,* and *Loligo, Aplysia* and *Doris* concentrate magnesium (Bethe, 1929; Bethe and Berger, 1931; Robertson, 1949, 1953.). This tolerance of, or even preference for, magnesium is unusual, and may prove to be characteristic of the marine molluscs. The greatest degree of ionic regulation is found in the cephalopods, amongst which the very active *Loligo* (squid) maintains greater concentration differences than *Eledone* (an octopus), or *Sepia* (cuttle fish).

In the cephalopods two different kinds of buoyancy mechanisms are associated with a high degree of ionic regulation. In *Sepia*, the spaces in the cuttlebone act as a float, counterbalancing the tissues which are denser than sea water. These spaces are partly filled with a liquid hypo-osmotic to the blood, and partly with a gas at less than atmospheric pressure. The osmotic pressure difference between the liquid and the blood of each animal is approximately equal to the hydrostatic pressure of the depth where it is found. It is probable that the water is withdrawn from the cuttlebone against the hydrostatic pressure by an osmotic concentration difference brought about by the activity of the epithelium adjacent to the cuttlebone (Denton, 1960). A mechanism of this type would make it possible, for example, to abstract water against a pressure of 150 feet by producing a concentration difference equivalent to 25% sea water. The gas in the spaces plays no significant part in this system, but merely diffuses into what would otherwise be a vacuum.

In the Cranchiid squids, e.g. *Verrilliteuthis*, *Galiteuthis*, and *Helicocranchia*, the weight of the tissues is counterbalanced by a large volume of coelomic fluid less dense (sp. gr. 1.011) than sea water (sp. gr. 1.026). This low density is due to an extraordinarily high concentration of ammonium ions. In sea water containing 490 mM Na/l., the coelomic fluids contained only 80 mM Na and 480 mM NH_4/l., the ammonium salt solution being less dense than the sodium salt solution. Ionic equilibrium is maintained by a high concentration of chloride. At the very low pH of the coelomic fluid (5.2), ammonia probably diffuses in from the blood and is trapped as ammonium ions (Denton, Shaw and Gilpin-Brown, 1958).

Cephalopod eye-fluids differ in composition both from sea water and from plasma. Magnesium is excluded, although it is usually concetrated in the plasma. Although in the vertebrates eye-fluids are very similar to a dialysate of the plasma (Chap. VI, p. 243), this is not true of *Sepia* (Table III.3).

TABLE III. 3. — COMPOSITION OF *Sepia* EYE-FLUIDS
(Expressed as percentage of plasma composition; Robertson, 1953)

Fluid	Sodium	Potas-sium	Calcium	Magnes-ium	Chloride	Sulphate
Vitreous humour...	115	62	113	9	97	49
Aqueous humour...	105	54	90	81	99	191
Plasma dialysate ...	98	98	84	96	102	105
Sea water	106	48	93	97	97	470

Annelids

The coelomic fluid of *Aphrodite* (the sea mouse) is almost identical to sea water in ionic composition, and is almost protein-free (Table III.2). Some degree of ionic regulation occurs in marine annelids, according to the published analyses of *Amphitrite* and *Glycera* (Smith, quoted in Cole, 1940) and *Arenicola* (Bialascewicz, 1933; Robertson, 1949), but no clear pattern emerges. They all concentrate potassium, and *Glycera* and *Arenicola* reduce sulphate. The marine polychaetes' powers of ionic regulation are feeble, and the degree of concentration or elimination rarely exceeds 10%.*

Analyses of the coelomic fluid of the echiuroid *Sipunculus* (Bethe and Berger, 1931; Bialascewicz, 1933) are so much at variance that it is impossible to draw any conclusions about the ionic regulation of the animal. *Goldfingia* concentrates sodium, potassium and calcium, and maintains low concentrations of magnesium and sulphate (Robertson, 1953). The regulation of most of the ions is of the order of 5–10%, but magnesium is reduced to 68% of sea water. The concentration of sodium is slightly greater than that of sea water and is probably to be correlated with this low magnesium.

* Robertson (1949) does not confirm Bialascewicz's figure of 139% of the sea water concentration for the potassium content of *Arenicola* blood.

Chordates

The hagfishes are the only vertebrates which may be primitively marine. Although *Myxine* is in osmotic equilibrium with sea water, it has remarkable powers of ionic regulation of a peculiar kind. Magnesium and sulphate concentrations in the blood are less than in sea water, as in many crustaceans, but the calcium and potassium concentrations are also lower. Sodium is strongly concentrated to maintain the osmotic pressure (Table III.2). Only *Nephrops* shows a similar pattern, but unlike *Myxine*, *Nephrops* concentrates calcium. The tunicates do not resemble *Myxine*, but have a "crustacean" pattern of ionic regulation, concentrating potassium and reducing magnesium and sulphate (Robertson, 1954). Calcium may be either diminished or concentrated.

Echinoderms

The perivisceral coelomic fluid of *Echinus* is very similar to sea water (Table III.2). A number of analyses of other echinoderm body fluids has been published, e.g. the star fishes, *Asterias* and *Marthasterias*, and sea cucumbers, *Cucumaria* and *Holothuria* (Cole, 1940; Robertson, 1949, 1953) but none of these animals shows any great degree of ionic regulation. In *Asterias rubens*, potassium is concentrated in ambulacral fluid to about 160% of the sea water concentration. This difference is maintained in a wide range of salinities (Binyon, 1962). In *Cucumaria*, ions do not differ significantly from their concentrations in sea water, except possibly potassium. *Holothuria* concentrates potassium and magnesium by about 3%, while *Marthasterias* concentrates potassium by 11% but very slightly reduces magnesium. In general, the echinoderms' powers of ionic regulation are poor.

8

Coelenterates

The mesogloeal fluid* of *Aurelia* (Table III. 2) is very similar to sea water except that the sulphate concentration is considerably reduced and there is a compensating rise in the chloride level (cf. p.116). This may be a characteristic of marine medusae as both Koizumi and Hosoi (1936) and Macallum (1903) found that a variety of different medusae contained low concentrations of sulphate in the mesogloeal "jelly". These latter authors reported rather large concentrations of potassium, but this may have been caused by the presence of cells in the jelly.

The Selective Advantages of Ionic Regulation

Among the animals examined, there are many degrees of ionic regulation of the body fluids and almost every ion is concentrated by some animal, yet excluded by another. Except for the buoyancy mechanisms of the squids, it is very difficult to correlate these differences with habitat, or mode of life, or to suggest what physiological advantages the various patterns of ionic regulation bestow upon their possessors.

Among the decapod crustaceans, the lowest concentrations of magnesium and sulphate are found in the more active animals. For example, the concentration of magnesium in the blood of the lethargic spider crabs, *Maia* and *Hyas*, is almost as high as in sea water, while the active crabs, *Carcinus* and *Portunus* (= *Macropipus*) have much lower magnesium concentrations. Robertson (1953) has suggested that the low concentration of magnesium in some crustacean bloods is correlated with the narcotic effect of this ion.[†] This attractive suggestion makes it difficult to account for the high concentration

---

* The analysis of *Aurelia* (Table III.2) refers to the almost protein-free fluid which exudes from the cut surface of the mesogloea.

† The use of magnesium sulphate as an anaesthetic for marine animals illustrates the narcotic effect of an excess of these ions in the blood.

of magnesium found in the blood of the supremely active squid *Loligo*. This discrepancy was noted by Robertson, who suggested that the depressive effect of the magnesium was counterbalanced there by the high concentration of potassium. An increase in potassium concentration is said to increase the facilitation response to electrical stimuli in some coelenterates (Ross and Pantin, 1940), but in general, an increase in blood potassium lowers the resting potential of nerve and muscle cells. Hoyle (1954) has argued that, in insects, a high concentration of potassium in the blood is correlated with quiescent behaviour (Chap. VI, p.272.).

The high concentration of calcium in the blood of many animals may help to maintain a state of saturation, or even supersaturation, of the blood with respect to calcium carbonate (Potts, 1954 a). Although the surface waters of the sea are supersaturated with calcium carbonate, most body fluids are more acid than sea water, probably because of the metabolic production of carbon dioxide. In the lamellibranchs, the blood is just saturated with the aragonite form of calcium carbonate, and the calcium carbonate of the blood is in equilibrium with that of the shell. If the pH of the blood is reduced by anoxia, solution of the shell occurs and the blood calcium rises. The slightly higher concentration of calcium in the blood, as compared with sea water, is one of the factors which help to maintain the saturation of the blood with calcium carbonate. On the other hand, the shell-less *Archidoris* also concentrates calcium in the blood.

Macallum's Hypothesis

A different sort of explanation of the significance of ionic regulation was proposed by Macallum (1926). He suggested that the inorganic composition of an animal's blood resembled the composition of the ocean at a geologically earlier period. In particular, he suggested that the low concentration of most

8*

vertebrate bloods is a relic of a time when the oceans were less concentrated than at present, and the low magnesium content of the blood of many crustaceans and vertebrates is an inheritance from a time when this ion had not reached its present concentration.

Unfortunately, there are several reasons for rejecting this bold hypothesis. Most marine animals are freely permeable to water and ions, a point which will be discussed shortly, and a slight change in the concentration of the environment produces a corresponding change in the composition of the blood within a few hours. When body fluids respond to changes in the environment so quickly, it is difficult to believe that they could maintain some similarity to the palaeozoic oceans through millions of years and generations. Again, closely related animals may show markedly different degrees of ionic regulation: for example in the hermit crabs, *Lithodes*, blood contains as high a concentration of magnesium as sea water, but *Pagurus* reduces the concentration of magnesium in the blood to about half that of sea water. Both these animals are probably descended from a common ancestor living in the Mesozoic. As it seems probable that sea water has not changed substantially in recent times, Macallum's hypothesis must be rejected (see also p.91, above).

Mechanisms of Ionic Regulation

The factors which create and maintain ionic concentration differences between an animal and its environment have been the subject of many investigations. The occurrence and extent of the concentration differences are the result of the interaction of both passive and active factors.

The passive factors are:

   1. The permeability of the animal's body wall to water and solutes.

2. The presence of protein in the body fluids which may produce Donnan effects, and which may bind some ions in indiffusible complexes.

The active factors are:

3. The excretion of salts and water from the body.
4. The active uptake of salts, and possibly water, in the gut and at the body surface.

Permeability of the Body Walls

The body walls of all marine invertebrates are permeable of both salts and water; in fact, most marine invertebrates are isosmotic with sea water because their body walls are so permeable. If a soft-bodied marine invertebrate is taken from normal sea water and placed in a different salinity, it soon becomes isosmotic with the new sea water. This new equilibrium is reached, partly as the result of the osmotic movement of water, and partly as the result of the movement of salt.

An animal which was permeable to water but impermeable to salt would behave as a perfect osmometer. That is to say, the product of the osmotic pressure of the body fluids and the water content of the body (and hence, approximately the volume) would be constant. If an animal were also permeable to salt, then the changes in volume would be less than those of a perfect osmometer. A few animals do behave almost as perfect osmometers. For example, when *Goldfingia* is transferred to sea water of a different salinity, it reaches a new equilibrium volume in a few hours and it maintains this new volume for several days. The changes in volume after injections of salt solutions can be accurately predicted, although after periods of several days, there is some return to the normal volume (Adolph, 1936).

The behaviour of the majority of the soft-bodied invertebrates deviates significantly from that of a perfect osmometer. For example, the nudibranch *Doris* swells rapidly in solutions hypo-osmotic to sea water, but the swelling is less than that of an ideal semi-permeable animal, and the volume starts to return to normal in a day or so (Bethe, 1934) (Fig. III.1). When the tectibranch *Aplysia* is transferred to dilute sea water, the initial expansion is much less than that of an ideal semi-permeable animal, and the volume returns to

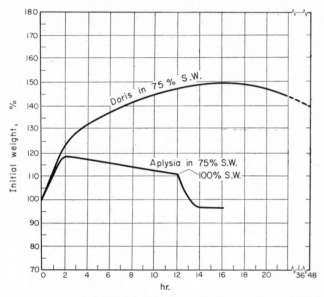

Fig. III.1. Weight changes in *Aplysia* and *Doris* after transfer to different concentrations of sea water. From Bethe, 1934.

normal in a few hours. If *Aplysia* is now returned to normal sea water, it shrinks rapidly to less than its original volume. This shows that the equilibrium in dilute sea water has been reached partly by the loss of solutes (Bethe, 1934).

Permeability to both salt and water can be illustrated in another fashion. When *Aplysia* was transferred to a solution isosmotic with sea water, but made up of half sea water and half a solution of sucrose, it shrank slowly until it died (Bethe, 1934). The large molecule of sucrose could not diffuse back into the animal as fast as the ions diffused out, and so the volume of the animal was reduced.

Dakin and Edmonds (1931) repeated these experiments with *Onchidium* (pulmonate) and in addition, used mixtures of sea water and urea solutions, and of sea water and magnesium sulphate solutions. In sucrose, the animal shrank steadily,

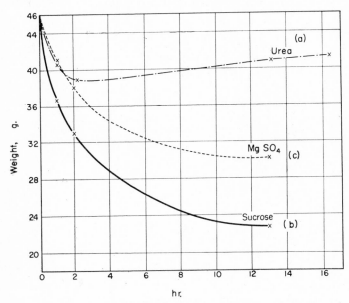

Fig. III. 2. Weight changes in *Onchidium* after transfer to different solutions. From Dakin and Edmonds, 1931.

suggesting that the body wall was much more permeable to sodium and chloride ions than to sucrose. In urea solutions, the body volume remained almost constant, presumably because the urea diffused in as fast as the salts diffused out. In magnesium sulphate solutions, the animal shrank slowly, suggesting that the permeability to magnesium and sulphate was less than to sodium and chloride (Fig. III.2).

It is not always clear from experiments of this kind whether the solutes are diffusing through the body wall, or entering or leaving by the gut or excretory organs. The transfer of an animal to a less concentrated medium may stimulate the excretory organ, and deviation in behaviour from a perfect osmometer could be due, at least in part, to the activity of the excretory organ. A few workers have attempted more critical experiments. Koizumi (1932, 1935) showed, by experiments in which the anterior and posterior ends of the animal were held clear of the surrounding sea water, that the body wall of *Caudina* (Holothuria) was permeable to salts, and Bethe (1934) made experiments with *Aplysia* in which the gut was ligatured, showing that the gut did not play a significant part in volume regulation.

Body walls are more permeable to small ions than to large ones (see also Chap. I, p.12). The experiments with *Onchidium* show that the animal is less permeable to magnesium and sulphate ions, than to sodium and chloride. The permeability of the isolated cuticle of the foregut of *Homarus* to different ions (Webb, 1940) (Table III.4), and that of the body wall of *Caudina*, are also in the inverse order of the ionic diameters (Koizumi, 1935 a).

TABLE III. 4. — THE RELATIVE PERMEABILITY OF THE CUTICLE OF THE FOREGUT OF *Homarus* TO DIFFERENT IONS
(Data from Webb, 1940; Boyle and Conway, 1941; Conway, 1960 b)

Ion	Permeability	Diameter Å (unhydrated)	Diameter Å (hydrated)
Sodium............	100	0.98	5.6
Potassium.........	169	1.33	3.8
Calcium	72	1.06	9.6
Magnesium	42	0.98	10.8
Chloride	100	0.98	3.8
Sulphate	52	1.89	7.2

Effects of Protein in the Body Fluids

The presence of protein in the body fluids may affect the distribution of ions between the body fluids and the outside medium to two ways: by binding some of the ions, particularly calcium, in indiffusible complexes, and by inducing a Donnan equilibrium affecting the distribution of all the ions (Chap. I, p.27). If a sample of body fluid is dialysed against sea water through a collodion membrane which is permeable to water and ions, but not to proteins, concentration differences caused by uptake or excretion are eliminated, and any concentration differences which remain are caused by a Donnan equilibrium or by ion binding. Using this technique, Robertson (1939, 1949, 1953), has shown that a small but significant Donnan effect is found in some crustaceans, where the blood protein is high, but it is undetectable in echinoderms, annelids, and lamellibranchs where the blood protein is low.

The composition of the blood of *Nephrops*, before and after dialysis, is given in Table III.5. The residual differences in concentration remaining after dialysis in sodium, potassium, magnesium, chloride and sulphate ions, may be safely attributed to a Donnan equilibrium produced by the presence of slightly acidic proteins in the plasma. This is shown by the correspondence between the dialysate and an ideal dialy-

TABLE III. 5. — COMPOSITION OF *Nephrops* PLASMA BEFORE AND AFTER
DIALYSIS WITH SEA WATER
(Expressed as mM/kg water; Robertson, 1949)

Fluid	Na	K	Ca	Mg	Cl	SO_4
Original plasma ...	517.7	7.6	I3.8	8.9	518.6	18.5
Sea water	453.6	9.6	10.0	51.7	529.9	27.3
Dialysate	458.6	9.8	11.1	53.3	524.0	26.8
Dialysate calculated from mean Donnan ratio	458.6	9.7	10.1	52.7	524.0	26.8

sate calculated from the mean Donnan ratio. The calcium concentration in the dialysed plasma, however, significantly exceeds the Donnan equilibrium concentration, implying that some of the calcium is bound.

Although the Donnan effects in crustacean blood are significant, they do not account for more than a small part of the ionic regulation in the living animal. The large differences in the plasma before and after dialysis must be attributed to active processes.

Excretion and Ionic Regulation

Pantin (1931c) suggested that the ionic regulation found in marine invertebrates was the result of the activity of the excretory organs. At that time, analyses of body fluids of marine animals were confined mainly to the crustaceans, in which potassium is concentrated relative to sea water, and magnesium and sulphate reduced. He suggested that because water and salts were removed by the excretory organs, they were replaced by inward diffusion. As the potassium ion was more mobile than sodium or chloride ions, and magnesium and sulphate ions less mobile, the resulting equilibrium would be one in which the body fluids were richer in potassium, and poorer in magnesium and sulphate, than sea water.

Robertson (1939) pointed out that this argument was partly fallacious, because inward diffusion would take place only down an electrochemical gradient. If magnesium and sulphate ions could not enter as rapidly as the other ions, then the more mobile ions would accumulate until they were in electrochemical equilibrium with the outside sea water, but the resultant fluid would be hypo-osmotic to sea water and no further water would enter. Thus, in the absence of some form of water uptake, the activity of the excretory organs would lead only to shrinkage. Robertson pointed out also, that calcium is less mobile than sodium or chloride, and so would be excluded by such a system, whereas it is usually concentrated. It might be added that a low concentration of magnesium is only characteristic of certain phyla and is not found in the molluscs. In order to account for the ionic regulation shown by many marine invertebrates, it is necessary to postulate both the active accumulation and the differential excretion of ions.

Although the activity of the excretory organs, combined with differential permeability, is insufficient to account for ionic regulation, the excretory organ may play an important part in reducing the concentration of some ions in the blood. The rate of urine production in most marine animals is so low that urine is difficult to collect, and data is limited (Table III.6). The urine produced is more or less isosmotic with the blood, but of different ionic composition, and so its production will not affect the total osmotic pressure of the blood. In the decapods, where the blood is poor in magnesium and sulphate, but rich in potassium and calcium, the activity of the renal organs tends to remove magnesium and sulphate and to conserve potassium and calcium. The conservation of potassium and calcium will not, in itself, raise the concentration of these ions above that of sea water, but

TABLE III.6. — COMPOSITION OF THE URINE OF SOME INVERTEBRATES WITH THE COMPOSITION OF THE BLOOD AND SEA WATER, EXPRESSED AS PERCENTAGE OF SEA WATER VALUES. (Robertson, 1949, 1953)

	Na	K	Ca	Mg	Cl	SO$_4$	NH$_3$ mM/kg water
Maia: blood ...	102	122	129	81	99	50	—
urine ...	102	119	128	87	97	108	—
Homarus: blood	111	86	151	14	100	31	—
urine	110	78	97	26	101	49	—
Sepia: blood ...	93	228	100	101	102	16.5	—
urine ...	74	114	70	69	102	36	146

will tend to augment the effect of active uptake. The correlation between the activity of the renal organs and the composition of the blood is imperfect, since in *Nephrops* where the potassium concentration of the blood is lower than in sea water, the antennary glands conserve potassium, (Robertson, 1949) implying that this ion is excreted elsewhere.

These conclusions, however, have little relevance unless the rate of urine flow is known. In general, the figures indicate that *Carcinus* in sea water produces 0.2–0.4% body weight/hr (Nagel, 1934; Webb, 1940); *Maia*, 0.12–1.61%/hr (Bialascewicz, 1933); *Cancer*, 0.13–0.42%/hr (Robertson, 1939); *Homarus*, 0.0–0.2%/hr (Burger, 1957). Since these animals are almost in osmotic equilibrium with the medium, there will be little osmotic inflow of water; the excreted water must come from swallowed sea water, from food, or from the active uptake of water. It is to be expected that flow rates in these conditions would be low, irrespective of the mode of formation of the urine, but at the same time, the formation of even these small volumes may have significant effects on the composition of the blood. For example, if a *Maia* produces, on average, 0.5% body weight/hr, a 100 g animal in one day will excrete 12 ml of urine containing 0.37 mM of sulphate. If the blood volume is one third of the body weight, the blood will contain 0.48 mM of sulphate. The sulphate excreted by the antennal glands in one day is almost equivalent to the total amount present in the blood. The capacity of the renal organs thus seems adequate to maintain the low concentration in the blood.

In *Sepia*, the blood is poor in sulphate and the renal organ preferentially removes it. In *Homarus* and *Maia*, as well as in *Sepia*, potassium is concentrated in the blood, and is to some extent salvaged from the urine, but in these animals the urine potassium is still higher than in sea water, so that its recovery from the filtrate is not very efficient. *Sepia* urine also contains a high concentration of ammonium ions which is accommodated by a lower concentration of the other cations. This high concentration of ammonium is associated with the carnivorous habit of the cephalopods. No figures are available for the concentration of ammonium in the urine of *Homarus* or *Maia*, but in the blood, the concentration is about 1 mM/kg water (Florkin and Duchâteau, 1943; Delaunay, 1931) and the urine concentration is probably not much higher.

Uptake of Salts and Water

Excretion, differential permeability, and the effects of the presence of protein in the blood, may account for some degree of ionic regulation, but when the concentration of any ion in the blood exceeds the concentration of the same ion in the dialysed plasma, that ion must be actively accumulated by the animal if there is no potential difference between the blood and the sea water. Ions may be provided by food, but often ionic regulation can be maintained through weeks of starvation and diet is probably a secondary factor. Most marine animals maintain concentration differences of the order of 1.2 : 1, or at the most 2 : 1, across the body wall. These concentration differences are very small compared with the 100 : 1 or 10,000 : 1 concentration differences found in brackish or freshwater animals, or even the 10 : 1 concentration difference which occurs between tissues and blood in marine animals, and the energy required to maintain equilibrium with the medium must be almost negligible.

In addition to the active uptake of ions, marine invertebrates must absorb water, possibly through the gut, to compensate for even a low rate of urine production. Metabolic water is certainly insufficient to account for 5–10% of the body weight of urine produced each day by unfed decapod crustaceans. The colloidal osmotic pressure of the blood will tend to draw water into the animal, but this would also seem to be insufficient to account for the observed rate of urine flow. The active uptake of ions at the body surface, by producing very localised concentration differences, might induce localised water uptake.

The ionic and osmotic changes which take place in a crustacean during moulting have been studied recently by Robertson (1960) in *Carcinus*. The very striking increase in body volume that occurs immediately after moulting is brought about by the rapid uptake of water from the environment. In *Carcinus*, this water uptake averages 66% of the premoult body weight. Shortly before moulting, the osmotic pressure of the blood rises to 105% that of sea water, but this increase will account for only a small part of the water intake. The greater part of the influx takes place by way of the gut after the crab has swallowed sea water. Of the sea water swallowed, the magnesium and sulphate ions are left behind in the gut, while much of the water and other ions are absorbed. As a result, shortly after the moult, the sulphate concentration in the gut fluids rises as high as six times that of sea water. Two thirds of the water absorbed appears in the blood, and the rest must be taken up by the tissues. Twelve hours after the moult, the blood concentration is still 103% that of the sea water, but later it becomes slightly hypo-osmotic for a while. As the solution passing through the gut wall is essentially isosmotic with sea water, some of the salt must enter the tissues along with the water.

The composition of the blood remains fairly constant during moulting, except that calcium rises to 164% of the sea water concentration just before the moult, as it is resorbed from the old shell, and falls to 93% as it is deposited in the new one; and sulphate falls from 46% of sea water before the moult, to 29.5% afterwards, when the sulphate-free liquid is absorbed through the gut wall.

Composition of the Tissues

Although the body fluids are very similar to sea water in ionic composition, the tissues are very different. The information available is confined almost entirely to two kinds of tissues, muscle and nerve. These are very rich in potassium, phosphate compounds, and a variety of organic compounds of low molecular weight, including amino acids, trimethylamine oxide, betaine and isethionic acid. In contrast to the body fluids, the tissues are poor in sodium and chloride. The potassium and chloride in *Loligo* nerve are in Donnan equilibrium with the potassium and chloride in the blood (Hodgkin, 1956), and this is probably true of the potassium and chloride in *Carcinus* nerve (Lewis, 1952), *Carcinus* muscle (Shaw, 1955a), the fast portion of *Pecten* adductor muscle (Potts, 1958), and *Loligo* and *Eledone* muscle (Manery, 1939; Hayes and Pelluet, 1947). It is very difficult to determine accurately the amount of intracellular chloride, as a small error in estimating the quantity of the chloride-rich extracellular fluid introduces a larger error into the calculation. However, in *Nephrops* and *Mytilus* muscles the deviation of calculated intracellular concentrations from the Donnan ratios is much larger than the standard error of the measurements (Potts, 1958; Robertson, 1957 b, 1961). When the potassium content of the tissue exceeds the Donnan equilibrium concentration, there must either be active uptake of potassium from the blood in addition to the extrusion of sodium, or some part of the potassium must be bound. Recent evidence of the intracellular concentrations in *Nephrops* abdominal flexor muscles indicates that this tissue both binds potassium and actively regulates it (Robertson, 1961). By comparing analyses of whole muscle with those for muscle press-juice, and using an experimentally determined value of 12% for the volume of extracellular space, Robertson has carefully calculated the intracellular composition of a number of inorganic and organic constituents of *Nephrops* muscle.

His data indicate that all the calcium in the muscle fibres is bound, 82% of the sodium, 60% of the magnesium and 26% of the potassium. The Donnan equilibrium ratios for potassium and chloride in *Nephrops* muscle are markedly different from the observed ratios (Table III.7). Even if one quarter of the potassium is bound, the concentration of free ions remaining is higher than the Donnan equilibrium concentration, and some active transport of potassium must take place.

TABLE III. 7. — SOME CONSTITUENTS OF THE OSMOTIC PRESSURE OF THE TISSUES OF SOME MARINE ANIMALS. EXPRESSED AS mM/KG WATER

Constituent	*Myxine*[6] muscle	*Nephrops*[1] muscle	*Carcinus*[2] nerve	*Loligo*[3] nerve	*Mytilus* fast[4] adductor	*Paracentrotus*[5] eggs
Sodium	137	24.5	41	50	79	52
Potassium	113	188	422	400	152	210
Calcium	2.2	3.72	—	0.4	7.3	4
Magnesium	10.8	20.3	—	10	34	11
Chloride	121	53.1	27	40	94	80
Sulphate	3.7	1.02	—	—	8.8	6
Carbonate	—	1.90	—	—	—	—
PO_4 + acid soluble P-compounds	82	164.2	19	10	29	68
Amino acids	—	476	444	87	295	—
Trimethylamine Oxide	—	59	—	—	—	—
Isethionic acid	—	—	—	270	—	—
Betaine	—	66	—	—	—	—
$\dfrac{K_i}{K_o}$	—	21.9	34.5	16.7	12.2	—
$\dfrac{Cl_o}{Cl_i}$	—	9.9	20.5	16.0	6.1	—

Data from: 1. Robertson 1961, corrected for extracellular fluid
2. Lewis,   1952, isolated nerve fibres
3. Hodgkin, 1956   ,,   ,,   ,,
4. Potts,   1958, corrected for extracellular fluid
5. Rothschild & Barnes 1953, no extracellular fluid
6. Robertson, 1960, whole muscle.

The potassium content of marine invertebrate nerves, and therefore their resting potentials, are much higher than in muscle (Table III.7). To balance the high potassium, the nerves must contain a high concentration of organic acids. *Sepia* giant axons contain a considerable amount of sulphonic and amino acids (isethionic, glutamic and aspartic acids); *Carcinus* nerve also contains a large quantity of glutamic and aspartic acids (Lewis, 1952). On the other hand, the muscles balance their high potassium content with greater quantities of inorganic phosphate and organic phosphate compounds.

The calcium content of the tissues is usually lower than that of the blood (e.g. *Nephrops*, Tables III.5 and III.7). The magnesium content of the muscle appears to be similar in different animals: in *Mytilus*, the blood magnesium is very high (53.5 mM/kg water) and the muscle contains 34 mM/kg water, while in *Nephrops*, the blood contains only 8.9 mM Mg/kg water whereas the muscle contains as much as 20.3 mM Mg/kg water. It is not clear how much of the calcium or magnesium in the tissues is in an ionic state. In *Sepia* nerve, the calcium is not ionic (Hodgkin, 1956), and in *Nephrops* muscle all the calcium and 60% of the magnesium is bound (Robertson, 1961).

Inorganic components account for about half of the total osmotic pressure of the tissues, and the rest is made up of a variety of organic compounds. Amino acids are of general occurrence, but in addition to isethionic acid in *Sepia* nerve large quantities of trimethylamine oxide and betaine have been found in some tissues. In *Homarus* muscle, the free amino acids amount to 256 mM/kg wet tissue, trimethylamine oxide to 75 mM/kg, and betaine to 67 mM/kg; *Homarus* digestive gland contained 170 mM, 14 mM, and 64 mM/kg wet tissue of these compounds respectively (Kermack, Lees Wood, 1955).* In *Nephrops* muscle, amino acids represent 40–50% of the total osmotic concentration, and trimethyl-

* The intracellular concentration in terms of mM/kg water would be at least 30% higher.

9

amine oxide and betaine 13% (Table III.7) (Robertson, 1961). *Myxine* whole muscle contains a high concentration of unidentified organic compounds (58%), presumably amino acids, as well as a high phosphate content (Robertson, 1960).

Very little information is available about the composition of the tissues of other phyla. *Caudina* muscle and blood corpuscles (Koizumi, 1935 b and c) and *Goldfingia* and *Thyone* muscles (Steinbach, 1940 a and b) also contain high potassium and much less sodium and chloride than the blood. However, it is difficult to estimate the amounts of extracellular fluid included in these analyses. *Arenicola* muscle (Cowey and Shaw, unpublished; Duchâteau-Bosson, Jeuniaux and Florkin, 1961) contains large quantities of free amino acids and high potassium (Chap. IV, Table IV.6).

Ascidian vanadocytes appear to contain a very high concentration of sulphuric acid. The blood plasma is neutral and has a lower sulphate concentration than sea water, but after cytolysis of the corpuscles, the acidity of the blood is equivalent to 0.022 N (Webb, 1939). This implies that the cell contents contain 1.83 N acid, since they occupy only 1.2% of the blood volume. The intact cells contain a very high concentration of sulphate, but free sulphuric acid of this strength would be strongly hyperosmotic to the plasma. It is difficult to conceive of any mechanism whereby the acid would be bound in the cells and only liberated by cytolysis.

The cytoplasm of the marine dinoflagellate, *Noctiluca*, is also acid (pH 4.6) and less dense (sp. gr., 1.018) than sea water (sp. gr., 1.026) (Iida and Iwata, 1943). Goethard and Hensius (1892, quoted in Krogh, 1939, pp.11–13) detected ammonia in the "cell sap" of *Noctiluca* and suggested that the buoyancy of these animals was due to a high concentration of ammonium salts. The quantitative measurements of Iida and Iwata, however, showed that the ammonium content (1.3 mM NH_4/l.) is quite insufficient to account for the buoyancy. They suggested, instead, that it was due to the replacement in the cell sap of sulphate by chloride. This has also been shown to be quantitatively insufficient (Davis, 1953) and it is now suggested that the low density is due to a high concentration of hydrogen ions (140 mM/l.) within the cell. However, a pH of 4.6 corresponds to a hydrogen ion concentration of $2.5 \cdot 10^{-2}$ mM H^+/l. and the buoyancy of *Noctiluca* remains unexplained. It is curious that low density ammonium solutions, first put forward as the principle of buoyancy in *Noctiluca* and since discarded, should be rediscovered in the cephalopods.

The eggs of marine invertebrates are similar to other cells (Table III.7). In *Paracentrotus* eggs, the potassium and chloride are possibly in a Donnan equilibrium with these ions in sea water (Rothschild and Barnes, 1953), but in *Sepia* eggs the chloride concentration is too high for a Donnan equilibrium (Bialascewicz, 1927). The proportion of the total osmotic pressure due to inorganic ions is very variable in the eggs of different animals, and amounts to only 10% in *Sepia* eggs (Bialascewicz, 1929).

The ionic concentration differences between cells and their environments must be actively created and maintained. If the potassium and chloride ions are in a Donnan equilibrium, the sodium must be actively excluded, and if they are not in equilibrium, potassium or chloride (probably the former) must be actively maintained as well. Most cells are quite permeable to all three monovalent ions. In the giant axons of *Sepia*, the rate of sodium turnover is about 25 mM Na/kg/hr (at 18°C), equivalent to about one third of the total sodium content of the cell each hour. This efflux is actively maintained against an electrochemical gradient, although a part may be due to exchange diffusion. Transmission of impulses in nerve affects the permeability to sodium and increases the rate of sodium turnover (Hodgkin and Keynes, 1955 a). The passive flux of potassium is about 16 mM K/kg/hr, or about 5% of the total. In *Carcinus* muscle, 70% of total sodium is exchanged in about 3 minutes (Shaw, 1955 c);

9*

it is suggested that much of this is due to exchange diffusion, but even in sodium-free Ringer, half the sodium is
lost in 10 minutes. The rate of exchange of potassium in
Carcinus muscle is 40% each hour. In *Mytilus* heart muscle,
the sodium turnover amounts to 460% of the total each
hour (Potts, 1959). Little is known about the fluxes of ions
between eggs and sea water, but they are in a dynamic equilibrium also. Sea urchin eggs take up ions from the sea after
fertilisation and during development (Oddo and Esposito,
1951; Needham, 1931, p.1250, 1950, p.38–39).

The rates of ion movement between the cells and body
fluids are of quite a different order from those between
body fluids and the surrounding sea water, and the energy
required at the cell surface to maintain the internal equilibria
may be many times greater than that required at the body
surface.

CHAPTER IV

OSMOTIC REGULATION
IN BRACKISH WATERS

Introduction and a Definition of Brackish Water

Brackish waters will be defined here as mixohaline waters of between 30‰ and 0.5‰ salinity (Venice System). The upper limit is fairly well defined, both geographically and physiologically. Salinities as low as 30‰ are found in open seas such as the Arctic Ocean, but significantly lower salinities are found only in partially enclosed seas such as the Baltic or the Bay of Bengal. The marine fauna becomes markedly impoverished only in salinities below about 30‰. The lower limit is not so clearly defined, but many "freshwater" lakes and rivers contain up to 0.5‰ salt. Less than 1% of the world's surface is covered by brackish waters, yet they are of considerable interest physiologically as a bridge between sea water and fresh.

Brackish waters are found in restricted coastal regions, such as estuaries or salt marshes, where the salinity often changes rapidly with the tides, and in larger land-locked seas such as the Baltic, the Caspian and the Aral Sea, where the conditions are stable. The Baltic declines in salinity from 30‰ in the Kattegat, to 5‰ at the head of the Gulf of Bothnia. The Caspian Sea has a salinity of 13‰ and Lake Aral of 11‰, but in each case the relative amounts of the different ions resemble those of sea water (Karpevick, 1958).

A gentle salinity gradient, such as that of the Baltic, provides an opportunity for the gradual adaptation of marine animals to a lower salinity during lateral migration, while

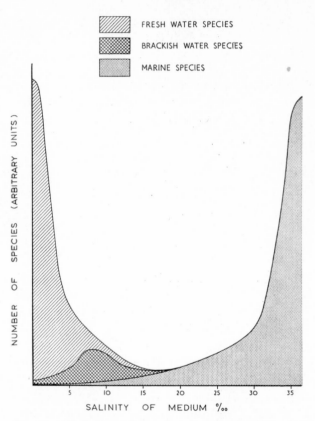

Fig. IV.1. Variation of the number of marine, brackish and fresh-water species with the salinity of the medium. Adapted from Dahl, 1956 and Remane, 1934.

the progressive dilution of an isolated arm of the sea would ensure either adaptation or extinction.

The fauna of brackish waters may be divided into three classes: marine animals which can tolerate low salinities, freshwater animals which can tolerate moderate salinitise, and true brackish water animals which are not found in either sea water or fresh water, although they may be able to survive in either. Most marine animals are unable to maintain their normal vigour in salinities much below 30‰, and the number of marine species declines rapidly with the salinity (Fig. IV.1). Seventy-five per cent of the numbers of marine species disappear in the Skagerrak when the salinity declines from 34‰ to only 30‰ (Dahl, 1956). Some animals such as *Mytilus edulis* or *Carcinus maenas*, although common in the sea, are also found in considerable numbers down to salinities of 10‰, or even lower, but marine species almost disappear at about 5‰. Most freshwater animals can tolerate salinities up to, but not greater than, their normal blood concentration, so that freshwater animals are not usually found in salinities higher than 10‰.

Characteristic brackish water animals such as the polychaete, *Nereis diversicolor*, or the prawn, *Palaemonetes varians*, are not commonly found in the sea (Plymouth Marine Fauna, 1931), although they may be able to survive well in normal sea water; therefore their absence from the sea must be attributed to ecological or behavioural rather than to physiological factors. On the other hand, few brackish water animals can live in fresh water, so that physiological factors usually limit their spread into this environment. The fauna of areas where the salinity varies between wide limits is usually restricted, but it may include some marine animals which evade low salinities, by closing their shells or retreating into the mud. For example, Milne (1940) recorded that the salinity inside the mantle cavity of *Mytilus* at low tide was 24‰, when the salinity outside had fallen to 7‰. In addition *Mytilus* is able to tolerate low salinities, but the limpet *Patella*, which is not a brackish water animal, was also able to survive solely by excluding the brackish water.

Animals are able to live indefinitely in a variable brackish water environment, either because they can regulate the concentration of the blood independently of the environment, i.e. they can osmoregulate, or because they can tolerate large changes in the concentration of the body fluids. The faculty of toleration is more widely distributed than that of osmoregulation. Even animals which can osmoregulate are often unable to maintain the same blood concentration in brackish or in fresh water as in sea water, and so their tissues must be able to tolerate some degree of change in blood concentration. For example, *Eriocheir*, the Chinese wool-handed crab, is about isosmotic in the sea, but maintains its blood equivalent to only 60% of sea water when it is in fresh water (Krogh, 1939, p.82). Animals which cannot osmoregulate can sometimes tolerate very low salinities, e.g. *Mytilus* lives in brackish water of only 6‰ salinity (Milne, 1940), or 4‰ (Beliaev and Tschugunova, 1952), and the starfish *Asterias* in water of 8‰ (Remane, 1941), but these animals can never survive in completely fresh water.

The Blood Concentrations of Brackish Water Animals

Even in animals which can osmoregulate, the concentration of the body fluids varies to some extent with that of the external medium. The relation between the concentrations of the medium and the body fluids of two crabs, the common shore crab, *Carcinus*, which can osmoregulate, and the spider crab, *Maia*, which cannot, is shown in Fig. IV.2. *Maia* is wholly marine in distribution, and its blood is always isosmotic with the medium, while *Carcinus* is commonly found in estuaries, and its blood concentration corresponds to about 60% sea water when it is living in only 15% sea water. The relation between the concentrations of blood and medium may be affected by other factors, such as temperature, oxygen-tension, age, sex and moulting cycles. Some animals display a hysteresis, the blood concentrations at any salinity differing according to whether the salinity was

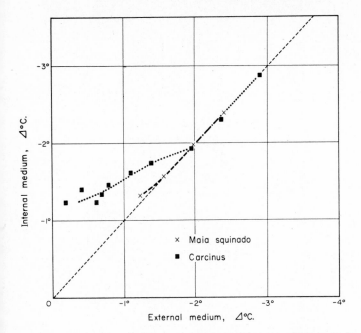

Fig. IV.2. Freezing points of the blood of the crabs *Maia squinado*
and *Carcinus maenas* as a function of the external medium.
From Duval, 1925.

approached from a higher or a lower concentration (Kinne
and Rotthauwe, 1952; Gilbert, 1959 a, b and c).

With these qualifications, the relation between the concentrations of medium and the blood in a number of brackish
water animals is shown in Fig. IV.3.

The Mechanisms of Osmotic Regulation

When the concentration of the body fluids is greater than
that of the medium, water enters by osmosis, and salts are
lost by diffusion. In order to maintain equilibrium, this water
must be removed and solutes replaced. The rate of urine

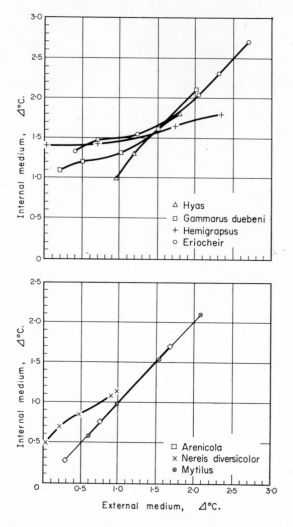

Fig. IV.3. The blood concentrations of some brackish water animals as functions of the external medium. *Hyas* from Schlieper, 1929. *Gammarus* from Beadle and Cragg, 1940. *Hemigrapsus* from Jones, 1941. *Eriocheir* from Scholles, 1933. *Arenicola* from Schlieper, 1929. *Nereis diversicolor* from Schlieper, 1929. *Mytilus* from Potts., unpub.

production is usually proportional to the osmotic concentration differences between the animal and the environment, and is probably equivalent to the osmotic inflow of water, but the possibilities of extra-renal water elimination should not be forgotten.

The energy required for osmotic regulation is the sum of the energy required to compensate for both the permeability to solutes and the permeability to water. These two factors will be considered separately.

Solute Loss

For simplicity, let us suppose that no potential difference exists between the body fluids and the external medium. The energy required for regulation will then vary with the external concentration in the following way.

If B is the concentration of any solute in the blood (M/l.),

M the concentration of the same solute in the medium (M/l.),

K the permeability of the body wall, area (A), to the solutes in M/unit area/molar concentration difference/hr,* then the *efflux* of solute will be

$$K A B \quad M/hr.$$

The *influx* of solute from the medium will be

$$K A M \quad M/hr,$$

and the net loss of solute will be

$$K A (B - M) \quad M/hr.$$

---

* The product KA for the whole body is made up of the sum of the products of the permeabilities and areas of each uniform part of the body surface.

The energy *(W)* required to replace the lost solute, by active uptake from the medium, will be

$$W = K A (B - M) R T \ln \frac{B}{M}. \qquad (1)$$

Thus, the energy required is a function of the concentration of both the blood and the medium. If the blood concentration were independent of the concentration of the medium (Fig. IV.4a, line A), then the energy required to replace the solute lost by diffusion would increase very rapidly as M declines (Fig. IV.4b, line A). If the blood concentration declined in brackish water (Fig. IV.4a, Line B), the energy required would be rather smaller (Fig. IV.4b, line B), but would still tend to infinity at low concentrations.

The permeability of the body wall will be different to each ion species, and the total energy required will be the sum of the energies needed to regulate the concentration of each ion. In practice, regulation of sodium and chloride ions together will account for about nine tenths of the total energy. The permeability of the body walls to both sodium and chloride appears to be similar (e.g. *Nereis*, Chap. IV, p.147; *Astacus*, Chap. V, p.200), so the total energy required will be about twice that required to replace either of these ions alone. In many cases, a potential difference exists between the body fluid and the medium, e.g. *Astacus* (Bryan, 1960a; Shaw, 1960c), *Rana* (Jørgensen, Levi and Zerahn, 1954). This occurs as the result of the preferential transport of either cations or anions. If the active uptake of sodium exceeds that of chloride, the body fluids become positive with respect to the medium, and the potential may be sufficient to draw the chloride in passively. In this case no energy is required to maintain the chloride concentration, but the energy required to maintain the sodium concentration is correspondingly increased.

If an animal were in equilibrium, and the body wall more permeable to chloride than to sodium, the flux of chloride

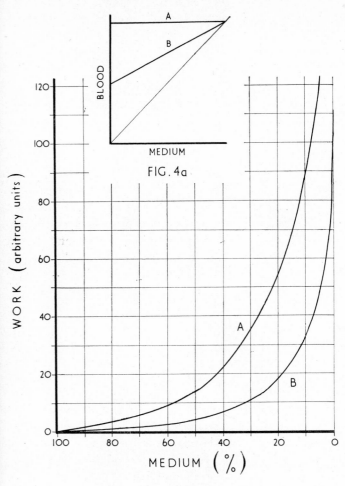

FIG. 4a

FIG. 4b

Fig. IV.4a. Diagram to illustrate two possible relations between the concentration of the blood and the concentration of the external medium. For explanation see text.
4b. The relation between ionic work and the concentration of the medium in animals permeable to salt but impermeable to water. A, blood concentration as in Line A, Fig 4a; B, blood concentration as in B, Fig 4a.

across the body wall could be much greater than the flux of sodium. If the animal was in distilled water, both the effluxes would have to be similar, to maintain electrical equilibrium. In this case, a potential difference will exist between the body fluids and the environment and the efflux of ions would be speeded or retarded according to Equation 6, Chap. I.

Water Uptake

The energy required to form urine by ultrafiltration is very small, but the energy required to replace salt lost in the urine or to resorb salt from the ultrafiltrate may be considerable.

If V is the rate of urine production, (l./hr), and U the concentration of any solute in the urine (M/l.), the energy required to replace the solute lost, by resorption from the medium, will be

$$W = R\,T\,V\,U\ \ln\frac{B}{M}. \tag{2}$$

The energy required for osmoregulation may be reduced if some of the salt is salvaged from the urine before it is voided. It is clearly more economical to recover some of the salt from the urine, which is initially at the same concentration as the blood, than it is to replace it by absorption from the medium which is less concentrated.

The energy required to recover some of the solute from the urine and to reduce the concentration of the ultrafiltrate from B to U will be

$$W = R\,T\,V\,U\left(\frac{B-U}{U} - n\,\frac{B}{U}\right) \text{cal/hr} \tag{3}$$

(Potts, 1954 c).

This is the work which must be done by the excretory organ. If the concentration of the urine is reduced below that of the medium, it becomes more economical to recover the solute from the medium. As long as U is finite, some solute will be lost, and work $= R\,T\,V\,U\,\ln\dfrac{B}{M}$ cals/hr must be done at the surface of the animal to replace it.

Hence, the total work which must be done by the animal as a consequence of its permeability to water, to maintain the concentration of any solute, will be

$$W = RTVU\left(\frac{B-U}{U} - \ln\frac{B}{U} + RTVU\,\ln\frac{B}{M}\right)$$
$$= RTV\,(B-U) + U\,\ln\frac{U}{M}. \qquad (4)$$

For all the constituents of the body fluids,

$$W = RTV\,(B' - U') + U_{Na}\,\ln\frac{U_{Na}}{M_{Na}} + U_{K}\,\frac{U_{K}}{M_{K}}\ \text{etc.} \quad (5)$$

where B' and U' are the total concentrations of the blood and urine respectively, U_{Na} and M_{Na} the concentrations of sodium in the urine and medium, etc. Hence, W can be independent of the concentration of any constituent in the blood.

To a first approximation,

$$W = RTV\,(B' - U') + U'\,\ln\frac{U'}{M'} \qquad (6)$$

when M' is the total concentration of the medium.

Again Equation 5 will not be strictly applicable if a potential difference exists across the barrier between blood and medium, or between urine and blood. However, if the blood is negative with respect to the medium, in general, the saving of energy on the cations will balance the extra expenditure on the anions, and vice versa.

W is at a minimum when the concentration of each constituent in the urine has been reduced to its concentration in the medium, when

$$W = R\,T\,V\ (B' - M') \qquad \text{from (6).}$$

This is also the energy which would be required to maintain water balance by the direct movement of water against the concentration gradient from the blood to the medium.

As the volume of urine produced is equivalent to the volume of water entering by osmosis,

$$V = P A \, (B' - M') \tag{7}$$

where $P A$ is the sum of the products of permeability to water (P) and area (A) over the whole surface of the animal.*

Hence, from Equations 6 and 7,

$$W = R T P A \, (B' - M') \left(U' \, \ln \frac{U'}{M'} + B - U \right). \tag{8}$$

Again, W is at a minimum when $U' = M'$, since

$$V = R T P A \, (B' - M')^2 \tag{9}$$

and it is at a maximum when no salt resorption takes place in the excretory organ, and $U' = B'$, when

$$W = R T P A \, (B' - M') \, B \ln \frac{B'}{M'}. \tag{10}$$

The energy required to compensate for the permeability to water in these two conditions is illustrated in Fig. IV.5. When the urine concentration is reduced from B' to M', the energy required is reduced by the factor

$$\frac{B' \ln \dfrac{B'}{M'}}{B' - M'} \text{ from (9) and (10).}$$

In fresh water, where M' is negligible compared with B' this factor reduces to $\ln (B'/M')$. In freshwater animals, this is about 0.1 or 0.2, but in brackish water animals, it is nearer to unity. This can be seen in Fig. IV.5, where the diver-

* More exactly, $P A = \Sigma \, P_1 A_1 + P_2 A_2 + \ldots$ for each small uniform area of the body surface.

gence between the lines $U = B$ and $U = M$ only becomes considerable at low salinities. In fact, all brackish water animals seem to produce urine isosmotic with the blood (e.g. *Carcinus*, Nagel, 1934; *Eriocheir*, Scholles, 1933; *Palaemonetes*, Panikkar, 1941) in salinities not less than about 10‰,

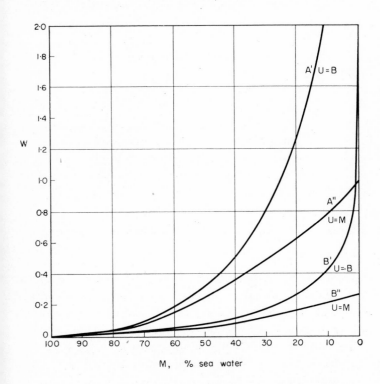

Fig. IV.5. The relation between osmotic work and the concentration of the medium in animals permeable to water but impermeable to salt.

A′ Urine isosmotic with blood; blood concentration
as in A of Fig. 4a.
A″ Urine isosmotic with the medium; blood concentration
as in A of Fig. 4a.
B′ Urine isosmotic with the blood; blood concentration
as in B of Fig. 4a.
B″ Urine isosmotic with the medium; blood concentration
as in B of Fig. 4a.
(From Potts, 1954 a)

10

although *Gammarus duebeni* produces a hypo-osmotic urine in lower salinities (Lockwood, 1961).

The total uptake of salt from the medium must be equivalent to the sum of the salt lost by diffusion and the salt lost in the urine. Energy required for osmotic regulation in hypo-osmotic media may be saved by lowering the blood concentration. This reduces the energy required to compensate for both the loss by diffusion (Equation 1) and the water uptake by osmosis (Equation 8). The energy may be reduced also by lowering the permeability to water and solutes (Equations 1 and 8), and by resorbing solutes from the urine (cf. Equations 9 and 10). Any reduction in the blood concentration produces a more than proportionate reduction in the energy requirements, while changes in permeability will produce proportionate changes. Resorption from the urine will produce little saving in brackish water, but may represent a very valuable saving in fresh water.

Specific Examples of Brackish Water Animals

Brackish Water Crabs

Carcinus maenas — The relation between the concentration of the external medium, and the concentration of the blood is expressed in Fig. IV.6 (data from Shaw, 1961 a). Earlier estimates were made by Nagel (1934), Bethe, v. Holst and Huf (1935), Huf (1936) and Webb (1940). The sodium space is equivalent to 38% of the body volume. Tracer studies have shown that both in sea water and in 50% sea water, the extra-renal sodium efflux is equivalent to about 14% of the body sodium each hour. The permeability is thus independent of the external medium between these concentrations. The relation between urine production and the medium is shown in Fig. IV.7. The urine is approximately isosmotic with the blood (Nagel, 1934; Webb, 1940). The renal sodium loss amounts to only 2.7% of the total loss in sea water, but rises to more than 20% of the total loss in 40% sea water (Fig. IV.10).

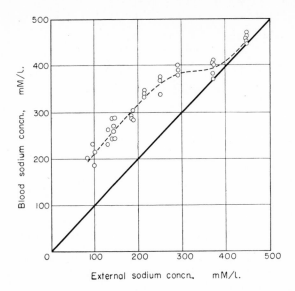

Fig. IV.6. *Carcinus maenas.* Variation of the sodium concentration in the blood with the sodium concentration in the medium. From Shaw, 1961 a.

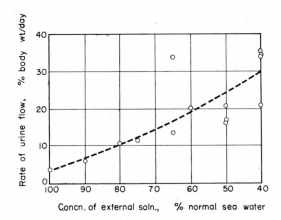

Fig. IV.7. *Carcinus maenas.* The relation between the rate of urine production and the concentration of the medium. From Shaw, 1961 a.

10*

In brackish water, the influx of sodium into the animal is due partly to passive diffusion from the external medium, and partly to active uptake. If no potential difference exists across the body wall, the ratio of passive influx: loss by diffusion will be equal to the sodium concentration in the medium: sodium concentration in the blood (Equation 5,

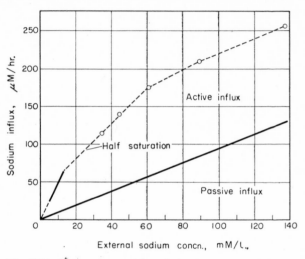

Fig. IV.8. *Carcinus maenas.* The relation between the sodium influx and the sodium concentration in the medium. Weight of crab 31.6 g. From Shaw, 1961 a.

Chap. I). The relation between the active and passive influxes is shown in Fig. IV.8. Shaw suggests that the relationship is of the kind discussed in Chap.I, p.34. The uptake system is fully saturated at external concentrations of about 70 mM Na/l. The active uptake declines sharply when the blood concentration rises above 400 mM Na/l. (Fig. IV.9). A 5% decline in the blood concentration is sufficient to activate the transport system fully. It follows that the blood concentration can only be maintained precisely over a very small range. A greater decline cannot stimulate the active transport system further, so that the blood concentration follows the fall in medium concentration at some distance (Fig. IV.6). However, it is curious to note that the concentration difference between blood and the medium, according to Shaw, remains about constant over the range 25–75% sea water, although the rate of urine production appears to increase (Figs. IV.6 and IV.7).

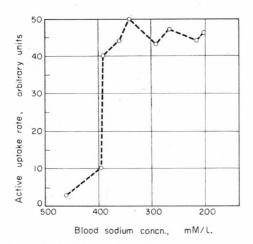

Fig. IV.9. *Carcinus maenas*. Relation between the sodium concentration in the blood and the rate of active uptake of sodium. From Shaw, 1961 a.

Using Shaw's figures, it can be calculated that the energy required for regulation in 40% sea water is equivalent to 2.4 cal/kg/hr (assuming $T = 15°C$). According to Schwabe (1933), *Carcinus* in sea water of 15‰ salinity consumes about 141 mg O_2/kg/hr, equivalent to about 400 cal/kg/hr. Thus, the energy required for osmotic regulation between the animal and the environment is only equivalent to a small part of the total metabolism, but all of this work must be performed by the outer surface of the animal.

To summarise, the losses and influxes into crabs in sea water and brackish water are expressed in Table IV.1 and Fig. IV.10.

TABLE IV.1. — SODIUM EXCHANGES IN *Carcinus maenas* IN SEA WATER
MEDIA (from Shaw, 1961 a)

Concentration			Fluxes mM/kg/hr				
External		Blood	Total	Renal	Diffusion	Passive	Active
% S. W.	mM/l.	mM/l.	flux	loss	loss	influx	influx
100	450	460	25.3	0.69	24.6	24.1	1.2
50	225	340	20.2	3.26	16.9	12.0	8.2
40	180	300	17.8	3.76	14.0	9.6	8.2

Calculated on the assumption that 100 % sea water contains 450 mM Na/l. and that the
passive efflux from the animal in 100 % sea water is 24.1 mM/kg/hr, and no potential
difference exists between the animal and the medium. Temperature unspecified.

The ability of *Carcinus* to transport ions against a concentration gradient was first clearly demonstrated by Nagel
(1934), who transferred some crabs which had adapted to
dilute sea water to a more concentrated medium, but one still
less concentrated than the blood. In the more concentrated
medium, the blood concentration rose significantly (Table
IV.2), although all the animals before transfer had blood
hyperosmotic to the second medium. As the body weight
of the animal remains constant to within 1% during such
transfers (Schwabe, 1933), the increase must have been caused
by the active uptake of salts against a concentration gradient.
No difference could be found between normal crabs and those
with the gut blocked, so the active transport must have taken
place at the outer surface.

TABLE IV.2. — ACTIVE UPTAKE OF IONS BY *Carcinus maenas*
(From Nagel, 1934)

	Medium		Blood	
	mM Cl/l.	Δ °C	mM Cl/l.	Δ °C
Before transfer...	242	0.89	344 (5)*	1.31 (5)*
24 hr after transfer	322	1.18	408 (6)*	1.56 (6)*

* Number of animals in brackets.

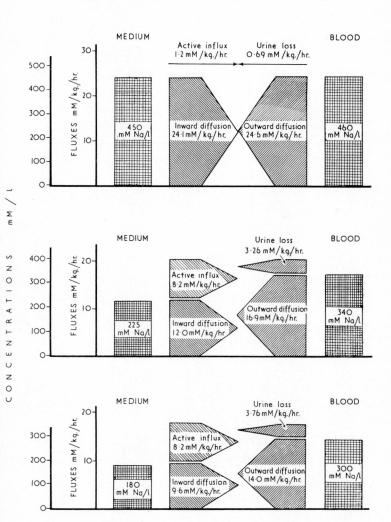

Fig. IV.10. The sodium fluxes through *Carcinus* in various media.

Comparison of Carcinus with marine crabs — *Carcinus* is able to live in dilute brackish water because it can maintain its blood concentration significantly higher than that of the medium, and because its tissues continue to function when the blood is equivalent to only 60% sea water. In order to maintain a blood concentration hyperosmotic to the medium, *Carcinus* concentrates ions against a gradient. While the majority of marine crustaceans can concentrate potassium and calcium (Chap. III), *Carcinus* is able to concentrate sodium and chloride as well.

Permeability to water — No direct comparisons of the permeability to water of *Carcinus* and a marine species have been made, but indirect evidence of permeabilities can be obtained from the rate of urine production, or from the rates of change of body weight when the excretory openings are blocked. These rates are proportional to PA (Equation 7), and if animals of similar size and shape are compared, some information may be deduced about P.

When *Maia* was transferred from sea water to water of 20‰ salinity, it increased in weight by nearly 3% in the first

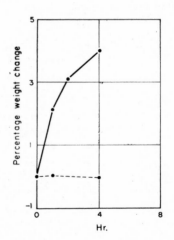

Fig. IV.11. Increase of weight of *Carcinus* and *Maia* with antennary glands open, after transfer to dilute sea water (20%). From Schwabe, 1933. (Solid line: *Maia*; broken line: *Carcinus*.)

hour, while *Carcinus* in the same conditions maintained an almost constant weight (Fig. IV.11). This reflects both a difference in permeability and in the ability of the excretory systems to remove water (Huf, 1936). When the excretory pores were blocked, the weight of *Carcinus* increased by less than 2%/hr in $\frac{1}{2}$ sea water, while that of the marine *Cancer* increased by 3.5%/hr (Fig. IV.12), and *Hyas* by nearly 3%/hr. These experiments suggest that *Carcinus* is less permeable to water than are marine crabs.

Permeability to salts — When a marine or brackish water animal is placed in an artificial sea water where the concentration of one ion is increased or decreased at the expense of the others, some corresponding change occurs in the blood. In general, marine crabs reach a new equilibrium more rapidly than *Carcinus* in these conditions. For example, when *Maia* and *Carcinus* were transferred to calcium-rich sea water, the concentration of calcium increased several times as rapidly in *Maia* blood as in *Carcinus* blood (Fig. IV.13). Some of the gain may be due to active uptake, but the very rapid change in the concentration of calcium in *Maia* blood suggests that the animal is much more permeable than *Carcinus*. The marine genera *Portunus* (= *Macropipus*) and *Hyas* are much more permeable to iodide ions than is *Carcinus*. After 5 hours in sea water containing iodide, the concentration of iodide in *Hyas* blood was 80% that of the medium, while in *Carcinus* it was only 20% (Fig. IV.14). The relative permeability to iodide was determined in this fashion for a number of crabs (Fig. IV.15). The concentration of iodide in the blood never exceeded that of the medium, and as *Hyas* and *Portunus* have poorer powers of ionic regulation than *Carcinus*, it is unlikely that the iodide was actively accumulated. The equilibrium concentration of iodide in *Carcinus* was lower in brackish water than in sea water (Fig. IV.16), probably because the urine output was higher and thus the rate of iodide excretion was also higher. Iodide was lost more rapidly from *Hyas* than from *Carcinus* after transfer to iodide-free sea water. Iodide accumulation was unaffected by block-

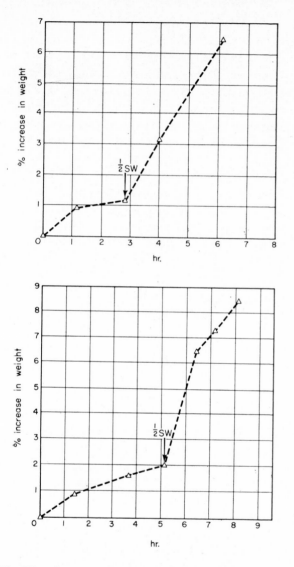

Fig. IV.12. Increases of weight of *Cancer* and *Carcinus* with antennary glands closed. At the points indicated by the arrows, the crabs were transferred to half sea water. Redrawn from Huf 1936. (*Cancer* above, *Carcinus* below.)

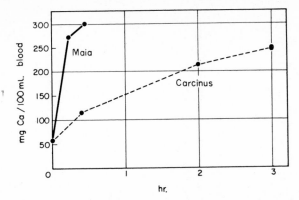

Fig. IV.13. Increase in the calcium concentrations in the blood of *Maia* and *Carcinus* after transfer to calcium-rich sea water. From Remane and Schlieper, 1958.

ing the gut; the main exchange probably occurred through the gills, but the carapace itself was slightly permeable (Bethe and Berger, 1931).

In the crab, *Carcinus maenas*, the total body potassium is exhanged at a rate of 3.6%/hr, but in *Portunus depurator*, the rate is 28%/hr (at 17°C) (Bryan, 1961).

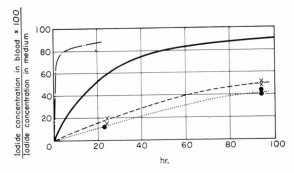

Fig. IV.14. Concentration of iodide in the blood of some decapod crustaceans after transfer to media containing iodide. Iodide concentration in the blood is expressed as a percentage of the concentration in the medium. From Nagel, 1934. (*Hyas*, upper line; *Portunus* spp., solid and dashed lines; *Carcinus*; dotted line.)

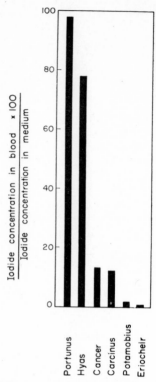

Fig. IV.15. The concentration of iodide in the blood of some decapod crustaceans 2½ hours after tranfer to a medium containing iodide. Iodide concentrations expressed as percentages of the concentration in the media. From Nagel, 1934.

The permeability of a number of species of American crabs has also been studied. Gross (1957) showed that the exoskeletons of crabs which did not osmoregulate were the most permeable to salts, regulating crabs were less permeable, and the freshwater crayfish, *Procambarus*, was the least permeable (Fig. IV.17). In these experiments, the permeability of each animal was measured by mounting a disc of exoskeleton, without hypodermis, between sea water and ½ sea water. The stronger solution, which simulated the blood, was placed on the inner side of the disc. The movement of water was negligible compared with the movement of salt. All these experiments confirm that brackish water crustaceans are less permeable than marine ones (cf. p.176).

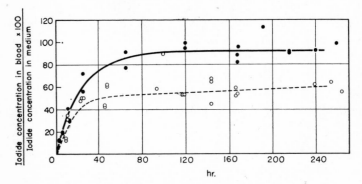

Fig. IV.16. Concentrations of iodide in the blood of *Carcinus* after transfer to media containing iodide. Iodide concentrations expressed as percentages of the concentrations in the media. Solid line in sea water, broken line in brackish water. From Nagel, 1934.

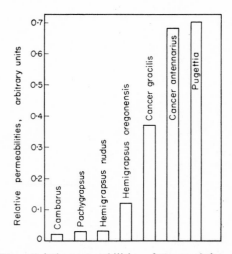

Fig. IV.17. Relative permeabilities of the exoskeletons of several decapod crustaceans to sea water. *Cancer* and *Pugettia*, marine, *Pachygrapsus* and *Hemigrapsus* spp., brackish, and *Cambarus*, fresh water. From Gross, 1957.

Nereis and Perinereis

Water exchanges. — *Nereis diversicolor* can live in a wide range of salinities; it is isosmotic in sea water, but hyperosmotic in dilute brackish water (Fig. IV.13). When it is transferred from sea water to brackish water, the animal takes up water by osmosis. At first, the rate of water uptake exceeds the rate of excretion and the volume of the animal increases; but as the blood is diluted, water uptake is reduced and eventually urine flow exceeds water uptake, and so the volume falls (Fig. IV.18). The final volume may (Jørgensen and Dales,

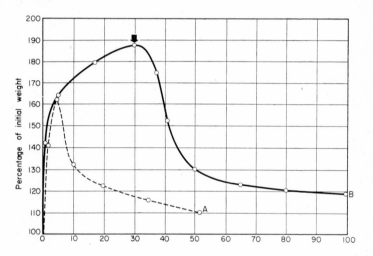

Fig. IV.18. *Nereis diversicolor.* Change of weight after transfer to 20% sea water (A), and to calcium-free sea water (B). At the point indicated by the arrow the worm was transferred to 20% sea water containing calcium. From Ellis, 1937.

1957) or may not (Beadle, 1937) be the same as the original volume. Urine flow is probably related to internal hydrostatic pressure, as an ingenious transfer experiment by Beadle demonstrates. *Nereis* living for 4 hours in ¼ sea water had the same blood concentration ($\equiv$ 55% sea water) as worms living for 3 days in ½ sea water, but those from ¼ sea water were the more distended. When the animals were transferred to isosmotic sea water, those from ¼ sea water lost weight, while those from ½ sea water remained constant. The weight loss (of the more distended worms) must have been due to a greater rate of urine production.

During the period of swelling, the blood is diluted as a result of both water uptake and salt loss. On the other hand, during the period of contraction, the water loss is not associated with any net salt loss, and it has been concluded that the animals produce a hypo-osmotic urine in these conditions (Ellis, 1937). However, subsequent work has shown that in the later period, active uptake balances loss of salts by diffusion and loss in the urine, both of which continue at a high level.

Marked differences in the rate of adaptation were found between worms from different localities (Ellis, 1937); the significance of this is unknown, but the possibility of regional variations should be kept in mind when making comparisons between experiments on different populations.

The presence of calcium, known to be effective in lowering surface permeability (Chap. I, p.13), was found to affect the rate of water uptake (Beadle, 1937; Ellis, 1937); thus, after transfer to more dilute brackish water, in the absence of calcium, the body volume continued to increase, instead of reaching a maximum and then falling (Fig. IV.18).

Sodium and chloride exchanges — Exchanges of sodium between worms and the medium have been investigated in *Nereis diversicolor* and *Perinereis cultrifera* with ^{24}Na as a tracer (Fretter, 1955) and exchanges of chloride have been studied in *N. diversicolor* and *N. virens* with ^{36}Cl (Jørgensen and Dales, 1957).

The rate of sodium uptake was measured in worms adapted for 36 hours to salinities of 45‰, 35‰, 17.5‰, and 9‰ (*ca.* 1¼ sea water, sea water, ½ sea water and ¼ sea water)

(Figs. IV.19 and IV.20). Exchange rates, expressed in terms of the weight of the worms in full strength sea water, were high: 10.9 μM/g/hr for *N. diversicolor*, and 35 μM/g/hr for *P. cultrifera* in sea water of 35‰ salinity. Total exchangeable sodium in *N. diversicolor* in sea water is 272 μM/g, so the rate of exchange is about 4% of the body sodium each hour;

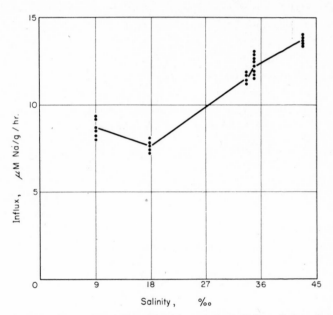

Fig. IV.19. *Nereis diversiolor*. The relation of the salinity of the medium to the influx of sodium. Temperature of solutions 12°C. From Fretter, 1955.

for *P. cultrifera*, the rate is even higher. Worms ligated at both ends showed the same rate of exchange as normal animals, so the gut was not implicated.

The chloride exchange experiments (Figs. IV.21 and IV.22) were made at a 10°C higher temperature, and the fluxes expressed in terms of the weight of the worm in the experimental conditions. The wide scatter of the chloride results, and the differences in techniques, make comparison difficult, but it appears that the chloride fluxes are about twice as high as the sodium fluxes. Jørgensen and Dales' results are of particular interest because they include some measurements made on *N. diversicolor* in fresh water.

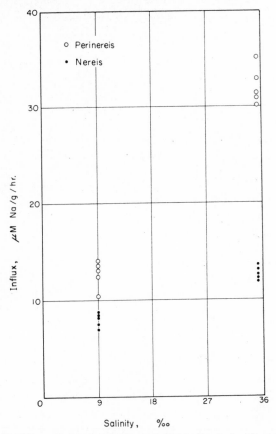

Fig. IV.20. *Perinereis cultrifera* and *Nereis diversicolor*. The influx of sodium in sea water of 9‰ salinity and 36‰ salinity. From Fretter, 1955.

In higher salinities, where the worms are isosmotic with the medium, sodium and chloride fluxes are about proportional to the medium concentrations (Fig. IV.19 and IV.21).

11

This could mean, either that active transport and excretion are negligible in these conditions and the ion flux is due to simple diffusion, or that the flux is largely due to exchange diffusion. However, the net fluxes calculated from tracer fluxes are almost identical with those obtained by direct measurements (Beadle, 1937, see below), so that exchange diffusion is probably not important.

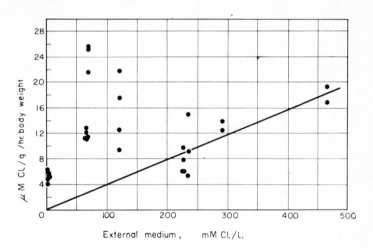

Fig. IV.21. *Nereis diversiolor.* The relation of the chloride concentration of the medium to the influx of chloride. Temperature 24-25°C. From Jørgensen and Dales, 1957.

When the animals are in sodium balance,

total Na influx = passive Na influx + active Na uptake
= passive Na efflux + Na lost in urine (11)

If it is assumed that there is no potential difference between body fluid and medium, then it follows from Equation 5, Chap. I, that

$$\frac{\text{passive influx}}{\text{passive efflux}} = \frac{Na_M}{Na_B}. \tag{12}$$

If in concentrated sea water of 44‰ salinity (589 mM Na/kg water), the rate of urine production and active uptake were negligible, it follows from Equations 11 and 12, and Fretter's data, that in 9‰ salinity (120 mM Na/kg water) the passive efflux will be 3.49 μM/g/hr, passive influx 2.56 μM/g/hr, and urine loss 4.35 μM/g/hr. If the urine were isosmotic with the blood, the rate of urine production would be equivalent to 2.8% of the water content/hr.

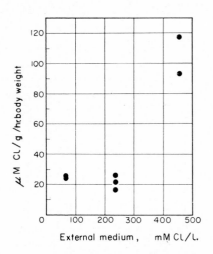

Fig. IV.22. *Nereis virens.* The relation of the chloride concentration of the medium to the influx of chloride. Temperature 24-25°C. From Jørgensen and Dales, 1957.

The chloride fluxes were about twice as large as the sodium fluxes. If it is assumed that in sea water of 35‰ salinity (470 mM Cl/l.) the fluxes (18.2 μM/g/hr) were due to passive diffusion, it follows from Equations 11 and 12 that in 9‰ salinity (120 mM Cl/l.) the passive influx was 4.65 μM/g/hr, the passive efflux 6.3 μM/g/hr, and urine loss 9.2 μM/g/hr. The rate of production of an isosmotic urine would be 5.7% of the body water/hr. These fluxes are illustrated in Fig. IV.23.

These rates of urine production are calculated on the assumption that no potential difference exists across the body wall. The fact that the two rates are sufficiently concordant

11*

(when allowance is made for the temperature difference), indicates that this is a reasonable assumption.

In fresh water (1.4 mM Cl/l.), the chloride influx was 5.5 μM/g/hr. The body fluid concentration in this medium was

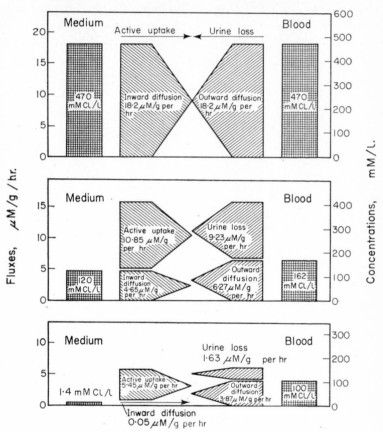

Fig. IV.23. *Nereis diversicolor.* Diagrammatic representation of the chloride fluxes through *Nereis.* Temperature 24-25°C.

100 mM Cl/l. If the permeability to the chloride is unchanged, influx by diffusion would be negligible, and diffusion loss would be 3.87 μM/g/hr. Loss in the urine would be only 1.6 μM/g/hr (Fig. IV.23). If blood and urine were isosmotic,

the rate of flow would be 1.4% of body water/hr. This is much smaller than the rate calculated for worm in $^1/_4$ sea water, although the osmotic gradient is greater; this suggests that the urine of worms in fresh water is no longer isosmotic, but hypo-osmotic to the blood. This is possible because the nephridium of N. *diversicolor* is more complex than that of non-regulating species (Jurgens, 1935), but it is reasonable to suppose that the urine is hypo-osmotic to the blood only at very low salinities (cf. *Astacus* and *Gammarus*, Chap. V, pp.177 and 182). If urine flow varies proportionately with the osmotic gradient, and if the urine of animals in $\frac{1}{4}$ sea water is isosmotic with the blood and flows at a rate of 5.4% body water/hr, in fresh water the urine flow would be 12.8% body water/hr, or about 10% body weight/hr. In these circumstances the urine concentration must be about one seventh that of the blood, *ca*. 16 mM Cl/l.

Jørgensen and Dales suggest, however, that the permeability of N. *diversicolor* in fresh water to both water and salts is only about a third that in brackish water. They attempted to compare the permeability by placing the worms first in a hyperosmotic solution and then in a hypo-osmotic one, and measuring the rate of change in weight. Allowing for loss of weight in handling, and after subjecting the worms to a concentration difference of 100 mM Cl/l. the loss of weight was 8.8% and 11.6%/hr in two experiments. This is comparable with a urine production of 5.4% in brackish water for a concentration difference of 42 mM Cl/l.

It was not really possible to repeat the experiment in fresh water, since the technique involves putting the worms in a hyperosmotic solution. However, worms from fresh water were dehydrated at an average rate of 6.7% body weight/hr and only rehydrated at 2.9%/hr for 100 mM Cl/l. concentration difference. The results of these experiments are ambiguous for the following reasons: first, they were done at a lower temperature (17–19°C); secondly, there was doubt about the blood concentrations during the experiment; and thirdly, no account was taken of urine production during the rehydration experiments, which might account for the slow weight gain. On the whole, Jørgensen and Dales' suggestion of a permeability change is possible, but not well-founded.

Exchange diffusion does not seem to contribute to the salt exchanges. Using conventional chemical methods, Beadle (1937) found that *N. diversicolor* lost 9% of the total body chloride in 5 hours when transferred from full-strength sea water to $\frac{1}{2}$ sea water (15°C), and lost 16% when transferred to $\frac{1}{4}$ sea water. It can be calculated from the tracer experiments that when the worms are transferred to $\frac{1}{2}$ sea water, the rate of net loss would be 5.65 $\mu M/g/hr$, or 10.4% of the total body sodium in 5 hours. Before the end of the experiment, the passive efflux would drop as the blood concentration fell, and some active uptake would occur, but this would not be considerable (Fig. IV.19). These two factors would reduce the net loss to some extent. The rate of loss in $\frac{1}{4}$ sea water, similarly calculated from the sodium fluxes, would be 15.5% of the total sodium, although active uptake would be appreciable before the end of the experiment in this case. Beadle's figure of 16% is in good agreement with the calculated rate. The net exchanges of sodium and chloride must be approximately equivalent to maintain electroneutrality.

Perinereis cultrifera is about three times as permeable to sodium as *Nereis diversicolor* (Fig. IV.20), and *Nereis virens* is about three times as permeable as *N. diversicolor* to chloride (Fig. IV.22). By transfer to the hyperosmotic solutions, Jørgensen and Dales showed that *N. virens* and *N. pelagica* were also between two and three times as permeable to water as *N. diversicolor*. *N. virens*, like *N. diversicolor*, can maintain its body fluids hyperosmotic to the environment, but because of its greater permeability it must work two or three times as hard to do so, and unlike *N. diversicolor*, it cannot survive in completely fresh water. *N. pelagica* is always isosmotic with the medium, and is restricted to high salinities. However, the ability to osmoregulate in low salinities is not the only factor in survival. Isolated muscles of *N. diversicolor* function normally in salinities down to 5–10% sea water, while those of *N. pelagica* do not function in less than 20% sea water (Wells and Ledingham, 1940).

When *N. diversicolor* was transferred from brackish water to sea water of 35‰ salinity, the uptake of sodium was much higher than in worms adapted to sea water (Fig.IV.24). *Perinereis cultrifera* behaved similarly, but the fluxes were even

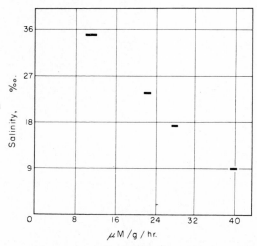

Fig. IV.24. *Nereis diversicolor*. The influx of sodium when trans-ferred to sea water of 35‰ salinity from more dilute media. The bar at 35‰ salinity represents the range of influxes in 12 worms in sea water. Temperature 12°C. From Fretter, 1955.
(Ordinate: Influx. Abscissa: Original salinity.)

larger. These very high levels of uptake must be the sum of the passive influx of sodium, combined with the active transport of sodium, even though in this case it is down the concentration gradient. The inward diffusion will be the same for all the worms, but the active transport or facilitated diffusion will be most strongly stimulated in those worms from the most dilute sea water. When *N. diversicolor* is adapted to 9‰ salinity, the inward diffusion is 2.56 μM/g/hr, and

the active uptake 5.27 μM/g/hr. When transferred to sea water
of 35‰ salinity, the passive influx will rise to 10 μM/g/hr,
but the rest of the influx (32.1 μM/g/hr) must be active
uptake down the concentration gradient. The high sodium
fluxes found in worms transferred from dilute sea water does
not accord with the suggestion that the permeability of the
worms is reduced in low salinities.

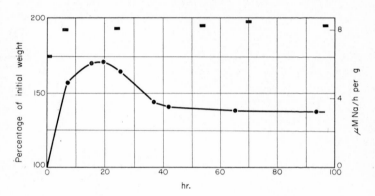

Fig. IV.25. *Nereis diversicolor*. Influx of sodium during the period
of weight regulation after transfer from sea water of 35‰ salinity
to that of 9‰. The continuous line represents the weight; the
dashes represent the sodium influxes. Temperature 12°C.
From Fretter, 1955.

In a final series of experiments, measurements were made of
the uptake of sodium by worms which had been transferred
from full strength sea water to water of 9‰ salinity (Fig.
IV.25). The uptake of sodium after transfer can again be
interpreted as the result of passive diffusion combined with
active uptake. After transfer, the passive influx will fall immediately to 2.56 μM/g/hr, and will then remain constant,
while the active uptake of ions will be stimulated as the blood
concentration falls. It can be seen that the rate of uptake does
not reach its maximum for some time after transfer, although
the rate is quite high shortly after transfer (*ca.* 7.6 μM/g/hr),
when the blood concentration must be almost unchanged.

The experiments recorded in Figs. IV.19 and IV.24 show that the rate of uptake depends very critically on the blood concentration, but the high level of influx shortly after transfer (Fig. IV.25) suggests that the external concentration, or possibly the concentration gradient across the body wall, can also stimulate the active uptake of ions. A careful study of the uptake during the first hours, or even minutes, after transfer would be of interest.

The energy required for osmoregulation — The energy required for osmoregulation in different environments can be calculated from the data above (Table IV.3). In *N. diversicolor*, the energy

TABLE IV.3. — THE ENERGY REQUIRED FOR CHLORIDE REGULATION
BY *Nereis diversicolor* IN VARIOUS MEDIA AT 25°C
(Calculated from Jørgensen and Dales, 1957)

Medium concn. mM Cl/l.	Body fluid concn. mM Cl/l.	Active influx $\mu MCl/g/hr$	Energy to maintain active influx cal/g/hr	Energy for differentiation of urine cal/g hr
120 (20% S.W.)	162	10·85	0·00177	—
65 (10% S.W.)	140	7·9	0·0033	—
1.4 (fresh water)	100	5·5	0·0127	0·00035

required for chloride transport in dilute sea water and in fresh water can be calculated from the fluxes and concentrations (Equation 8). The total energy required for osmotic regulation will be about twice as great as that required for chloride regulation alone (Chap. IV, p.129).

The oxygen consumption of *N. diversicolor* in brackish water is about 100 mm³/g/hr at room temperature (Beadle, 1931), equivalent to 0.5 cals/g/hr. At 25°C, the oxygen consumption will probably be twice this, so the energy required for osmotic regulation will vary from about 0.2% of the total metabolic energy in 20% sea water, to about 2.5% of the total in fresh water.

Procerodes (=Gunda)

The small flatworm, *Procerodes ulvae*, lives in the intertidal zone where hard water streams enter the sea, and it is subjected alternately to hard fresh water and almost undiluted sea water. Although it can survive for long periods in fresh water, it is not found in permanent fresh water. To some

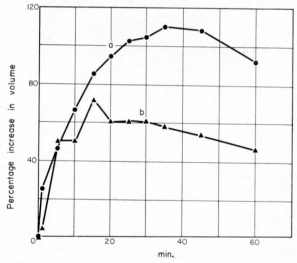

Fig. IV.26. Changes in volume of *Procerodes* (*Gunda*) after transfer from sea water to Plymouth tap water (soft), (a), and to Wembury stream water (hard), (b). From Pantin, 1931.

extent, it is adapted to meet temporary osmotic stress, in contrast to most brackish or freshwater animals which are adapted to meet a permanent stress.

After transfer from sea water to hard fresh water, *Procerodes* swells rapidly by osmosis, but later returns to an equilibrium volume in a similar way to *Nereis* (Fig. IV.18 and IV.26).

About a quarter of the body salts is lost in the first 50 minutes, and the final concentration of the body fluids when equilibrium is reached is only 6–10% of sea water (Pantin, 1931 a and b). When transferred from sea water to diluted sea water, the rate of swelling and the final volume are less than when it is transferred to fresh water, but the animals still lose salt. Although *Procerodes* can live for long periods in hard fresh water, it can survive for only a short while in soft fresh water. After transference to soft water, the rate of swelling is more rapid than in hard water, and continues until the animals disintegrate. The addition of 1–2 mM Ca/l. to the soft water reduces the rate of swelling and of salt loss. Nothing is known about excretion in *Procerodes*, or of its ability to absorb salts against a concentration gradient, but the dynamics of osmoregulation are probably analogous to those of *Nereis diversicolor*. If this is so, transfer to hard water leads to an influx of water and a loss of salts. When the concentration difference between the animal and the medium is sufficiently reduced the excretory system will be able to cope with the reduced influx of water, and an active uptake mechanism can maintain the reduced salt concentration. In these respects, *Procerodes* does not differ from animals which live continuously in brackish water, but in its initial response to fresh water, it shows an interesting adaptation to temporary osmotic stress. Beadle (1934) observed that in the swollen state following transfer to fresh water, some water appeared to be stored in vacuolated cells in the gut, where presumably it remained until the animal returned to sea water.

The ability of the tissues to tolerate a ten- or twenty-fold change in concentration twice each day is one of the most remarkable features of *Procerodes*, and deserves further study. It would be interesting to know if the change in concentration of amino acids, or of other organic constituents in the tissues, was greater than that due to water movements alone.

The Composition of the Tissues

The concentrations of the body fluids of most brackish water animals can fluctuate within wide limits, in spite of the animals' powers of osmoregulation. The ability of the tissues to tolerate such wide variations is an essential attribute of brackish water animals. The importance of tissue tolerance is illustrated by the penetration into brackish water of some animals such as *Mytilus edulis* or *Asterias rubens*, which cannot osmoregulate at all (see also p.122). The variation of the composition of the tissues with salinity has been studied in several brackish water invertebrates. When the concentration of the blood falls, the changes in the tissues are similar in these animals. These changes include (1) a slight increase in the water content; (2) a decrease in the concentration of those ions to which the tissues are permeable, particularly sodium and chloride and to a lesser extent potassium; (3) a decrease in the concentration of free amino acids and other organic compounds. In each case, the decrease in the concentration of organic compounds is considerably greater, and the decrease in the ion concentrations somewhat larger, than those due to the change of water content alone. In contrast, the decrease in the concentration of phosphate compounds is about proportional to the increase in water content.

Crustaceans

The composition of the muscles of *Carcinus* living in different media has been investigated by Shaw (1955, c and d; 1958, a and b). The composition of individual muscle fibres of crabs from full strength sea water (550 mM Cl/l.) and from 40% sea water are shown in Table IV.4. The freezing-point depression of the isolated fibres was a little higher than that of the blood at all concentrations, probably because of the autolysis of organic compounds such as adenosine triphosphate; the living muscle is probably isosmotic with the blood (Shaw,

TABLE IV.4. — THE COMPOSITION OF MUSCLE FIBRES OF *Carcinus*
LIVING IN FULL-STRENGTH SEA WATER AND 40 % SEA WATER
(Data from Shaw, 1955 c and d, 1958 a and b; note that these analyses refer
to individual muscle fibres uncontaminated by extracellular fluid.)

Constituents	100 % S.W. mM/kg. fibre water	40 % S.W. mM/kg fibre water	Composition expected in 40 % S.W. from change in water content
α-Amino N cpds. ...	434	191	353
Trimethylamine oxide	90	58	73
? Betaine (N-cpd.)	93	66	76
Arginine+inorganic phosphate	82	64	67
Adenosine triphosphate	9	8	7
Potassium	146	93	118
Sodium	53	32	43
Chloride	53	34	43
Water (%).............	74·0	77·8	—

Chloride in 100 % sea water = 533 mM/l.

1958 b). The last column in Table IV.4 shows the composition
of the muscles when allowance is made for the change in
water content only. It is clear that there is a very substantial
reduction in the quantity per cell of amino acids, trimethylamine oxide and betaine, smaller reductions in the amounts
of sodium, potassium and chloride, but no significant change
in phosphate content. As the fall in ionic constituents and
phosphate compounds is less than the fall in blood concentration, the reduction in the organic compounds is proportionately greater. When *Carcinus* was returned to sea water
after adaptation to brackish water, the changes were reversed.

Changes in the individual amino acids have been investigated
by bioassay in whole muscle of animals from full strength
sea water and ½ sea water (Table IV.5) (Duchâteau, Florkin and
Jeuniaux, 1959). Again, the last column shows the composition
when allowance is made for the change in water content only.

TABLE IV. 5. — THE FREE AMINO ACID CONTENT OF MUSCLE OF
Carcinus FROM SEA WATER AND 50 % SEA WATER
(Re-calculated in terms of mM/kg water*; from Duchâteau,
Florkin and Jeuniaux, 1959)

Constituents	100 % S.W. mM/kg whole muscle	50 % S.W. mM/kg whole muscle	Composition expected in 50 % S.W. from change in water content
Alanine............	26	21	23
Arginine	46	43	41
Aspartic acid ...	3	2·5	2·6
Glutamic acid ...	43	26	38
Glycine............	187	98	165
Proline	79	37	70
Water (%).........	74·7	—	—

* Including extracellular water.

It is apparent that the quantities per cell of alanine, arginine
and aspartic acid do not change, but very large reductions
do take place in glutamic acid, glycine and proline. The amino
acids which have disappeared from the muscles are not converted to polypeptides, but it is not known if they are converted to
protein, or transported to some other part of the body, such
as the digestive gland (Shaw, 1958 b).

The trimethylamine oxide content of Indian prawns, *Penaeus*
and *Metapenaeus*, varies from 118 mg N/100 g tissue,
or about 110 mM/kg water, in animals in full strength sea
water, to zero in animals in fresh water (Velankar and Govindan,
1960). The changes in concentration of the body fluids are
not recorded, but the blood concentration is likely to be higher
in sea water than in fresh water.

Molluscs

Mytilus edulis living in diluted sea water of 4‰ salinity is
slightly hyperosmotic to the medium (Beliaev, 1951), but
British specimens are not known to adapt to less than 10‰,
where they are still isosmotic to the medium. Osmotic adjust-

ment to a new salinity takes place rapidly, but ionic regulation continues in brackish water (Seck, 1958; Potts, 1954 a) and the relative concentration of potassium in the blood even increases, although this may be a consequence of its loss from the tissues. It is clear that the ability of *Mytilus* to survive in a wide range of salinities is due to the ability of the tissues to function in a wide range of blood concentrations. *Mytilus* heart muscle continues to function well between 40% and 160% sea water, and the ciliated cells of the gills between about 40% and 150% sea water, while similar tissues of the marine oyster *Ostrea* and the freshwater mussel *Anodonta* have much more restricted ranges of normal function (Pilgrim, 1953, a and b). The composition of the tissues in various salinities has been investigated by Krogh (1939), Seck (1958) and Potts (1954). When the animals are adapted to a lower salinity, the cells swell and extracellular fluid decreases. In full strength sea water, the muscle cells contain high concentrations of sodium, potassium and chloride ions, considerable amounts of phosphate compounds, and a very high concentration of free amino acids, accounting in all for about three quarters of the total osmotic pressure (Table IV.6). In $\frac{1}{2}$ sea water, the intracellular concentrations of sodium and chloride ions and

TABLE IV.6. — THE COMPOSITION OF THE FIBRES OF THE VENTRAL PORTION OF THE ADDUCTOR MUSCLE OF *Mytilus edulis* FROM FULL STRENGTH SEA WATER AND $\frac{1}{2}$ SEA WATER
(From Potts, 1958)

Constituents	100% S. W. mM/kg water	50% S. W. mM/kg water	Composition expected in 50% S. W. from change in water content
Sodium	79 ± 12	27 ± 7	61
Potassium	152 ± 5	106 ± 6	117
Chloride	94 ± 17	23 ± 6	72
Acid soluble PO$_4$ compounds	39	29	30
Amino acids	295 ± 6	183 ± 6	237

Chloride in 100% sea water = 573 mM/kg water.

of free amino acids are greatly reduced, and in contrast, potassium ions and phosphate compounds have been conserved. Some of the reductions in concentration are the result of an increased water content of the fibres, but when allowance is made for the water movement (Table IV.6, col. 4), it is clear that in the cells considerable quantities of sodium and chloride have been lost, and a large part of the free amino acids has disappeared, but the amounts of potassium and phosphate per cell are only slightly reduced. After transfer to brackish water, the concentrations of free amino acids, phosphate and potassium in the blood rise slightly, but this can only account for a small part of the loss from the tissues.

In the brackish water clam, *Rangia cuneata*, the concentrations of free amino acids increases with salinity, but by far the greater part of the change is accounted for by alanine alone (Allen, 1961).

Annelids

The muscle of *Arenicola marina* also adapts to brackish water by changes in amino acid content (Table IV.7). Two amino acids alone (glycine and alanine) account for more than 90%

TABLE IV. 7. — COMPOSITION OF MUSCLE FIBRES OF *Arenicola marina*
IN FULL STRENGTH SEA WATER AND 50% SEA WATER
(From Cowey and Shaw, unpublished)

Constituents	100% S.W. mM/kg water	50% S.W. mM/kg water	Composition expected in 50% S.W. from change in water content
Sodium	117	60	108
Potassium	179	128	166
Chloride	97	38	89
Glycine	257	60	239
Alanine	150	36	139
Total free amino acids ..	431	109	401
% water	74.4	79.9	

of the total amino acid content (Cowey and Shaw, unpublished; Duchâteau-Bosson, Jeuniaux and Florkin, 1961).

In *Perinereis cultrifera*, where salinity changes are followed by changes in blood concentration, the tissues respond in the concentration of free amino acids. In *Nereis diversicolor*, on the other hand, where there is some degree of osmoregulation, the blood changes and the free amino acid changes in the muscles are correspondingly smaller (Jeuniaux, Duchâteau-Bosson and Florkin, 1961).

CHAPTER V

OSMOTIC REGULATION
IN FRESHWATER ANIMALS

Introduction

Fresh water is a more exacting environment than the sea for the maintenance of animal life. Although natural waters always contain significant quantities of salt, the concentration may be only 0.01% of the concentration of sea water, so survival in fresh water must depend on the ability of animals to osmoregulate. A small body of fresh water may have the further disadvantage of wide variations in temperature, oxygen content and pH, or it may at times dry up altogether.

The salts in fresh water are derived in part from oceans, and in part from the weathering of rocks. When sea spray evaporates, the minute salt particles remaining may be carried for thousands of miles before returning to earth in rain water, which always contains some salt, even in continental areas. The salts in fresh water may be concentrated by evaporation. Rain water in America contains from 0.17 mM Cl/l. in a coastal region, to 0.03 mM Cl/l. inland. Greater or lesser quantities of soluble minerals, especially calcium and magnesium salts, may be added by the leaching of rocks. The concentration of calcium in fresh water varies from several millimoles in hard waters, to less than 0.1 mM/l. in soft waters. The biological importance of hard and soft waters has long been recognized; but calcium is only one of a number of essential

164

ions, and the distinction between sodium-rich and sodium-poor water may also be of considerable importance.

The compositions of a very hard and a soft water from Britain are given in Table V.1, which includes, for comparison, the concentrations of the same ions in sea water. A soft water from a well-watered continental area might contain even smaller quantities of salt than the example given.

TABLE V.1. — THE IONIC COMPOSITION OF A SOFT WATER (ELAN VALLEY RESERVOIR, WALES) AND A HARD WATER (A WELL AT BURTON-ON-TRENT) COMPARED WITH SEA WATER

	Concentration mM/kg water		
	Elan Valley*	Burton water**	Sea water***
Sodium	0·248	2·22	475·40
Potassium	0·0051	1·46	10·07
Calcium............	0·067	3·98	10·34
Magnesium	0·043	1·67	54·17
Chloride	0·226	2·54	554·40
Sulphate	0·045	3·95	28·56
Bicarbonate	—	2·02	2·37

* By kind permission of A. H. Coombes, Birmingham City Analyst.
** Recalculated from Macan and Worthington (1951)
*** Barnes, 1954 (sea water of 34·33°/₀₀ salinity).

Freshwater Animals

Representatives of most of the major groups are found in fresh water, but notable absentees include the cephalopods, echinoderms, protochordates, brachiopods and chaetognaths. The inhabitants of fresh water are descended from both marine and terrestrial ancestors. The freshwater crustaceans, fishes, lamellibranchs, prosobranch gastropods (e.g. *Viviparus* and *Hydrobia*), and coelenterates are all derived from marine ancestors. Aquatic insects, arachnids, the pulmonate snails and probably also the freshwater oligochaetes and leeches, are descended from terrestrial forms, even though

12*

these may have been limited to damp habitats like the terrestrial annelids, which are generally in contact with a film of soil water and osmoregulate in some respects like aquatic animals. Many of the freshwater animals descended from terrestrial ancestors have retained aerial respiration, e.g. insect larvae and the pulmonate snails. These forms are more insulated from their environment than those freshwater forms respiring by means of gills, or directly through a permeable skin.

Osmotic Pressure of the Blood

The osmotic concentrations of the body fluids of freshwater animals vary from about 50 mOsm/l. in the lamellibranchs to about 650 mOsm/l. in some crabs (Table V.2). A variation of 10–20% on either side of the mean is quite common within a population of a freshwater species (e.g. Lockwood, 1959), and the mean may also vary seasonally (Hardisty, 1956) or with temperature (Lockwood, 1960).

The blood of freshwater animals is almost always less concentrated than the blood of marine ones, but the range of concentrations is considerable. It is difficult to account for this variation. Factors which may affect the blood concentration of a freshwater animal include the surface: volume ratio and hence the absolute size of the animal, the permeability of the body wall, the metabolic rate, and the period of time the group has been adapted to fresh water. The vertebrates have relatively uniform blood concentrations (between $1/4$ and $1/3$ sea water) and this may be related to their descent from a common freshwater ancestor. The crustaceans, in contrast, have a very wide range of blood concentration; this may reflect both the fact that the group has invaded fresh water several times, and the greater size range within the crustaceans. For example, *Eriocheir*, which has a high blood concentration, and still breeds in the sea, is probably a recent immigrant to fresh water, while the smaller branchiopods with a lower blood concentration are an ancient group of fresh-

TABLE V.2. — OSMOTIC CONCENTRATION OF THE BODY FLUIDS OF SOME ANIMALS IN FRESH WATER

Class	Species	Mean conon. of blood, mOsm/kg water	Author
Rhizopoda:	*Pelomyxa*	*ca.* 90	Løvtrup & Pigon, 1951
Ciliata:	*Zoothamnium*	*ca.* 50	Kitching, 1938
Hydrozoa:	*Chlorohydra viridissima*	40-50	Lilly, 1955
Oligochaeta:	*Lumbricus terrestris* (in fresh water)	167	Ramsay, 1949a
Lamellibranchiata:	*Anodonta cygnaea*	44	Potts, 1954a
Gastropoda:	*Viviparus viviparus*	94	Potts (unpub.)
	Lymnaea peregra	124	Potts (unpub.)
Insecta:	*Aedes aegypti* (larva)	266	Wigglesworth, 1938
	Sialis lutaria (larva)	339	Shaw, 1955a
	Ephemera vulgara (larva)	237	Fox & Baldes, 1935
Crustacea:	*Eriocheir sinensis*	636	Scholles, 1933
	Potamon niloticus	506	Shaw, 1959c
	Astacus fluviatilis	436	Scholles, 1933
	Palaemonetes antennarius	403	Parry, 1957
	Gammarus pulex	276	Lockwood, 1961
	Daphnia magna	136	Fritsche, 1916
Agnatha:	*Petromyzon fluviatilis*	264	Morris, 1956
Osteichthyes:	*Acipenser stellatus*	292	Kalashnikov & Skadovskii, 1948
	Amia calva	291	Dekhuyzen, 1904
	Salmo trutta	326	Parry, 1960
	Protopterus	258	Smith, 1930
Amphibia:	*Rana esculenta*	237	Botazzi, 1906
Reptilia:	*Emys orbicularis*	237	Botazzi, 1906

water crustaceans. Among the freshwater molluscs, the pulmonate *Lymnaea* has the highest blood concentration, the prosobranch *Viviparus* a lower concentration, and the lamellibranch *Anodonta*, with the larger relative gill area, the lowest concentration. The small lamellibranch *Dreissena*, which is a very recent immigrant to fresh water, and the even smaller lamellibranch *Pisidium*, both have blood concentrations of 54 mOsm/l., a little higher than *Anodonta* blood (Potts, unpub.).

The very low osmotic pressures of the blood of lamellibranchs may be correlated also with their low metabolic rates,
and the low osmotic pressure of *Hydra* tissues may be
associated with the low metabolic rate and small size of this
animal. The rather high osmotic pressures of the minute
protozoans may be related to their higher metabolic rates,
but there is also evidence that the body surface is more
impermeable than that of *Hydra* and some other freshwater
animals (Table V.5).

The Composition of the Blood

The body fluids of freshwater animals show many similarities
to sea water in spite of the lower osmotic concentration.
Sodium and chloride are generally the most abundant ions,
while the concentration of potassium is very much lower.
The amount of calcium present is usually less than that in
related marine animals, but usually it is proportionately less
reduced than the total ions (Table V.3). The relatively high
concentration of calcium in the blood of *Potamon*, *Astacus* and
Anodonta is probably related to the presence of a skeleton
of calcium carbonate in these animals (Chap. III, p.101),
while the lower concentration of calcium in frog blood may
be related to its possession of a skeleton of the more insoluble
calcium phosphate. Insect blood generally has a high calcium
concentration, e.g. the lace-wing *Sialis* (Neuroptera) (Table
V.3), *Hydrophilus* (Coleoptera) 11 mM/l. (Florkin, 1949),
Saturnia (Lepidoptera) 7.1 mM/l. (Drilhon, 1934), but the
significance of this is not known. Not all the calcium is
ionised; for example, Schoffeniels (1951) found that about
25% of the calcium in *Anodonta* blood was not ionised (cf.
Ligia, Chap. III, p. 94).

In contrast to calcium, very little magnesium is found in
the blood of freshwater animals (Table V.3). The insects,
however, are peculiar in containing high concentrations, e.g.
Sialis (Table V.3), *Hydrophilus* 20 mM/l. (Florkin, 1949), and

TABLE V.3. — THE OSMOTIC CONSTITUENTS OF THE BLOOD OF SOME
FRESHWATER ANIMALS

Animal	Concentrations in mM/kg water or mM/l. blood							Author
	Na	K	Ca	Mg	Cl	HCO₃	Otherions	
Rana esculenta[1]	109	2·6	2·1	1·3	78	26·6	lactate 3·5	Boyle & Conway, 1941
Salmo trutta[2] ...	161	5·3	6·3	0·93	119	n. d.	phosphate 1·0	Phillips & Brockway, 1958
Potamon niloticus[2]	259	8·4	12·7	n. d.	242	n. d.		Shaw, 1959 c
Astacus fluviatilis[2]	212	4·1	15·8	1·5	199	15		Drilhon-Courtois, 1934 Huf, 1934 Duval & Portier, 1927
Sialis lutaria[2]	109	5	7·5	19	31	15	amino acids 152	Shaw, 1950 b
Anodonta cygnaea[1]	15·6	0·5	6	0·2	11·7	12	amino acids 0·2	Potts, 1954

1 mM/kg water
2 mM/l. blood
Analyses of common ions in the blood and coelomic fluid of the earthworms *Lumbricus terrestris*, *Eisenia foetida* and *Hilodrilus caliginosus* have been published recently (Kamemoto, Spalding, and Keister, 1962).

Sphinx (Lepidoptera) 23 mM/l. (Drilhon, 1934). Other freshwater animals have a low magnesium concentration, e.g. *Eriocheir* in fresh water 3.4 mM/l. (Berger, 1931), *Salmo trutta*, the brown trout, 0.9 mM/l. (Phillips and Brockway, 1958). Florkin (1949) has emphasised that the ratio of monovalent ions to divalent (Na + K/Ca + Mg) is about 10 in marine animals and about 20 in freshwater ones. This is a consequence of the high concentration of magnesium in marine, and low magnesium but moderate calcium concentrations in freshwater animals.

The concentration of sulphate in the body fluids of freshwater animals is so low that measurements are not often attempted, but a few estimates are available, e.g. *Hydrophilus* 0.14 mM SO_4/l. (Florkin, 1949), *Anodonta* 0.7 mM/l. (Potts,

1954 a). It is interesting to observe that these two ions, magnesium and sulphate, commonly excluded to some degree from marine animals, are usually present only in very low concentrations in the blood of freshwater animals.

Bicarbonate ions form a relatively larger part of the total anions in the blood of freshwater animals than in marine ones. Even the absolute quantities of bicarbonate may be larger, e.g. freshwater *Anodonta* 12 mM/l., but marine *Mytilus* only 6 mM/l. (Potts, 1954 a); freshwater *Astacus*, 15 mM/l. but marine *Homarus* 6 mM/l. (Duval and Portier, 1927). This high concentration of bicarbonate in freshwater crustaceans and molluscs may also be correlated with the presence of a calcareous exoskeleton, but it could help to conserve chloride ions which have to be obtained from the environment. The very high concentration of bicarbonate in frog blood is related to pulmonary respiration, as a consequence of which the blood is equilibrated with the relatively stagnant air of the lungs.

Since inorganic constituents account for only about a half of the total osmotic pressure of *Sialis* blood, the rest must be made up by organic compounds of which free amino acids are important. Large quantities of amino acids and other organic compounds have been reported in many insects, and are characteristic of both aquatic and terrestrial forms (Florkin, 1949). When the chloride content of the blood of some aquatic insects is artificially raised or lowered, the free amino acids vary reciprocally, so that the total osmotic pressure remains constant (Schoffeniels, 1960 a).

Osmotic Regulation in Freshwater Animals

The osmotic and ionic relationships of freshwater animals are similar to those of animals living in brackish water. To some degree, all animals are permeable both to ions and water. In freshwater animals, water is gained by osmosis and salt lost by diffusion. The most important variables in osmotic regulation of freshwater animals are, therefore, their permeability to water, their permeability to salts, the concentration of salts in the urine and the urine loss, and the rate of uptake of salts.

The Rate of Urine Production and the Permeability to Water

The rates of urine production in a variety of freshwater animals are collected in Table V.4. These rates have been estimated in a number of ways: by direct cannulation, by the rate of increase in weight when the excretory openings are blocked,

TABLE V.4. — RATES OF URINE PRODUCTION OF SOME FRESHWATER ANIMALS

Animal	Weight (g)	Urine flow % body wt./day	Blood conc. mOsm	Temp. °C	Author
Rana esculenta	58	30.5	220	22	Hevesy, Høfer & Krogh, 1938
Salmo gairdnerii ...	280	8.65	314[1]	5	Holmes, in press
Carrassius auratus	48	4	300[2]	–	Krogh, 1937 b
Lampetra fluviatilis	35[3]	15.6	269	17	Morris, 1956
Eriocheir sinensis ...	60	3.6	636	13–14	Scholles, 1933
Astacus pallipes ...	28.7	8.2	435	20	Bryan, 1960 c
Potamon niloticus ...	20	<0.6>0.05	542	–	Shaw, 1959 c
Palaemonetes antennarius	0.08	53	404	20	Parry, 1957
Daphnia magna ...	0.0039[4]	240[7]	136[5]	–	Krogh, 1939
Asellus aquaticus ...	0.1[4]	20[7]	300	–	Lockwood, 1959
Gammarus pulex ...	0.04	47[8]	276	20	Lockwood, 1961
Sialis lutaria	0.07	4.5	339	20	Shaw, 1955 a
Lumbricus terrestris[6]	4	61	167	19	Wolf, 1940
Anodonta cygnaea ...	74	45	44	15	Potts, 1954 b
Zoothamnium sp. ...	1.5×10⁻⁸	575	50	–	Kitching, 1938

1. Parry, 1960
2. Estimated by comparison with other freshwater teleosts.
3. Hardisty, 1956
4. Animals weighed by W.T.W.P.
5. Fritsche, 1916
6. Immersed in water.
7. Calculated from permeability to D_2O (Krogh, 1939),
8. Calculated from rate of exchange of T_2O.

by the rate of clearance of dyes or other substances, and from the permeability to heavy water. For reasons discussed in the Introduction (Chap. I, p.23), the rate of urine production calculated from the permeability to heavy water may be substantially lower than the true rate, but in both *Sialis* and *Palaemonetes*, the rates calculated by such methods compare well with the rate of urine production determined in the same animals by volume methods. In the few cases where the rate of urine production has been measured at different temperatures, it increases rapidly with temperature, e.g. the frog produced 3.5–4.3 ml/kg/hr at 2°C, 8.5–8.6 ml/kg/hr at 10°C, and 12.1–22.4 ml/kg/hr at 22°C (Hevesy, Høfer and Krogh, 1935); *Petromyzon* produced 60 ml/kg/day at 2.5°C, 150 ml/kg/day at 9°C, and 300 ml/kg/day at 17°C (Wikgren, 1953).* These figures indicate a Q_{10} of about 2 for the permeability to water. The permeability of *Sialis* larva cuticle to heavy water has a Q_{10} of about 3 (Shaw, 1955 a).

It is difficult to compare the permeabilities implied by Table V.4 with one another, because of variations in osmotic concentration, temperature, and surface: volume ratio of the animals, but in a few cases absolute permeabilities have been measured. Some estimates derived from the data in Table V.4, together with measurements from other sources, are collected in Table V.5. The permeabilities of most freshwater animals are remarkably low, the most permeable being the frog, with a permeability of 3.9 μ/sec at 20°C, and the least permeable the goldfish, *Carassius*, with a permeability of only 0.02 μ/sec.† The majority of freshwater animals have permeabilities between 1 and 0.1 μ/sec. The figure of 1.58 μ/sec recorded in Table V.5 for the lamprey is based on Wikgren's estimate of the rate of urine production; the normal rate is only half as large (Morris, 1956) so the permeability is usually about

---

* The rate of urine production recorded by Wikgren is larger than reported elsewhere, because of his experimental technique (Morris, 1956), but the variation with temperature is valid.

† This latter figure is based on only one determination of urine production at an unspecified temperature and in unnatural conditions.

TABLE V.5. — PERMEABILITY TO WATER
(See also Chap. I, p.10)

	Permeability recorded	Perme-ability μ/sec.	Author
Collodion membrane		1200	Krogh, 1939
Human erythrocyte		125	Dick, 1959
Zoothamnium sp. ...	28–56 days for 1 ml to pass through 1 cm² at 1 atmosphere	2·5–5·1	Kitching, 1938
Amoeba	0·017 μ/min/atm	0·35	Prescott & Zeuthen, 1953
Chlorohydra	0·6 u³/υ²/min/atm	12·5	Lilly, 1955
Sialis lutaria (larva)	$1·8 \times 10^{-2}$ cm/hr	0·05	Shaw, 1955 a
	$1·5 \times 10^{-2}$ cm/hr	0·04	
Astacus fluviatilis ...	M. N.* 2 years	0·2	Wikgren, 1953
Lampetra fluviatilis ...	M. N. 91 days	1·58	Wikgren, 1953
Anguilla anguilla ...	M. N. 5 years	0·08	Wikgren, 1953
Carassius auratus ...	Rate of urine production,4% body wt./day	0·02	Krogh, 1937 b
Rana temporaria	30 days for 1 M to pass 1 cm² at 1 M/l. conc. difference	3·9	Hevesy, Høfer and Krogh, 1938
Frog body cavity egg	–	1·21	Prescott & Zeuthen, 1953
Frog ovarian egg ...	–	89·1	Prescott & Zeuthen, 1953

* M.N. = minute number.

o.8 μ/sec. For comparison, the permeability of a collodion membrane just impermeable to protein is 1200 μ/sec (Krogh, 1939, p.24), and human erythrocytes have permeabilities of 125 μ/sec. Ovarian eggs of the frog have a permeability of 89 μ/sec, but frog's eggs about to be laid have permeabilities of only 1.4 μ/sec. Only a few estimates have been made of the permeabilities of marine animals. Some marine ciliates have permeabilities ranging from 1–2 μ/sec, lower than the freshwater Zoothamnium (Kitching, 1938) but the marine ciliates are themselves probably descended from freshwater ancestors. In general, freshwater animals seem to be less permeable than their marine counterparts (see also Chap. IV, p.138).

For comparative purposes, the data in Table V.4 have been arranged to show what the rates of urine production would be if all the animals had the same blood concentration, the same body weight, but retained their normal body proportions, and were at the same temperature (Table V.6). The differences between the rates of urine production are then a function of the absolute permeabilities and the surface: volume ratios. It can be seen that the crustaceans, *Eriocheir*, *Astacus*, *Palaemonetes*, *Asellus* and *Gammarus* would have remarkably similar rates of urine production. The much higher rate for *Daphnia* is not altogether improbable, as the complex of limbs and carapace has a large surface: volume ratio, but this estimate is based on only one inadequately recorded measurement of the permeability at an unknown temperature. The low permeability of *Potamon* is outstanding, and calls for further investigation. The surface: volume ratio of this crab is unlikely to be very different from that of *Eriocheir*, and so *Potamon* must either have a permeability only one tenth that of any other freshwater crustacean, or alternatively it must excrete water extra-renally.

The permeability of *Sialis* larvae is of a different order from that of most crustaceans although similar to *Potamon*. Shaw (1955) showed that the larva was covered with a lipoid layer about $0.1\,\mu$ thick, which probably accounts for this low permeability. A similar waterproofing layer is common in the insects, and the larva is not well waterproofed in comparison with terrestrial forms.

The freshwater protozoon *Zoothamnium* is rather more permeable than most freshwater animals (Table V.5). In spite of its simple shape, the hypothetical urine production of *Lumbricus* in fresh water (Table V.6) is very large, so the absolute permeability must be very high. The hypothetical urine production in *Anodonta* is much larger than in any other

TABLE V.6. — COMPARISON OF RATES OF URINE PRODUCTION OF A
VARIETY OF ANIMALS IN FRESH WATER, REDUCED TO 1 G WEIGHT,
15°C AND 1 M/L. CONCENTRATION OF BODY FLUIDS
(From TABLE V.4)

Species	Comparative urine production % body wt./day
Protozoa:	
Zoothamnium sp.	21
Annelida:	
Lumbricus terrestris	440
Mollusca:	
Anodonta cygnaea	4350
Arthropoda:	
Eriocheir sinensis	22
Astacus fluviatilis.........	40
Potamon niloticus	$<3 \cdot 7 > 0 \cdot 25$
Palaemonetes antennarius	56
Daphnia magna............	276
Asellus aquaticus	31
Gammarus pulex	41
Sialis lutaria...............	$3 \cdot 8$
Vertebrata:	
Lampetra fluviatilis	165
Carassius auratus.........	48
Salmo gairdnerii	215
Rana esculenta	297

Surface areas have been calculated on the assumption that the area varies as $W^{2/3}$ and the permeability has a Q_{10} of 2.

animal, and may be related to the very large surface:volume ratio, but may also imply a large absolute permeability.

The vertebrates form a relatively uniform group. Apart from the goldfish, *Carassius*, the other freshwater vertebrates are subject to a greater influx of water than are crustaceans of comparable weight and blood concentration. The surface: volume ratio of fishes is larger than that of the air-breathing frog, so the absolute permeabilities of fishes must be lower.

The permeability to water of a number of marine and brackish water animals can be compared on the same basis as Table V.6. For example, a 50 g *Carcinus* in 40% sea water has a blood concentration which is 250 mOsm/l. hyperosmotic to the medium, and produces urine equivalent to about 30% of its body weight/day (Shaw, 1961 a). This is equivalent to about 440% body weight/day/molar concentration difference in a 1 g crab. A number of the marine crabs, *Maia*, of average weight 32 g, transferred to a 75% sea water medium, gained weight at an initial rate of 2.5%/hr (Schwabe, 1933). This is equivalent to 760% body weight/day/molar concentration difference in a 1 g crab. It may be concluded that brackish water and marine crabs are far more permeable to water than are the freshwater crustaceans. Soft-bodied marine invertebrates are even more permeable than crustaceans. For example, a 3 g *Doris* transferred to 75% sea water gained weight at the rate of 10% body weight/hr (Bethe, 1934). This is equivalent to 4000% body weight/day/molar concentration difference for a 1 g animal. These crude comparisons suggest that marine animals are distinctly more permeable to water than are freshwater ones.

Concentration of the Urine and Renal Salt Loss

Many freshwater animals produce a urine hypo-osmotic with the blood, but some, e.g. *Eriocheir*, *Palaemonetes*, and *Potamon*, produce an isosmotic urine (Tables V.7 and V.8). Some freshwater animals approach the most economical concentration of the urine, in which the concentration of each ion would be that of the surrounding medium. Sodium and chloride concentrations as low as 1 mM/l. have been recorded for a number of animals (Wikgren, 1953) (Table V.7), but the ionic content of the urine of most freshwater animals is usually greater than that of the surrounding water.

Most of our information about the composition of the urine is confined to the total osmotic concentration, but some detailed analyses are available. A proportion of the osmotic

TABLE V.7. — THE CONCENTRATION OF SODIUM IN THE BLOOD AND
URINE OF *Astacus* IN VARIOUS MEDIA AT 20°C
(Bryan, 1960 a, b, and c)

Medium	Concentration mM Na/l.	
	Blood	Urine
*0·00	200	1–2
0·02	168	1
0·5	203	1
2·0	204	6
10·0	204	11

* 20 hr after transfer from 2.0 mM/l.

pressure of the urine is due to substances such as ammonium
or bicarbonate ions of metabolic origin, but other ions
such as sodium or chloride which are lost in the urine
must be replaced. In *Sialis* larva, the excretory fluid in
the rectum has an osmotic concentration equivalent to
2/3 that of the blood, but 90% of this is due to ammonium
bicarbonate (Shaw, 1955 b). On the other hand, in *Eriocheir*
urine, inorganic constituents account for practically all the
osmotic concentration (Scholles, 1933) (Table V.8) and Krogh's
experiments (1939) with *Eriocheir* show that only a small part
of the ammonium ions produced is excreted by the antennary
glands, and the greater part is lost by diffusion through the
body wall or via the gut. The higher concentration of ammonium in the urine of *Sialis* may be attributed to the lower
permeability of the larva, which reduces the osmotic inflow
of water and therefore the rate of urine production, and also
the loss of ammonia by diffusion. Most freshwater animals
are more permeable than *Eriocheir*, so it is probable that the
amounts of ammonium in the urine are relatively small in
freshwater animals.

The total concentrations and relative quantities of ions in the
urine of a freshwater animal may be inconstant, and vary with
diet, environment, and the condition of the animal, e.g. *Astacus*

TABLE V.8. — THE COMPOSITION OF *Eriocheir* BLOOD AND URINE IN
FRESH WATER AND IN AN ARTIFICIAL SEA WATER
(Scholles, 1933)

Medium	Fluid	Concentration mM/l.			
		K	Ca	Mg	Cl
Fresh Water					
	Blood	5·1	10·0	3·4	280
	Urine	7·0	4·7	0·7	264
Sea Water					
	Blood	8·7	11·5	15·8	440
	Urine	10·0	10·7	35·0	500
	Water	10·3	7·6	39·8	494

(Table V.7 and Fig V.1). In contrast to *Astacus*, the chloride
content of *Lampetra* urine is independent of the external
chloride concentration (Morris, 1960). *Eriocheir* preferentially
excretes magnesium when living in sea water, but conserves it
when in fresh water (Table V.8), and *Aedes detritus* conserves
both sodium and potassium in distilled water, but excretes
sodium in sodium-rich solutions and potassium in potassium-
rich ones (Table II.2). Bryan (1960 a) found that temperature
shock could produce a several-fold increase in the sodium content of *Astacus* urine, and the urine of fed animals contained a
higher concentration of sodium than that of starved animals.

With these reservations about the constancy of urine composition, the rate of salt loss in the urine can be calculated
(Table V.9). The range of renal salt loss is very large, from
4.4 mM Na/kg/hr in the freshwater prawn, *Palaemonetes antennarius*, down to less than 10 μMCl/kg/hr in the frog and
goldfish. The highest rates of loss are in *Palaemonetes* and *Eriocheir*, which produce urine isosmotic with the blood. The rate
of loss is lower in *Eriocheir* than in the prawn, mainly because
the much smaller prawns have a larger surface:volume ratio.
Potamon also produces an isosmotic urine, but the rate of urine
production is so low that salt loss is only about one tenth that
of *Eriocheir* (Tables V.4 and V.9). All the remaining animals in

the table produce a urine containing between one tenth and one hundredth the concentration of salt in the blood. The calculated rate of salt loss in *Lumbricus* immersed in water (Table V.9) is almost certainly larger than when it is in the soil.

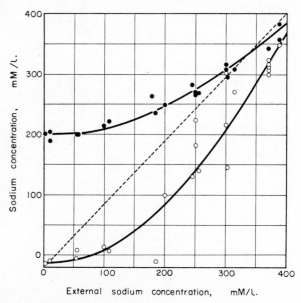

Fig. V.1. *Astacus pallipes*. The sodium concentration in the blood and urine as functions of the concentration in the medium. Blood ●, Urine ○. Temperature 20°C. From Bryan, 1960c.

Extrarenal Salt Loss

In addition to salt lost in the urine, salt is also lost by diffusion through the body wall; this loss also varies with external conditions.

Palaemonetes — The freshwater prawn of circum-Mediterranean regions, *Palaemonetes antennarius* has been studied recently (Parry, 1957; Parry, 1961 b; Parry and Potts, unpub.). In fresh water (0.5 mM Na/l), the efflux of sodium averages 5.3 mM Na/kg/hr. The urine production is about 2% body weight/hr,

13

TABLE V.9. — RENAL SALT LOSS IN SOME AQUATIC AND SEMI-AQUATIC ANIMALS

	Urine flow ml/kg/hr	Blood concn. mM/l.	Ion	Urine concn. mM/l.	Net loss μM/kg/hr	Weight g	Author
Eriocheir sinensis	1·5	280	Chloride	264 (Cl)	420	60	Scholles, 1933
Palaemonetes antennarius	22	210	Sodium	200 (Na)	4400	0·08	Parry, 1957 1961 b, Parry & Potts (unpub)
Potamon niloticus	<0·25 >0·02	259	Sodium	240 (Na)	60–5	20	Shaw, 1959 c
Astacus pallipes............	3·4	203	Sodium	6·0 (Na)	20·5	29	Bryan, 1960 a
Gammarus pulex	20	152	Sodium / Chloride	27 (Na)	·540	0·04	Lockwood, 1961
Gammarus duebeni	30	255	Sodium / Chloride	83 (Na)	1·66	0·04	Lockwood, 1961
Rana esculenta	10·4	72	Chloride	1 (Cl)	10·4	58	Krogh, 1937a
Salmo gairdnerii	3·6	314	Chloride	1·9–11 (Cl)	6–37	280	Holmes, 1961
Carassius auratus	1·67		Chloride	2·5–4·1 (Cl)	4–7	48	Krogh, 1937b
Lampetra fluviatilis	6·5[4]	100[1]	Chloride	6·0[1] (Cl)	39	35[2]	1. Morris, 1956 2. Hardisty, 1956
Lumbricus terrestris	25[4]	25[3]	Chloride	3·4[3] (Cl)	85	4[4]	3. Ramsay, 1949 b 4. Wolf, 1940
Sialis lutaria larva	1·9	109	Sodium	12 (Cl)	23	0·7	Shaw, 1955 b

and the renal salt loss amounts to 4.4 mM Na/kg/hr, so the extrarenal loss of sodium is about one mM Na/kg/hr.

Eriocheir — A number of measurements have been made of the rate of extra-renal salt loss from the Chinese wool-handed crab, *Eriocheir sinensis*. Koch and Evans (1956) found that individual crabs lost 24–450 (mean 200) μM Na/crab/hr* when the excretory pores were blocked, but the weights of the crabs were not recorded. More recently, Shaw (1961b) has found that the mean rate of total loss in deionised water is 2.1 mM Na/kg/hr (average weight 153 g, temperature not recorded). If the renal sodium loss is the same as the renal chloride loss (Table V.9), then the extra-renal loss will amount to 1.7 mM Na/kg/hr. These results agree with a single measurement of the rate of chloride loss made by Krogh (1939, p.82), who found that a 144 g *Eriocheir* lost 1.4–2.8 mM of both sodium and chloride/kg/hr during the first day in deionised water. However, on the second day, the rate of loss declined to only 750 μM/kg/hr. Similarly, Berger (1931) found that a 151 g crab lost 1.4 mM Cl/kg/hr during the day after transfer to deionised water, but the loss declined to only 0.28 mM/kg/hr on the second day, and to only 100 μM/kg/hr after a week. The decline cannot be accounted for by the fall in the blood concentration alone during this time. It may be analogous to the reduced rate of loss found in *Gammarus* at very low concentrations (see below). In *Eriocheir*, Krogh found that on the second day, when the total chloride loss was 750 μM/kg/hr, the renal loss amounted to 24% of the total loss.† This is similar to the proportion calculated by Shaw (1961 b) from the initial rate of loss of sodium and Schwabe's (1933) estimate of the rate of urine production.

It is clear that the rate of extra-renal loss and possibly also the renal loss, can vary widely in different conditions.

* Calculated from Koch and Evans' graphs.
† Note that the estimated renal loss in Krogh's experiment was 24% of the total, not 14% as published.

13*

Gammarus — A reduction of the rate of loss of salt in very dilute solutions has been observed in *Gammarus pulex*, where the rate of total loss of sodium declines from about 0.45 mM Na/kg/hr in a medium containing 0.3 mM Na/l. to about half this level in a solution containing 0.09 mM Na/l. In a medium containing 14 mM NaCl/l. the renal sodium loss is 0.54 mM NaCl/kg/hr, but this probably declines in less concentrated solutions, cf. *Astacus* (Table 7). At least some part of the observed reduction could therefore be due to the change in the renal loss (Table V.10) (Lockwood, 1961).

TABLE V.10. — EFFLUX OF SODIUM FROM *Gammarus pulex* VARIOUS MEDIA
(from Shaw and Sutcliffe, 1961)

Medium mM Na/l.	Sodium loss mM/kg/hr
0.30	0.45
0.06	0.30
salt-depleted animal in 0.06	0.22

Potamon — The total loss of sodium from the freshwater crab *Potamon* in distilled water amounts to 800 μM/kg/hr (Shaw, 1959 c), less than in *Eriocheir*, but the renal loss is very much less, between 5 and 60 μM/kg/hr. Potassium loss is only 50 μM/kg/hr, one sixteenth of the sodium loss; Shaw points out that the potassium concentration in the blood is only one thirtieth of the sodium concentration (Table V.3), so the permeability to potassium must be about twice as large as the permeability to sodium.

Asellus — In deionised water, the freshwater isopod *Asellus aquaticus* loses about 1% of the total body sodium/hr (Lockwood, 1960). The sodium concentration of the blood is 137 mM/l., and the sodium space about 80% of the water content.

If the water content is 80% of the total weight, the sodium loss will be 87 μM/kg/hr. The rate of urine production estimated from heavy water measurements is about 1.25%/hr (Table V.4). Thus, if the urine were isosmotic with the blood, the urine loss would exceed the observed loss. The maxillary gland of *Asellus* has a complex structure (Schwabe, 1933) and the urine is probably very dilute compared with the blood, in which case practically all the loss would be extra-renal. The rate of loss is independent of the temperature (Lockwood, 1960), whereas permeability to water usually has a large Q_{10}.

Astacus — Extensive investigations of the sodium balance of the freshwater crayfish, *Astacus pallipes*, (Shaw, 1959 a; Bryan, 1960, a, b and c) have clarified the scattered observations of earlier workers (Krogh, 1939, p.91; Wikgren, 1953). Bryan measured the rate of loss of [22]Na in a large variety of conditions, and his results have been collected in Table V.11. In media containing 0.5–10 mM Na/l. the extra-renal loss of sodium is about 370 μM Na/kg/hr at 20°C, between ten and a hundred times the renal loss. Shaw (1959 a) found that at 12°C, the extra-renal loss was about 150 μM/kg/hr. In more concentrated solutions, the rate of loss is greater because the blood concentration is higher. This was shown clearly by experiments in which the rate of loss of sodium by diffusion was measured in the same two animals, when the blood concentrations had been raised artificially, and when the blood concentrations were at the normal levels. In both cases, the rate of loss by diffusion was proportional to the concentration of sodium in the blood (Table V.12, col. 4). It should be noted that the rate of loss by diffusion (Table V.11) are rates of total loss, and the rates of net loss will be considerably smaller in more concentrated solutions, because sodium will also enter by diffusion.

Immediately after transfer to distilled water, the rate of loss of sodium falls by 30% compared with the loss in 2 mM NaCl/l. This reduction appears before the blood concentration falls (Table V.11, lines 1 and 4). Thus, the loss cannot be

TABLE V.11. — RENAL AND EXTRA-RENAL SODIUM LOSS FROM *Astacus pallipes* IN VARIOUS MEDIA AT 20°C

(Bryan, 1960 a, b, c)

Medium mM Na/l.	Urine concn. mM Na/l.	Urine flow ml/kg/hr	Na lost in urine μM/kg/hr	Blood concn. mM Na/l.	Rate constant of loss (h⁻¹)	Number of determinations	Total loss[4] μM/kg/hr	Extra renal loss μM/kg/hr
0.01[1]	0.1	3.4	3	203	0.00235	15	212	209
0.02[2]	1	2.8	3	168	0.00236	1	176	173
0.5[2]	1	3.4	3	203	0.004	?	360	357
2.0[2]	6	3.4	20	204	0.00428	19	380	358
10.0[2,3]	11	3.2	35	204	0.0044	2	397	362
200[2]	100	0.8	80	246	0.0045	1	486	406
245[2]	130	0.8	104	280	0.00633	1	786	682
2[1]	300	4.05	1215	310	0.00622[5]	2	2065	850

1. Experiments made shortly after transfer to medium.
2. Experiments made after animals had been adapted to medium.
3. Data from Bryan (1960 c., Fig. 2).
4. Calculated from the rate constant of loss and the blood concentration, on the assumption that the sodium space is equivalent to 46.9% of the body volume, and that the density was 1.118. The first assumption may not be quite correct at a high blood concentration.
5. With excretory pores blocked.

TABLE V.12. — COMPARISONS OF THE RATE OF EXTRA-RENAL
SODIUM LOSS FROM TWO *Astacus*, WHEN THE BLOOD CONCENTRATION
WAS RAISED TO 310 mM Na/L. AND WHEN THE BLOOD CONCENTRATION
WAS NORMAL, AT 20°C
(Bryan, 1960 c)

	Blood concentration mM Na/l.	Rate of loss of sodium mM/l. blood/hr	Rate of loss
			Blood concentration
Animal 1	186	0·88	0·0047
	310	1·55	0·0050
Animal 2	180	1·30	0·0072
	310	2·35	0·0076

attributed wholly to diffusion, but neither can it be attributed
to exchange diffusion of the usual kind, because the loss
does not increase if the concentration of the medium is raised
above 2 mM/l. Bryan adduces evidence supporting the theory
that the sodium pump transporting ions into the animal is
slightly leaky; when the pump is inoperative as in distilled
water, the leak stops, and hence the efflux of ions is reduced
(Bryan, 1960 b). This point is discussed further below.

In animals with a depleted blood concentration, the renal
loss may amount to only 1% of the total loss, but in animals
with artificially raised blood sodium, the renal loss may exceed the extra-renal loss (Table V.11, line 8 and Bryan, 1960 c).

Fish — The loss of chloride from fish was first investigated
by Krogh (1937 b). A catfish, *Ameiurus*, (19.5 g) lost chloride in
glass-distilled water at the rate of 30 μM/kg/hr, and the stickleback, *Gasterosteus*, (7.5 g) lost it at the rate of 260 μM/kg/hr. In
both of these fish, the rate was much increased by the presence
of heavy metals in the media. A goldfish, *Carassius*, (48 g) in
a divided chamber, lost chloride at a rate of 140 μM/kg/hr
from the hind end of the body alone. On the other hand, an
eel (98 g) lost only 9.2 μM Cl/kg/hr in glass-distilled water.
In both the stickleback and the goldfish, the rate of loss is

much larger than the rates of renal loss found in the three fishes in Table V.9, but in the eel and the catfish, the two rates of loss are of the same size.

Frog — The total rate of loss of chloride from the frog in distilled water is similar to that of the catfish. It declined from a rate of 60 μM/kg/hr on the first day, to 12 μM/kg/hr in 11 days at 22°C (Krogh, 1937 a). In a second frog, in which urine was collected and analysed separately, the concentration of chloride in the urine varied irregularly between 0.5 and 1.0 mM/l. corresponding to a rate of loss of 5-10 μM/kg/hr, while the extra-renal loss declined progressively from 16 μM/kg/hr to 0.8 μM/kg/hr after 10 days. The decline is therefore due to a reduction in the rate of loss through the skin, rather than to a reduction in the renal loss. In contrast, the calcium lost in the urine declined during the 10 days of the experiment from 3.2 μM/kg/hr to 1 μM/kg/hr, while the calcium lost through the skin remained almost constant at 2.8 μM/kg/hr. More recently, the toad, *Bufo marinus*, was shown to lose sodium at the rate of 27 μM/kg/hr, but after dehydration, the rate of loss of sodium increased to 172 μM/kg/hr. This increase was probably due to the release of the antidiuretic hormone following dehydration (Chap. IX, p.345) (Bentley, 1958 a). As the rate of urine production would be low when the toad is dehydrated, most of this loss must have taken place through the skin.

General — From the foregoing discussion of individual animals, it can be seen that extra-renal salt loss is extremely variable (Table V.13). The range of permeabilities is surprisingly large, but the permeabilities are much lower than in marine or brackish water animals. Even *Eriocheir* is less permeable than the brackish water *Carcinus maenas* which would lose 18 mM/kg/hr, or *Nereis diversicolor* which loses 3.9 mM/kg/hr in fresh water. However, the permeability of an animal to salt is not constant as the extra-renal salt losses of many animals can be drastically reduced if the animals are kept for some time in salt-free water, e.g. the frog and *Eriocheir*. These apparent reductions in permeability may be related to changes in the salt absorption mechanism which occur as the animals become adapted to the new conditions, or they may be due to real changes in the permeability of the body wall to salt. Most of the data in Table V.13 are derived from animals put into distilled water and the extra-renal loss from animals in natural fresh water may be rather larger.

TABLE V.13. — EXTRA-RENAL LOSS OF SALTS FROM SOME FRESHWATER ANIMALS

Animal	Rate of loss $\mu M/kg/hr$	Temperature	Author
Nereis diversicolor ...	3870 Cl	25°C	Jørgensen & Dales, 1957
Eriocheir sinensis ...	1700 Na		Shaw, 1961 b
Astacus pallipes	370 Na	20°C	Bryan, 1960 a
Potamon niloticus ...	800 Na		Shaw, 1959 c
	50 K		
Palaemonetes			
antennarius	1000 Na	20°C	Parry & Potts, unpub.
Ameiurus sp.	30 Cl		Krogh, 1937 a
Gasterosteus aculeatus	260 Cl		,, ,,
Anguilla anguilla......	9·2 Cl		,, ,,
Rana esculenta	16 Cl	18°C	Krogh, 1937 b
	2·8 Ca	18°C	,, ,,

The permeability to salts is to some extent independent of the permeability to water; for instance, *Potamon*, which apparently has a very low permeability to water, is more permeable to salt than most other freshwater animals.

In *Palaemonetes*, *Gammarus pulex* and the frog, the renal salt loss may exceed the salt loss by diffusion, but in most other animals the renal salt loss is small compared with the extra-renal loss. This does not mean that the osmotic work performed by the renal organs is not important in these cases; on the contrary, the renal losses are small only because the kidneys are so efficient. If the urine were to remain isosmotic with the blood, in practically every case, the renal loss would exceed the diffusion loss, as it does in *Astacus* if the level of blood concentration is artificially raised. In this respect, freshwater animals resemble *Nereis diversicolor;* when this animal is in brackish water, (9‰ chlorinity) the renal chloride loss (9.2 mM/kg/hr) exceeds the diffusion loss (6.3 mM/kg/hr) but when it is in fresh water, the renal loss is reduced to 1.6 mM/kg/hr, while the diffusion loss is still 3.9 mM/kg/hr. Only in *Potamon* is the urine loss negligible in comparison with the diffusion loss, even though the urine is isosmotic with the blood.

Active Uptake of Salts

Most freshwater animals are able to replace the lost salt by active uptake from the medium. It is possible that some animals which are very impermeable to both salts and water, such as the larva of *Sialis lutaria*, obtain all the salts they require in their food. Shaw (1955 b) was unable to detect any active uptake of sodium by *Sialis* from tap water, and similarly, Krogh (1937 b) found no evidence of active uptake by elvers of *Anguilla*, even after their salt content had been depleted by keeping them in distilled water. However, most freshwater animals are able to take up ions from extremely low concentrations in the medium. Direct uptake is probably the main source of ions for most freshwater animals even if they are feeding, and it is the only source when they are starved.

Before the development of radioactive isotope techniques, the ability of animals to take up ions against a concentration gradient was studied by placing salt-depleted animals in dilute salt solutions and measuring the net changes in concentration. These experiments necessarily involved animals not in equilibrium with their environments, but in spite of this they did demonstrate active uptake, the threshold concentrations below which net uptake was impossible, and the ion selectivities of the transport systems. Krogh (1937 b, 1938) and his school showed that a large variety of freshwater animals, including fishes, a leech, molluscs, a crab and the frog, could all take up salts from very dilute solutions. The threshold was usually less than 1 mM NaCl/l. For example, the gastropod *Viviparus* could reduce the concentration of a sodium chloride solution to 0.105 mM Cl/l., a concentration lower than that of most natural waters; the frog could reduce the concentration to as low as 0.01 mM/l., and so would be able to take up salts from the softest rain water. In contrast, the crab *Eriocheir* had a threshold of 0.2–0.4 mM/l. and *Lymnaea peregra* a threshold of 0.56 mM/l., and so these animals would not be able to gain salts from soft water.

The maximum rates of net uptake recorded, i.e. the excess of uptake over loss, were as follows (μM Cl/kg/hr): the leech, *Haemopsis*, 480; *Lymnaea*, 165; *Viviparus*, 173; *Unio*, the freshwater mussel, 300; *Eriocheir*, 455; *Astacus*, 150; frog, 810; and *Salmo gairdnerii*, 300.

By placing salt-depleted animals in different solutions, Krogh was able to show that the sodium and chloride transport systems could work independently. Both sodium and chloride ions were taken up together from sodium chloride solutions, but the frog could take up chloride from solutions of ammonium chloride, calcium chloride, and potassium chloride without the equivalent cation. The chloride taken up was balanced by excreted bicarbonate ions. Similarly, sodium ions can be taken up from solutions of sodium sulphate in exchange for ammonium ions, excluding the sulphate. Sodium ions can also be taken up from solutions of sodium carbonate but in excess of the ammonium ions produced. Krogh suggested that sodium taken into the body is balanced by an increase in the bicarbonate ions in the blood produced metabolically, while an equivalent quantity of bicarbonate ions in the solution is converted to carbon dioxide. This hypothesis obviates the need to postulate an ability to take up bicarbonate ions. Sodium can also be taken up from mixtures of sodium and potassium chloride without any accompanying potassium uptake. On the other hand, in *Eriocheir*, sodium and lithium compete for the same uptake mechanism, so that the presence of lithium inhibits sodium uptake (Koch and Evans, 1956). The uptake of ions is independent of the osmotic uptake of water, since Krogh found that chloride could be taken up from a 1 mM NaCl/l. solution in a glucose solution isosmotic with the blood. Different ions are absorbed in different ways by animals and Table V.14 shows the various paths of entry of some commonly used inorganic ions in the frog, the goldfish and *Eriocheir*.

TABLE V.14. — MODE OF ENTRY OF SOME IONS INTO FRESHWATER
ANIMALS

Animal	Active uptake	Passive entry	Impermeable
Frog	Br, Na	I, NO_3, CNS	I, NO_3, CNS
Goldfish	Na, Cl, Br		
Eriocheir	Na, Cl, Br, CNO, CNS, K	I, NO_3	

The introduction of radiotracers has made possible much more detailed studies of the processes of ion uptake, including the measurement of the rate of uptake when the animal is in equilibrium conditions.

The active uptake of sodium has been demonstrated in the axolotl (Jørgensen, Levi and Ussing, 1946), the goldfish (Meyer, 1951; Sexton and Meyer, 1955), and the crab *Eriocheir* (Koch and Evans, 1956). Koch, Evans and Schicks (1954), using isolated perfused gills of *Eriocheir*, showed that the site of active uptake was the branchial epithelium. More recently, detailed studies have been made of active uptake in a number of crustaceans, including *Astacus*, *Eriocheir* and *Gammarus pulex*, in the frog, and in the larva of the mosquito *Aedes detritus*. The crustaceans show many similarities one to another in the dynamics of active uptake, but differ in many respects from both the frog and the insect larva. These three types of uptake mechanism will be discussed separately below.

Astacus — The active uptake of sodium ions by *Astacus* in various conditions of external and internal sodium concentration has been investigated by Shaw (1959 c, 1960 a and b) and Bryan (1960, a, b and c). Shaw's experiments were done at 12–13°C and Bryan's at 20°C; Shaw's animals had a blood concentration of 180–190 mM Na/l. and Bryan's, 203–204 mM Na/l. This difference is probably attributable to the temperature difference.

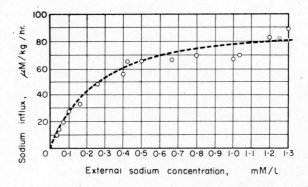

Fig. V.2. *Astacus pallipes*. The relation between the rate of sodium uptake by a sodium depleted crayfish and the sodium concentration in a medium. Temperature 12°C. From Shaw, 1959 c.

In fresh water containing 0.30 mM Na/l., the sodium influx averages 150 μM/kg/hr. The minimum equilibrium concentration, or threshold, of a sodium depleted crayfish averages 0.04 mM/l., varying from 0.02–0.09 mM/l. in different individuals (Shaw, 1959 a). The relation between external sodium concentration, and the sodium influx for a crayfish which had been depleted of sodium until it was in balance with its threshold concentration, is shown in Fig. V.2. The relation between the external concentration and the rate of influx is similar to that of *Carcinus* and can be defined in terms of Shaw's equation (Chap. I, p.34): $f_{max} = 0.15$ mM/kg/hr, $S = 0.2$–0.3 mM/l.

At 20°C in fresh water containing 0.50 mM Na/l. the total influx of sodium was 360 μM/kg/hr (Bryan, 1960 a), compared with 150 μM at 12–13°C, above. In a medium containing 10 mM/l. the influx increases only slightly to 397 μM/kg/hr (Table V.11, col. 8) and the blood concentration is un-

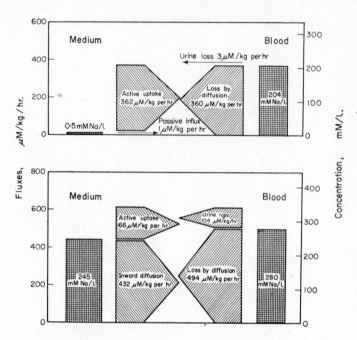

Fig. V.3. *Astacus pallipes* (*fluviatilis*). Diagrammatic representation of the sodium fluxes through the crayfish in fresh water and brackish water. Temperature 20°C.
Calculated from Bryan, 1960 a and b.

changed, which again suggests that the influx is almost independent of external sodium concentrations above 1 mM Na/l. At very high external concentrations, the influx does increase significantly; in a medium of 200 mM Na/l. it reached 486 μM/kg/hr (1 determination) and in 245 mM Na/l. it reached 786 μM/kg/hr (1 determination, cf. Table V.11, col. 8). The increases, 130 and 430 μM, may be attributed to a

passive influx. When the blood concentration is 204 mM
Na/l., the passive efflux is 360 μM/kg/hr (Table V.11),
so the permeability is apparently similar in both directions.
The passive fluxes will be proportional to external and internal
concentrations only if no potential difference exists across the
body wall (Chap. I, p.19). Simple calculations based on Equation 1, Chap.I (and assuming that no potential difference

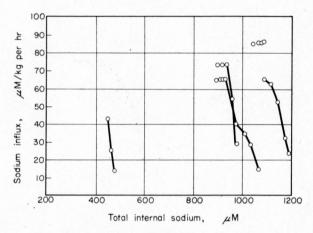

Fig. V.4. *Astacus pallipes.* The relation between the rate of active
uptake of sodium from a solution containing 0.03mM Na/l. and
the sodium content of the animals. Temperature 12°C.
From Shaw, 1959 c.

exists between the animal and the medium) show that, in a
medium containing 245 mM Na/l. the passive influx would be
432 μM/kg/hr, and the active uptake 166 μM/kg/hr (Fig. V.3).
The reduction in the rate of active uptake will be the consequence of a higher blood concentration (see below) (cf. *Nereis*,
Chap. IV, p.150; *Carcinus*, Chap. IV, p.135).

The rate of influx of sodium does not depend only on the
external, but also on the internal sodium concentration (Fig.V.4).
The rate of uptake from a constant external concentration is
very sensitive to changes in internal sodium content (Shaw,
1959 c) (blood concentration and total sodium being in pro-

portion). A 5–10% fall in total body sodium causes a five-fold increase in the rate of influx from the same external concentration. However, the rate of influx cannot be increased indefinitely by continuing to lower the sodium content of the blood, but reaches a well-defined maximum for each animal (Fig. V.4). The relation between internal sodium content and influx

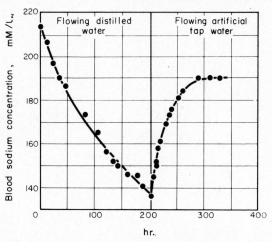

Fig. V.5. *Astacus pallipes* Changes in the sodium concentration in the blood during washing out in distilled water and during subsequent period of active uptake after return to tap water containing 2.0 mM Na/l. Temperature 20°C. From Bryan 1960 b.

is not exactly reproducible, but is affected by a hysteresis which suggest a time lag, or "back-lash", in the control mechanism. Some of Bryan's experiments also clarify the relation between the rate of sodium uptake and its total concentration in the animal. Salt-depleted crayfish took up sodium from a 2 mM Na/l. solution although, as would be expected from the hysteresis, they did not replace all the lost sodium. The curve of net uptake in relation to time was exponential in character (Fig. V.5), so that

$$\ln\left(\frac{1 - \text{Na gained}_t}{\text{Na gained}_\infty}\right)$$

against time (t) is a straight line (Fig. V.6). At first sight, "it appears that the rate of net uptake is lower as the degree of sodium depletion is increased, and is not related to the length of time in distilled water" (Bryan, 1960 b), but if any one individual is considered, it is clear that the rate of uptake is

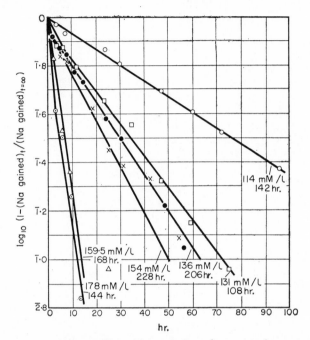

Fig. V.6. *Astacus pallipes.* The variation of net uptake rates with time during recovery of salt depleted animals. The figures show the level to which the blood sodium had been depleted and the time in distilled water that it took to achieve this. Temperature 20°C. From Bryan, 1960 b.

greatest when the blood concentration is lowest. If it is assumed that the final sodium concentration in the blood of each animal in Fig. V.6 was 200 mM/l. the initial rate of gain of sodium for each animal can be calculated from the rate constant which can be obtained from the slope of the line, and the total increment of sodium (Table V.15). For example, when

14

the blood concentration of animal 1 was 114 mM Na/l., it took up sodium at a net rate of 550 μM/kg/hr; when the blood concentration had risen to 160 mM/l., the net gain had declined to 256 μM/kg/hr; at 180 mM/l., it was 128 μM/kg/hr; at 190 mM/l., it was only 64 μM/kg/hr, etc. Thus, the increase in the rate of sodium uptake, above normal equilibrium level, is directly proportional to the depletion of the sodium content of the animal. Bryan's animals had not been depleted to the stage where the rate of uptake reached a maximum (Fig. V.4).

TABLE V.15. — COMPARISON OF NET UPTAKE RATES OF ANIMALS
SHOWN IN FIG. V.6

Initial blood concentration mM/l.	Increase in blood concentration[1] mM/l.	Rate constant (h^{-1})	Initial rate of uptake[2] μM/kg/hr
114	86	0·015	550
131	69	0·032	950
136	64	0·037	1000
154	46	0·046	900
159·5	40	0·19	3300
178	22	0·21	200

1 Assuming that the final blood concentration is 200 mM Na/l.
2 Calculated from K (rate constant) and the increase in the blood concentration, assuming a density of 1.118 and a sodium space of 46.9 %.

In each animal, the gross uptake of sodium is larger than the net gain by an amount equivalent to the net loss. The rate of loss can be calculated for each animal from the fall in blood concentration and the time it was washed in distilled water. In most cases, the loss is small compared with the net gain, so approximately, the total rate of uptake is proportional to the depletion of the animal's sodium. This is also illustrated by the relatively straight parts of each curve in Fig. V.4. It is clear that Bryan's animals maintained a linear relation between influx and depletion over a much wider range than Shaw's, and were capable of an active uptake more than ten times normal.

It is apparent from Fig. V.6 that animals which take longest to regain lost sodium are those which lose most sodium during the washing in distilled water: for example, the blood concentration of animal 1 dropped by 90 mM Na/l. in 142 hours and required 100 hours to recover, while the blood of animal 6 dropped only 22 mM/l. and recovered in 12 hours. This led Bryan to conclude that the rate of net uptake is lower as the degree of sodium depletion is increased. An animal with a low rate of loss will replace lost sodium more rapidly than an animal with a high rate of loss, provided their total uptake rates are the same, but this explanation is quantitatively insufficient, because animals with a low rate of loss took up sodium more rapidly than those with a high rate, e.g. Table V.1, 15, lines 1 and 6. One explanation of this could be that some of the sodium lost by the gills is recovered by other gill filaments before it leaves the branchial cavity. Some of the animals in Table V.15 have tremendous powers of sodium uptake; if all the animals have similar permeabilities, those with the most powerful uptake systems would recover most of the lost sodium and so have the smallest net losses.

Shaw noted that the efflux in distilled water was 20% less than that in fresh water, and he attributed the difference to exchange diffusion. Bryan found that the efflux in distilled water was 36% less than in a 2 mM/l. solution (Table V.11), and of this reduction only 5% was due to a fall in the urine concentration, but he attributed the reduction not to exchange diffusion, but to a leak in the sodium pump which occurs only when the pump is working. If the level of sodium in the animal is raised artificially so that active uptake ceases, the influx of ^{22}Na practically stops, in a 2 mM Na/l. solution, although in these conditions exchange diffusion would continue. Again, in depleted crayfish which were taking up sodium rapidly, the rate of loss of ^{22}Na was several times larger than normal during the period of rapid uptake, and declined to the usual level when the animals reached equilibrium. This shows that the pump leaked most when working hardest. If, when

14*

the animal is in fresh water, in the time taken for 6 ions to be lost by diffusion, 8 ions are actively transported and 2 have leaked out by the activity of the pump, then the animal will be in equilibrium. When the animal is in distilled water, active uptake and the associated loss will cease, and only 6 ions will be lost where 8 were lost before, a reduction of 25%. On the other hand, a seven-fold increase in the rate of transport in fresh water, such as would occur after sodium depletion, would increase the rate of loss by 2–3 times.

The sodium pump is unaffected by the character of the anion present in the external medium. The influx from sodium sulphate solutions is similar to that from sodium chloride of the same sodium concentration, although chloride accompanies the sodium whereas sulphate does not. The sodium taken up from sodium sulphate solutions must be exchanged for some other cation, e.g. ammonium, but the rate of uptake has no effect on the rate of ammonium output, and may exceed it. Shaw (1960 a) suggests that sodium ions are exchanged for ammonium and/or hydrogen ions produced metabolically. The presence of potassium or calcium ions in the external medium has no effect on the rate of sodium uptake, but the presence of 1 mM NH^+_4/l. or 0.1 mM H^+/l. (pH 4) depresses the sodium uptake by 70–80%. It is probable that the presence of these ions in the external medium interferes with the sodium pump by depressing the efflux of ammonium or hydrogen ions, for which the sodium is exchanged. In *Eriocheir*, sodium uptake is inhibited by carbon dioxide (Koch, Evans and Schicks, 1953; Dumont, 1957).

To summarise, sodium balance in the crayfish in solutions of moderate sodium content is a function of three variables (ignoring the hysteresis): the uptake rate, the external concentration, and the internal concentration; the rate of loss may be considered constant. The relation between these variables is illustrated in Fig. V.7, where the curves have been drawn on the assumption that the rate of uptake is proportional to the sodium depletion up to a certain maximum. When an animal is in equilibrium

with an external sodium concentration *A*, the rate of uptake
will be *A'*, where *A' = L*, the rate of loss. If the external
sodium concentration now falls to *B*, the rate of uptake will
fall to *B'*, where *B'* is less than *L*. The blood concentration
will therefore decline, and this will stimulate the rate of uptake
until a new equilibrium is established, where a new rate of

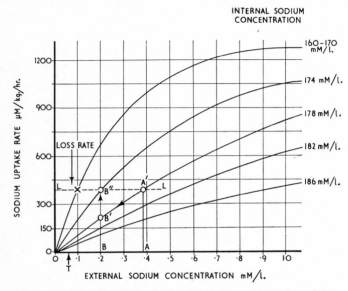

Fig. V.7. *Astacus pallipes.* A diagrammatic representation of the
relation between sodium uptake rate, the external sodium concentration and the internal sodium concentration. For explanation of
letters see text. Adapted from Shaw, 1959 c.

uptake, *B''*, once again equals the rate of loss. Because the rate
of uptake is so sensitive to changes in internal sodium concentration, large changes in the external sodium concentration
result in only small alterations internally.

The chloride pump is similar but subordinate to the sodium
pump. In animals in equilibrium with the threshold concentration (0.03 mM Cl/l.). the relation between influx and external
concentration is similar to that for sodium (Fig. V.3). In

distilled water, the chloride loss averages 70% of the sodium loss (Table V.16, line 5). When salt depleted animals are transferred to a solution of 0.3 mM NaCl/l. the chloride efflux increases several times (Table V.16, line 1) so that the net uptake of chloride in these conditions is only a small part of the gross influx, whereas in the same conditions sodium efflux is only 30% of the gross influx. Substitution of potassium chloride for sodium chloride has little effect on the gross influx, but net uptake is even further reduced (Table V.16, line 2); if sodium is then added as sodium sulphate, the influx is increased (Table V.16, line 3). Animals depleted of chloride but not sodium, can take up chloride from potassium chloride solutions with a much smaller concomitant loss (Table V.16, line 4). In these conditions, the ions were not accompanied by equivalent amounts of potassium, but must have been exchanged for bicarbonate or hydroxyl ions (Shaw, 1960 c).

TABLE V. 16. — CHLORIDE FLUXES IN *Astacus*, VARIOUS CONDITIONS (12°C)
(from Shaw, 1960 c)

Condition of animal	Medium conc./l.	Chloride influx μM/animal/hr	Chloride efflux μM/animal/hr	Net uptake μM/animal/hr
NaCl depleted	0·3 mM NaCl	8	7·5	0·5
NaCl depleted	0·14 mM KCl	6	5·94	0·05
NaCl depleted	0·14 mM KCl + 1 mE Na_2SO_4	9·7	8·5	1·2
Cl depleted ...	0·14 mM KCl	5·5	1·4	3·9
Normal	deionised water	–	0·8*	–

* For an animal of 10 g

It is clear from these experiments that the chloride pump works most easily in parallel with the sodium pump, but if there is a marked fall in the ratio of chloride and sodium in the blood, it can operate independently. The chloride pump continues to operate in the presence of a concentration of ammonium which would inhibit the sodium pump. During chloride uptake from potassium chloride solutions, the inside of the animal was about 29 mV negative to the external medium; in these conditions, chloride ions must be transported against both electrical and concentration gradients.

Shaw (1960 c) has suggested that the sodium pump sets the level of the blood sodium, and that the chloride pump operates on the Cl/Na ratio in the blood. This theory postulates that the chloride pump operates, or rather idles, continuously, bringing about a Cl–Cl exchange across the body surface; but when it is stimulated (e.g. by a fall in the Cl/Na ratio, or by the difference between sodium and chloride concentrations in the blood) it operates more effectively by exchanging some other anion for chloride.

A combination of Bryan's and Shaw's theories for sodium and chloride pumps could explain almost all the observed phenomena, but neither author has fully explored the effects of changes in the external and internal concentrations on the electrical potential difference developed between the crayfish and the ambient medium. Changes in the potential across the body wall could produce large changes in the passive efflux of ions (Chap. I, p.20; Equation 2). Animals in equilibrium with solutions of 0.4 mM NaCl/l. and 2.0 mM NaCl/l. are, respectively, 6.6 mV and 4.1 mV positive to the medium (Bryan, 1960 a), while during stimulated chloride uptake (from 0.3 mM KCl/l. see above), the animals were 29 mV negative to the medium. If uptake was inhibited by carbon dioxide, the potential fell to about − 10 mV. When no uptake occurs, the potential should reach a level at which the passive effluxes of cations balance those of the anions. The animals are then slightly negative, so the body wall is probably more permeable to chloride ions than to sodium, since the negative potentia enhances the passive loss of sodium and retards that of chloride When there is active uptake of sodium, the situation becomes more complicated, but if sodium uptake predominates, the animal will tend to be positive, if chloride predominates, to be negative. Transfer from distilled water to sodium chloride solutions may be accompanied by a change from negative to positive, increasing the passive efflux of sodium, but decreasing that of chloride. The greater sodium efflux in sodium chloride solutions compared with that in distilled water, observed by both Shaw and Bryan, might be due to this effect rather than to exchange diffusion or leaky pumps, and the very rapid efflux of sodium associated with rapid uptake could be due to a similar effect. Similarly, the increased chloride influx, following the addition of sodium to potassium chloride solution, might be dissociated with a decrease in the negative potential when the sodium uptake starts, which would reduce the electrochemical gradient for chloride. On the other hand, the chloride efflux is also increased in these conditions, and this does suggest the working of a leaking or idling pump. The chloride efflux is minimal in distilled water and in 0.14 mM KCl/l. (Table V.16, line 5), when the animal is probably negative to the external medium. More information is required about potentials across the body wall in different media before it is possible to define accurately the proportion of the effluxes taking place by diffusion, exchange diffusion, and leaking pumps.

Other crustaceans — The relation between the rates of uptake and the internal and external concentrations in a number of other crustaceans appears to be similar to that of *Astacus*, although no other animal has been studied so intensively.

In *Eriocheir*, the external concentration (S) at which the influx is half the maximum (see Chap. I, p.34) is about 1.0 mM Na/l. (Shaw, 1961 b). This is only slightly lower than that for the brackish water amphipod, *Gammarus duebeni*, where $S = 1.5$ mM Na/l. The maximum rate of influx (f_{max}) in *Eriocheir* is thus about 2.0 mM/kg/hr, but crabs which had been adapted to 2% sea water (9 mM Na/l.) had higher uptake rates in the same solutions than those which had been adapted to 10% sea water (45 mM Na/l.). This appears to have been due to an increase

in f_{max} rather than to a reduction in S.* No doubt the increase
is analogous to that observed in salt-depleted *Astacus* (see
p.199).

In *Potamon*, f_{max} is also about 2.0 mM/kg/hr in salt depleted
animals but S is less than 0.1 mM Na/l. (Shaw, 1959 c). The uptake system is very sensitive to small changes in the sodium
content of the animal. The loss of 50 μM of sodium from a
crab, corresponding to about 4% of the total body sodium,
doubles the rate of uptake from a solution containing 0.5 mM
Na/l.

In *Gammarus pulex*, f_{max} is about 0.3 μM/animal/hr, or approximately 7.5 mM/kg/hr, but S is only 0.15 mM Na/l. f_{max},
S and the minimum equilibrium concentrations of a number of
crustaceans are collected in Table V.17.

TABLE V.17. — THE PROPERTIES OF THE ACTIVE UPTAKE MECHANISM
OF SOME CRUSTACEANS AND THEIR LOWEST EQUILIBRIUM CONCENTRATIONS

Animal	f_{max} mM/kg/hr	S mM/l.	Min. equil. conc. mM/l.	Author
Carcinus............	10	20	90	Shaw, 1961 a
Gammarus duebeni	20	1.5	0.2	Shaw & Sutcliffe, 1961
Eriocheir	2.0	1.0	0.2	Shaw, 1961 b
G. pulex............	7.5	0.15	0.06	Shaw & Sutcliffe, 1961
Potamon............	2.0	0.1	0.05	Shaw, 1959
Astacus	0.15	0.2–0.3	0.04	Shaw, 1961 b

In the course of the adaptation of these crustaceans to fresh
water, there has been a progressive decrease in the permeability
of the body wall to both salt and water (see p.143), and an increasing ability to take up ions from low external concentrations. The rate of uptake at low concentrations may be increased, either by an increase in f_{max}, or by a decrease in S. In

* See Shaw (1961 b) Fig. 1.

fact, freshwater animals often have a lower value for f_{max} than brackish water ones (Table V.17), but S is also lower. For example, S decreases by a factor of 10 between the brackish water *Carcinus* and *Gammarus duebeni* maximally adapted to fresh water, and declines by a further factor of 10 between *G. duebeni* and *G. pulex*. Shaw (1961 b) has pointed out that a decrease in S is most effective in allowing an animal to maintain salt balance in very dilute solutions. The salt balance can be maintained when active uptake is equal to the net loss by diffusion, neglecting salt loss in the urine, i.e.

$$f = f_{max} \frac{M}{S+M} = k'(B-M),$$

where B is the blood concentration, M the medium concentration, and k' some constant relating to the permeability. Shaw compared the lowest equilibrium concentrations in two animals with the same f_{max} and the same blood concentration (300 mM Na/l.) but with different values of S of 40 mM Na/l. and 2.5 mM Na/l., respectively (Fig. V.8). If the permeabilities of the body surfaces are high and $k' = 32$ (arbitrary units), animal 1 will remain in balance at an external concentration of 180 mM Na/l., and animal 2 at a concentration of 150 mM Na/l. If the permeability is halved ($k' = 16$), the advantage of the lower S value becomes more apparent, since animal 1 can maintain sodium balance in a solution of 90 mM Na/l., but animal 2 in a solution of only 25 mM Na/l. If the permeability is halved again ($k' = 8$), the difference between the two animals is even more pronounced, salt balance being maintained at 32 and 2.5 mM Na/l., respectively. In this case, to maintain the sodium balance in a solution containing 0.05 mM Na/l., animal 2 would have to reduce the permeability by a further factor of 8, but animal 1, to achieve the same result, would have to reduce it by a factor of 1600. This illustrates very dramatically, the advantages of a transport system with a high affinity for sodium (and hence a low value for S) associated with a moderate reduction in the permeability to sodium.

Both *Eriocheir* and *Astacus* respond to salt depletion by an increase in f_{max} rather than by a reduction in S. This implies that the individuals respond by increasing either the concentration or the activity of the cation carrier, rather than by altering its affinity for sodium.

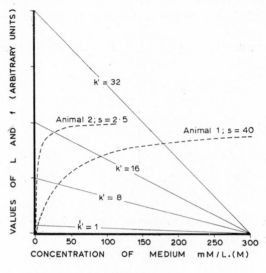

Fig. V.8.

Asellus — The interpretation of tracer studies in the freshwater isopod, *Asellus aquaticus* (Lockwood, 1960) is complicated by the presence of a considerable amount of sodium bound in the uric acid deposits in the cells of Zenker's organ. In deionised water, the rate of loss of sodium is independent of temperature, and amounts to about 1% of the total body sodium in an hour, equivalent perhaps to 880 μM/kg/hr. In a solution of 1.1 mM Na/l. the flux of sodium through equilibrated animals (at 20°C) amounts to 3.5% of the free sodium/ hr, or 2.28 mM Na/kg/hr. The difference between these two estimates is probably the result of some kind of exchange diffusion. Although the rate of net loss is independent of temperature, the rate of uptake is not. Animals which have been washed out in distilled water until their sodium content had fallen to 50–70% of normal, took up sodium more rapidly at 11°C than at 1°C (Table V.18). The sodium pump is particularly efficient, and the sodium concentration in the blood is independent of the external concentration down to 90 μM Na/l. but it is reduced in media more dilute than this.

TABLE V.18. — UPTAKE OF SODIUM BY SODIUM DEPLETED *Asellus*
(Calculated from Lockwood, 1960. Expressed as mM/kg/hr.)

Temperature	Net uptake	Loss in deionised water at the same temperature	Total uptake*
1°C	0·21	0·68	0·87
11°C	1·06	0·68	1·74

* Excluding exchange diffusion

As the rate of loss is independent of the temperature, while the active uptake system is more active at higher temperatures, the steady state sodium concentration in the blood in any medium is higher at higher temperatures. A similar relation between temperature and blood concentration has been noted in many other animals, e.g. *Astacus* (p.191), *Palaemonetes* (Panikkar, 1941), *Gammarus pulex* (Lockwood, 1961), *Salmo trutta* (Gordon, 1959 a). It has often been observed that marine and brackish water animals penetrate further into brackish or fresh water in warmer climates than in cool ones (Panikkar, 1950), and the balance between the rates of salt uptake and salt loss at different temperatures may explain this. However, this is not the whole story, since at very low temperatures (below 5°C) the blood concentration of *Asellus* rises again (Lockwood, 1960), and a similar rise has been observed in *Gammarus pulex* (Heuts, 1943).

Aedes — In the yellow-fever mosquito, *Aedes aegypti*, the concentration of sodium in the blood is about 100 mM/l., and all the sodium in the larva is normally exchangeable (Stobbart, 1959). At 28°C, the flux of sodium through starved larvae is about 1.2 mM Na/l. blood/hr in solutions containing between 2 and 8 mM Na/l. (Treherne, 1954; Stobbart, 1959).* The efflux in distilled water is only about 0.5 mM Na/l. blood/hr, or even less. As the rate of uptake is independent of the external sodium at concentrations between 2 and 8 mM Na/l., the uptake is probably related to the external concentration by a curve similar to that for *Astacus* (Fig. V.2).

In solutions containing about 2 mM Na/l., the flux through fed larvae is very much greater, about 8 mM Na/l. blood/hr. The fluxes through sodium deficient larvae immediately after transfer to a medium containing sodium, were relatively enormous (Table V.19). These sodium deficient larvae had been reared in distilled water, and the blood contained only about 30 mM Na/l. After about 10 hours in the new medium, the blood sodium had risen to 90–100 mM Na/l., and the fluxes declined to about the rates found in normal larvae.

TABLE V.19. — FLUXES OF SODIUM THROUGH SODIUM-DEFICIENT *Aedes detritus* LARVAE IMMEDIATELY AFTER TRANSFER TO A MEDIUM CONTAINING 2 mM Na/l.
(from Stobbart, 1960)

Larvae	Influx mM/l./hr	Efflux mM/l./hr
Fed	105	60
Starved	14	5

About 90% of the exchange takes place through the anal papillae, the osmoregulatory function of which had been demonstrated first by Wigglesworth (1933). If the anal papillae are damaged by treatment with a 5% sodium chloride solution, the sodium flux through the starved larvae drops to about 115 μM

* The results of Treherne and Stobbart are expressed in terms of a litre of blood, but an animal contains about 85% blood.

Na/l. blood/hr (Stobbart, 1959). If the papillae are left intact, but the gut blocked, the sodium flux is reduced by a "relatively small amount" (Stobbart, 1959).* These two facts together suggest that most of the exchange takes place through the anal papillae, and practically all the rest through the gut. The rate of exchange in larvae with both the gut blocked and the anal papillae destroyed was negligible (Treherne, 1954). The fluxes were about 30% higher at 35°C than at 20°C (Treherne, 1954), a temperature quotient much lower than in most biological reactions.

An unexpected feature of the sodium exchange in *Aedes aegypti* is that the rate of exchange in well fed larvae is six or seven times as fast as it is in starved larvae. This makes it improbable that the efflux is passive, because it is unlikely that feeding would increase the permeability of the membrane. Stobbart suggests that a greater part of the efflux in the fed larvae is mediated by a carrier mechanism, consisting of a sodium pump on the inside of the wall of the anal papilla, operating in conjunction with a carrier substance constituting an exchange diffusion system of limited capacity. The pump transports sufficient sodium to balance the small passive loss, but the bulk of the movement takes place by exchange diffusion through the membrane mediated by the carrier. This hypothesis is supported by the low temperature coefficient of the fluxes, and by their magnitude. If the carrier is saturated when the external concentration is 2 mM Na/l., the rate of exchange will be independent of the external sodium at higher concentrations; but at a sufficiently low concentration of sodium, if Stobbart's hypothesis is correct, the sodium efflux from the larvae should be proportional to the external sodium concentration. In distilled water, the total efflux would be equivalent to the net loss and the efflux from fed and starved larvae in distilled water should be the same. There is insufficient evidence to decide how much of the net efflux takes place via

---

* In the only published experiment with an animal with the gut blocked, the reduction was about 20%.

the malpighian tubes and the rectum, and how much is lost by diffusion.

When the anal papillae are destroyed, the blood sodium declines from 100 mM/l. to 80 mM/l. This suggests that the influx via the anal papillae is larger than the efflux, but that the gut can also take up sodium against a concentration gradient.

In the absence of measurements of the potential difference between the blood and the external medium, it is impossible to decide if the increased efflux which takes place during rapid uptake (Table V.19) is due to passive diffusion down an increased electrical gradient, or to a leaky pump losing more ions as it works harder. While at first sight, exchange diffusion would seem to have no survival value, Stobbart (1959) points out that these very large influxes in sodium deficient larvae would be impossible, unless the capacity of the exchange diffusion system had been enhanced. Alterations in the capacity of such a system might thus have considerable survival value.

Analogy with the crustacean active uptake system is difficult because the influxes have not been recorded at very low concentrations. However, the sodium pump in *Aedes* is saturated at an external concentration of 2 mM Na/l., so the affinity of the system for sodium must be very high, and the value for S, very low, as in some freshwater crustaceans. On the other hand the great variation of the influx with the state of nutrition has no parallel in the crustaceans.

Sialis — The larva of *Sialis lutaria*, the lace-wing, is apparently unable to take up ions from external solutions, but the gut can take up ions against a small concentration gradient (Shaw, 1955 b). The larvae are so impermeable that it is impracticable to deplete their salt content by washing them in distilled water, but the active uptake of ions can be stimulated by the removal of a considerable proportion of the blood. Animals depleted in this way absorb sodium ions from a solution containing 85 mM Na/l. and transfer them (at a rate of 250 μM/kg/hr) to the blood, at a concentration of 120 mM Na/l. The blood was

18 mV positive with respect to the gut contents, probably as a result of this active transport of sodium ions. The normal chloride content of the blood is only 31 mM/l., and under the influence of the positive potential, chloride ions would diffuse into the blood from concentrations in the gut as low as 15 mM/l. Whether the larvae are able to actively transport chloride from lower concentrations was not investigated. In fresh water, the renal loss of chloride was negligible, but the diffusion loss was 360 μM/kg/hr (calculated from the data given in Shaw, 1955 b). The larva of *Sialis* is carnivorous and the chloride loss may be replaced from the food. The low permeability of the body wall, the efficiency of the excretory system, and the carnivorous habit, combine to make the active uptake of ions from the external medium almost superfluous.

Frog — A fairly detailed picture of the ion transport system of frog skin has been obtained from the study of the properties of isolated diaphragms of skin. Such a piece of skin will maintain an electrical potential of up to 140 mV between solutions of sodium chloride placed on either side, the inner being positive to the outer. At the same time, there is a transfer of sodium chloride from the outer to the inner solution, even against considerable concentration gradients. Simultaneous measurements of the potential, the concentrations, and the fluxes, show that sodium is actively transported against an electrochemical gradient, but that chloride only diffuses passively down the electrochemical gradient (Koefoed-Johnsen, Levi and Ussing, 1952).* These facts suggest that the potential is brought about by the active transport of sodium ions across the skin; this has been confirmed by use of a short-circuit current technique. When the potential across the skin is maintained at zero by the application of an external e.m.f., with identical solutions of sodium on either side, the current generated by the skin is equal to the net sodium flux.

* But compare the situation in the intact frog (Chap. V, p. 190)

In these circumstances, chloride ions diffuse in both directions at an equal rate and so do not contribute to the current (Ussing and Zerahn, 1951).

When chloride is present, the potential across the skin is a complex function of the sodium transport, because of the leakage of chloride through the skin. If chloride is replaced by

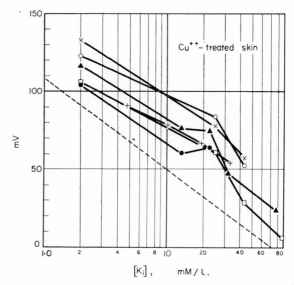

Fig. V.9. Frog skin. The relation between potential and potassium concentration inside (K_i). Ringer solution on both sides. Active transport had been poisoned by 10^{-5}M Cu outside.
From Ussing, 1960.

a non-penetrating anion such as sulphate, or if the skin is made impermeable to chloride by treatment with 10^{-5} M copper sulphate, the potential across the skin becomes a simple function of the concentration of sodium on the outside of the skin and of the potassium inside (Koefoed-Johnsen and Ussing, 1958). The potential behaves as if the inside of the skin were a potassium electrode, i.e. E is a function of log K_i; while the outside behaves as a sodium electrode, i.e. E is proportional to log Na_0 (Figs. V.9 and V.10). Potassium outside has no effect

15

on the potential, and so the outer surface must be relatively impermeable to it, but the potential is dependent on the potassium inside, and sodium transport is inhibited if it is absent. The potential is independent of the sodium concentration inside, provided it is greater than 10 mM Na/l. The inside of the skin is therefore relatively impermeable to sodium ions.

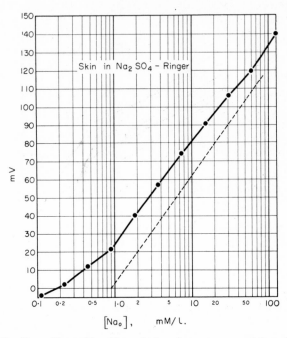

Fig. V.10. Frog skin. The relation between potential and the sodium concentration outside. (Na_0) Sodium sulphate Ringer on both sides. From Ussing, 1960.

Koefoed-Johnsen and Ussing (1958) suggested the following hypothesis to account for these observations. The active transport of sodium is brought about by the activity of the stratum germinativum of the skin. The inner surface of the cells is similar in some respects to the surface of nerve or muscle fibres, that is, it is permeable to potassium and chloride ions and relatively impermeable to sodium ions. The outer surface, on the other hand, is permeable to sodium and chloride, but impermeable to potassium ions. The inner membrane is provided with a cation pump which can extrude sodium ions from the cell into the inner solution against an electrochemical gradient. There is some evidence (see below) that this cation pump can also transport potassium into the cells. When mobile anions are absent, the total potential across the skin can be described in terms of the equation:

$$E = \frac{RT}{F} \ln \frac{Na_o}{Na_{cells}} + \frac{RT}{F} \ln \frac{K_{cells}}{K_{plasma}}$$

where Na_o and K_{plasma} are the sodium and potassium concentrations in the outer and inner solutions respectively, and Na_{cells} and K_{cells} their concentrations in the cells.

Although the potential can thus be described in terms of diffusion potentials in the absence of mobile anions, it must be actively maintained in the presence of chloride ions. If chloride is allowed to penetrate the skin, sodium chloride will accumulate inside the cells, potassium will leak into the inner solution, the potential will decline, and the cells will swell. Measurements of the potential made with micro electrodes show that the potential is developed in two steps, in accordance with this theory. Measurements of the electrical potentials and the changes in the volume of the stratum germinativum of the skin in various solutions (Engbaek and Hoshiko, 1957) confirm these predictions. The potassium and chloride in the cells are not in a Donnan equilibrium with the inner solution, so that the potassium ions are also actively transported. The inner layer of the skin is freely permeable to water, the outer layer less so, but the permeability of the outer layer is increased by the presence of the antidiuretic hormone, or oxytocic principle (Ussing, 1960).

The properties of the sodium pump of frog skin are rather different from those of the sodium pump of freshwater crustaceans. Although the relation between influx and external sodium concentration is similar (cf. Fig. V.2 and Fig. V.11),

15*

saturation of the system is reached at a much higher concentration, (Fig. V.11) (*ca.* 35 mM Na/l.). Shaw's constant, S, is therefore about 18 mM Na/l. (cf. p.34). In the frog, the dynamics of sodium balance must be fundamentally different from those in *Astacus* and the other crustaceans. As most of the experimental work has been done on isolated frog skin, little is known about the relation between the internal sodium

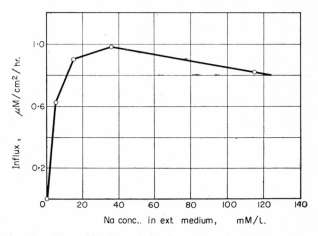

Fig. V.11. Frog skin. The relation between sodium influx and the external sodium concentration. From Kirschner, 1955.

concentration and the sodium pump. In the intact animal, the antidiuretic hormone, liberated in response to an increase in concentration, facilitates salt uptake (Chap. IX, p.347). This is probably a secondary effect, brought about by the dilation of pores in the skin.

The passive efflux of sodium ions increases as the external sodium concentration increases (Fig. V.12). The efflux into 100 mM Na/l. Ringer is three times as large as the influx into sodium-free choline Ringer. Kirschner (1955 a) suggests that transport takes place in association with a carrier. When the external sodium is low, ions diffusing out have a high probability of meeting an unoccupied carrier and of being returned, but if the external sodium is high, the carrier is likely to be fully occupied. The relation between efflux and external sodium concentration in frog skin is reminiscent of that of *Astacus* (p.197), and Bryan's theory of a leaking pump provides an alternative explanation. In contrast, Kirschner's hypothesis applied to *Astacus* cannot explain Bryan's observation that the

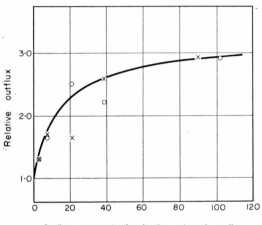

Sodium concentration in the external medium, mM / L.

Fig. V.12. Frog skin. The relation between sodium efflux and the external sodium concentration. The x and the o represent the data from two separate experiments. The efflux is expressed in terms of the efflux into sodium free choline ringer. This reference efflux was 0.46 μM/cm^2/hr in one experiment and 0.60 μM/cm^2/hr in the other. From Kirschner, 1955.

sodium efflux from salt loaded *Astacus* is less than the efflux from normal animals.

There is evidence that a potassium pump in frog skin can function independently of the sodium pump (Steinbach, 1937).

The Tissues of Freshwater Animals

In general, the tissues of freshwater animals contain lower concentrations of organic solutes than those of marine forms (cf. Table V.20 and Table III.5). The sulphonic acid, taurine, present in high concentration in marine molluscs, is character-istically absent from freshwater forms (Simpson, Allen and Awapara, 1959) and in the freshwater crayfish, *Astacus*, betaine (present in *Homarus*) is not detectable (Cowey, 1961). The freshwater crab, *Potamon*, probably a recent immigrant from the sea, most nearly resembles a marine animal in tissue composition; its muscles are strikingly similar to those of *Carcinus* in 40% sea water (Table IV.4), and in particular they contain large quantities of free amino acids and trimethylamine oxide. The muscles of the freshwater crayfish, *Astacus pallipes* contain 110 mM amino acids /kg water (Cowey, 1961). Frog muscle contains much smaller quantities of free amino acids and *Anodonta* muscle even less. *Sialis* contains a surprisingly small quantity of sodium (Shaw, 1955 b), even though the blood contains 120 mM Na/kg water. The chloride of *Sialis* tissues is immeasurably small, but the blood also contains relatively little.

In frog muscle, and probably also in *Sialis*, the potassium and chloride are in a Donnan equilibrium with the same ions in the blood, but in *Potamon*, the intracellular concentration of chloride is rather higher than the Donnan equilibrium con-centration.

The muscles of freshwater teleosts contain moderate quanti-ties of both free amino acids and trimethylamine oxide. Con-trary to the earlier belief that trimethylamine oxide did not occur in freshwater fish, the quantities of trimethylamine oxide appear to be of the same order as in marine fish, or even elasmobranchs (Anderson and Fellers, 1952; Parry, 1961).

Ionic equilibria in the freshwater coelenterate, *Pelmatohydra*, and in the freshwater ciliate, *Spirostomum*, have been investi-gated with the aid of radioactive tracers (Lilly, 1955; Carter, 1957). In many respects, these two animals may be compared with the individual cells of the higher Metazoa. Unlike the tissues of Metazoa, both animals are hyperosmotic to the sur-rounding medium, but this would not affect ionic equilibria provided that the water balance were maintained. Both *Pelmato-*

hydra and *Spirostomum* were found to accumulate potassium to a considerable degree. The sodium content of *Pelmatohydra* is almost independent of external concentration in solutions of 0.1–5.5 mM Na/l. In low concentrations, sodium is accumulated, and in higher concentrations excluded from the animal.

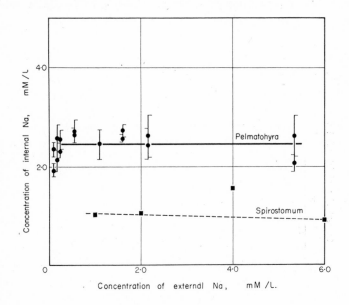

Fig. V.13. *Pelmatohydra* and *Spirostomum*. Relation between the internal sodium concentration and the sodium concentration in the external medium. *Pelmatohydra* from Lilly, 1955; *Spirostomum* from Carter, 1957.

The sodium concentration in *Spirostomum* is more or less constant in external concentrations varying from 1.2–4.1 mM Na/l. but the experimental range of concentrations was not sufficiently wide to decide if *Spirostomum* could accumulate sodium at low concentrations (Fig. V.13). *Pelmatohydra* accumulates [82]Br* over the range 0.1–2.6 mM/l., but the animals did not survive

* For technical reasons, [82]Br was used in place of a chlorine isotope; it is assumed that the animal treats both halides alike.

in higher concentrations of bromide. In interesting contrast to this, *Spirostomum* excluded [82]Br over the experimental range 1.7–4.6 mM/l. (Fig. V.13). If it is capable of accumulating bromide, it can only be at exceedingly low concentrations.

Carter (1957) points out that, in the solutions used, which contained more than 1 mM/l. of both sodium and bromide

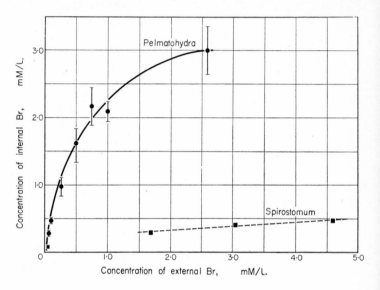

Fig. V.14. *Pelmatohydra* and *Spirostomum*. The relation between the internal bromide concentration and the concentration of bromide in the external medium. *Pelmatohydra* from Lilly, 1955; *Spirostomum* from Carter, 1957.

ions, *Spirostomum* behaved very like metazoan striated muscle or nerve cells, accumulating potassium and excluding sodium and bromide ions. In addition, the potassium and halide ions were roughly in a Donnan equilibrium. However, the variations of potassium efflux with external concentration (see below) do not support the hypothesis of a Donnan equilibrium. *Pelmatohydra* differs from *Spirostomum* in accumulating bromide (Fig. V.14), but the coelenterates contain a mesogloea which may resemble the extracellular fluids of the higher Metazoa.

TABLE V.20. — IMPORTANT OSMOTIC CONSTITUENTS OF TISSUES OF SOME FRESHWATER ANIMALS

Animal	Tissue	Concentrations of ions in the tissues, mM/kg water						Amino acids	Other N Cpds.	Total, as % blood	Author
		Na	K	Ca	Mg	Cl	PO_4				
Anodonta cygnaea[1] ...	Fast adductor muscle	5.3	21.3	12	4.5	2.4	20	3	–	100	Potts, 1958
Potamon niloticus[1] ...	Muscle	44	111	n. d.	n. d.	32	78	170	42 TMO	78	Shaw, 1959b
Sialis lutaria[1]	All tissues	1	135	7	35	<1	n. d.	n. d.	n. d.	52	Shaw, 1955b
Rana temporaria[1] ...	Muscle	13	140	5	14	1	49	10	Carnosine 16	100	Harris, 1960, p.143.
Salmo salar[1]	Muscle	20.5	264	2.5	n. d.	3.2	n. d.	49*	46 TMO	100	Parry, 1961 a, Cowey, Daisley and Parry, 1962
Pelmatohydra oligactis[2]	Whole animal	2.5	14	n. d.	n. d.	1.5	n. d.	n. d.		45	Lilly, 1955
Spirostomum ambiguum[2]	Whole animal	1	7	n. d.	n. d.	0.3	n. d.	n. d.			Carter, 1957

1. mM/kg water
2. mM/l. water

The efflux of sodium from *Pelmatohydra* in distilled water cannot be explained in terms of a one-compartment system, and it is possible that some of the sodium and bromide is in the mesogloea, and not in the cells (Lilly, 1955). The sodium content of *Pelmatohydra* remains constant in a wide range of external concentrations, but the halide content varies. At higher external concentrations, the halide content of the cells must be considerable. In this respect, *Pelmatohydra* differs from *Spirostomum*.

With the exception of frog tissues, only a few measurements are available of the fluxes of ions through the cells of freshwater animals (Table V.21). In frog muscle, the sodium efflux is maintained by an active process working against an electrochemical gradient. Keynes (1954) estimated that sodium extrusion requires 0.025 cal/g muscle/hr at 11°C, or about 16% of the resting metabolism of the muscle. As the potassium is in a Donnan equilibrium across the fibre membrane, no energy is required and the passive influx is equal to the passive efflux. Changes in the

TABLE V.21. — THE IONIC FLUXES THROUGH THE CELLS OF SOME FRESHWATER ANIMALS

Cells	Temp. °C	Ion	Extracellular conc. mM/l.	Intracellular conc. mM/l.	Rate const. (h⁻¹)	Efflux mM/l. /hr	Author
Frog muscle	17	K	2.5	88	0.2	17.6	Keynes, 1954
,, ,,	17	K	5.0	99	0.32	31.6	,, ,,
,, ,,	17	Na	117	13	0.67	8.7	,, ,,
Anodonta ventricle ...	5	Na	14.7	7.1	4.6	3.3	Potts, 1959
Pelmatohydra		Na	1	2.5	0.35	0.875	Lilly, 1955
		K	0.054	14	0.20	2.8	,, ,,
Spirostomum	18	Na	1	1.02	12.2	12.4	Carter, 1957
	18	Na	6	0.91	12.4	11.3	,, ,,
	18	K	0.04	3.0	0.35	1.05	,, ,,
	18	K	1.00	9.4	0.27	2.54	,, ,,

external potassium concentration, by altering the resting potential of the muscle, affect the electrochemical potential of the potassium on either side of the membrane (Chap. I, p.31), and therefore alter the efflux (Table V.21). In *Anodonta* ventricle, the efflux of sodium also takes place against an electrochemical gradient and the energy required, 0.046 cal/g/hr, is similar to that of frog muscle, but very much less than the energy required by the marine lamellibranch *Mytilus*.

It is not possible to calculate the energy required to maintain ionic equilibrium in *Pelmatohydra* and *Spirostomum*, because the potentials across the body walls have not been investigated.

The efflux of sodium from *Pelmatohydra* is of the same order as that from frog or *Anodonta* muscle, if allowance is made for the different internal concentrations, although in *Pelmatohydra* it is probably the influx which is actively maintained. In contrast, the flux of sodium through *Spirostomum* is very large, and is independent of the external sodium concentration. If the flux takes place by exchange diffusion (Carter, 1957), the rate would be limited by the low internal concentration.

The fluxes of potassium are of the same order of size in both *Pelmatohydra* and *Spirostomum*, and are comparable with those in frog muscle. The effluxes from *Spirostomum* are roughly proportional to the internal concentrations of potassium. This suggests that the resting potential of *Spirostomum* is low, and that potassium is lost by simple diffusion down a concentration gradient. If the potassium were in a Donnan equilibrium, an increase in the external potassium concentration, by lowering the resting potential, should increase the efflux even if the internal potassium concentration were unchanged (Table V.21, lines 1-2). This does not appear to be so (Table V.21, lines 9-10).

Amino acids in the tissues play a part in intracellular regulation in *Eriocheir*, as in the brackish water invertebrates *Carcinus*, *Mytilus* and *Arenicola* (Chap. IV, p.158). If *Eriocheir* is transferred from fresh water to sea water, the concentration of intracellular amino acids is increased and the cells are able to maintain a relatively constant volume. Isolated nerves of *Eriocheir* similarly show the same response to increased salinity by increasing the concentration of free amino acids. It is not the increase in osmotic concentration of the extracellular fluids *per se* which induces the response, as the addition of sucrose to the perfusing fluid does not produce the salinity response. Since isolated tissues can react in this way, the response cannot be hormonally controlled and the origin of the amino acids must be intracellular (Schoffeniels, 1960 a).

Freshwater Eggs and Embryos

The eggs of marine animals are usually permeable to both water and salts, while those of freshwater animals (and of their terrestrial descendants) are often relatively impermeable. Embryonic life continues for a longer period in fresh water than in sea water so that the regulatory mechanisms necessary for life in fresh water are functional at hatching, and the eggs are provided with a greater quantity of yolk to make this extended development possible. In addition to the food materials in the yolk, a greater proportion of the ions required for development are also supplied.

Trout eggs on laying take in an additional 18% water (Manery and Irving, 1935), but after this the eggs have been regarded as impermeable to both water and salts. This conclusion was based on the observation that the eggs did not show volume changes after immersion in media of different salinities (Gray, J., 1932; Svetlov, 1929). However, the experiments of Krogh and Ussing (1937) showed that the eggs were permeable to heavy water during the first 6 hours after hatching, relatively impermeable for the following 12 days (at 10°C) and then showed an increasing permeability as development proceeded. As the volume remains constant during this time, there must also be an excretion of water. Additional evidence for the movement of water in the embryo during the development, is shown by the fact that the water content of the embryo at hatching is greater than that of the yolk at laying (Gray, J., 1932; Hayes, 1949). The same is probably true of amphibian eggs (Table V.22) (Needham, 1950).

TABLE V.22. — WATER ABSORPTION DURING DEVELOPMENT IN SOME FRESHWATER EMBRYOS

(From Needham, 1950, p.38)

Species	Wet weight of yolk	Additional water	Weight of embryo	Calculated organic combustion
Salmo trutta	1·0	+ 0·7	= 1·56 +	0·14
Salmo salar	1·0	+ 1·5	= 2·34 +	0·16
Ambystoma	1·0	+ 0·74	= 1·88 +	0·07

The chorion of the trout and other teleost eggs is a mechanical structure produced at laying. The membrane of the egg maintains a concentration difference of 258 mOsm/kg water inside to only 11 mOsm/kg water outside (Gray, 1932). This membrane has a potential difference of 13–18 mV, inside negative. If the eggs are transferred to distilled water, the potential increases to 60–100 mV (Pumphrey, 1931). After hatching, the total osmotic concentration of the body fluids of the embryo increases to 296 mOsm/kg water (Busnel, Drilhon and Raffy, 1946; Parry, 1961 a).

The volume of the fluid in the sub-chorionic space varies with the composition of the medium and is larger in eggs fertilised in soft water than in those fertilised in hard water. Although in many marine teleost eggs, the fluid in this space has the same composition as the medium, in salmon and trout eggs, it has a total osmotic content and a sodium concentration several times higher than the medium, at least during the first day after fertilisation (Parry and Swift, pers. comm.).

Some inorganic ions are also taken up during development. Calcium and sodium are both absorbed from the medium by salmon eggs, since the final quantities of these ions are four times and three times, respectively, their quantities in the newly-laid eggs. On the other hand, phosphate and potassium are lost during development (Hayes, Darcy and Sullivan, 1946). The eggs of the giant salamander *Cryptobranchus* also take up calcium, which increases during development from 0.64 mM/egg to 1.28 mM/egg (Needham, 1950, p.39).

Frog eggs on laying are almost isosmotic with the adult body fluids (Backmann and Runnstrom, 1912), but immediately after laying the osmotic concentration drops sharply (from 240 to 180 mOsm/l.). The volume increases by 15–20% during the first 2 to 4 hours after laying. This swelling practically ceases after the first cleavage, but is resumed again after about 24 hours. After 2 days, the osmotic concentration of the egg begins to increase and by the fifth day is almost back to the initial concentration. This increase in concentration is not due to an increase in chloride concentration, but must be attributed to organic solutes. After hatching, the water content increases but the osmotic concentration is maintained, due at least in part, to the active uptake of chloride, which begins when the gills first appear (Krogh, Schmidt-Nielsen and Zeuthen, 1938). The perivitelline fluid is almost isosmotic with the external medium, but the slightly higher osmotic concentration of the frog perivitelline fluid (*ca.* 4 mM Cl/l.) may account for the increase in the volume of the perivitelline space during development.

CHAPTER VI

OSMOTIC REGULATION
IN TERRESTRIAL ANIMALS

Introduction

Osmotic regulation in land animals is dominated by the urgent need to conserve water. Several aspects of osmoregulation common to all animals, are most appropriately discussed here, because our knowledge of tetrapod and insect physiology is more intensive than that of other groups. In consequence, a major section of this chapter deals with glandular secretion and ionic regulation in the tissues.

The transition from an aquatic to a terrestrial life has been made several times, and some animal groups have radiated into an immense variety of form. The most successful of these invaders, insects, tetrapods and terrestrial arachnids, are found first in the Devonian period. The radiation of some later arrivals, such as the operculate gastropods, the onchidiid slugs (Opisthobranchiata), the isopods and the crabs, has been more limited. A remarkable variety of other groups has also become adapted to life on land, even though their representatives may be confined to damp habitats. These include the earthworms, leeches, Onycophora *(Peripatus)*, triclad platyhelminths *(Terricola)*, nemertines *(Geonemertes)*, nematodes, and even an ostracod *(Mesocypris)* (Harding, 1953). The operculate gastropods have established several independent radiations on land, including the Heliciidae, Cyclophoridae, Pomatiasidae, and Hydrobiidae.

Osmotic Pressure of the Blood

The variety of blood concentrations in terrestrial animals reflects to some degree their several independent invasions of this environment. The tetrapods are directly descended from the freshwater fishes, and the concentrations of all tetrapod body fluids, like those of freshwater fishes, are approximately equivalent to $\frac{1}{4}$ or $\frac{1}{3}$ sea water (Tables V.1 and V.2). Crabs such as *Birgus* or *Coenobita*, which are completely terrestrial as adults, have much higher blood concentrations, which may be indicative of their recent marine origin. The high concentrations found in the completely terrestrial isopods, such as *Oniscus* or *Porcellio*, suggest that their ancestors colonised the land directly from the shore, as *Ligia* does today. The insects have much lower electrolyte concentrations, even including forms such as *Petrobius* which lives on the shore (Table VI.1). It is possible that the insects are descended from freshwater ancestors, although it has been suggested that they evolved for a time in the interstitial water in the soil (Croghan, 1959). Soft-bodied land animals such as earthworms, living in damp habitats, are in some ways analogous to freshwater animals and have low blood concentrations (see also Chap. V, p.166).

The Composition of the Blood

In most groups of terrestrial animals, the greater part of the osmotic pressure of the blood is accounted for by sodium and chloride ions (Table VI.2). The concentrations of potassium are usually small, so that the ratio Na/K is 20 or more; the concentration of magnesium is usually less than 5 mM/kg water; and the concentration of sulphate so low that it is generally not assayed. In these respects, terrestrial animals resemble freshwater animals. Even in the littoral *Ligia*, the concentrations of magnesium and sulphate are less than half those in sea water, although the blood is slightly hyperosmotic to sea water.

TABLE VI.1. — OSMOTIC CONCENTRATIONS OF THE BLOOD OF SOME
LAND ANIMALS

Animal	Blood concentration mOsm/kg water		Author
	Mean	Range	
Gastropoda:			
Helix pomatia	228	183–252	Rouschal, 1940
Limax maximus	134	—	Rouschal, 1940
Annelida:			
Pheretima posthuma ...	–	220–270	Bahl, 1945
Crustacea:			
Ligia oceanica	1156	807–1324	Parry, 1953
Oniscus sp...............	560	436–672	Parry, 1953
Porcellio sp.	700	672–737	Parry, 1953
Birgus latro	*ca.* 900*	*ca.* 640–1230*	Gross, 1955
Arachnida:			
Euscorpius italicus......	607	580–638	Rouschal, 1940
Tegenaria atrica.........			
Insecta:	407	—	Croghan, 1959
Petrobius sp.	426	—	Croghan, 1959
Mantis religiosa.........	477	455–500	Rouschal, 1940
Tenebrio mollitor			
(adult)	527	504–545	Rouschal, 1940
Amphibia:			
Bufo vulgaris	239	—	Botazzi, 1906
Reptilia:			
Testudo graeca	321	—	Burian, 1910
Aves:			
Gallus domesticus	–	299	Korr, 1939
Mammalia:			
Homo sapiens	285	—	Smith, 1956

* Recorded as 90% „sea water" etc.

Analyses of body fluids of several earthworms have been published recently (Kamemoto, Spalding and Keister, 1962). The blood of *Lumbricus terrestris* living in soil contains 85.7 ± 6.6 mM Na, $5.5 + 1.0$ mM K, 8.3 ± 1.5 mM Ca and 39.0 ± 8.3 mM Cl/l. The coelomic fluid has a lower concentration of sodium, potassium and calcium.

The concentration of chloride in earthworm body fluids is very low compared with either the sodium concentration or the total osmotic pressure (Bahl, 1947; Ramsay, 1949 a and b); the

16

TABLE VI.2. — COMPOSITION OF THE BLOOD OF SOME LAND ANIMALS

Animal	Blood composition, mM/kg or mM/l.						Amino acids	PO$_4$	Author
	Na	K	Ca	Mg	Cl	HCO$_3$			
Ligia oceanica	586	14	36	21	596	—	—	5	Parry, 1953
Tegenaria atrica	207	9.6	—	—	193	—	—	—	Croghan & Lockwood, 1959
Petrobius sp.	208	5.8	—	—	194	—	—	—	Lockwood & Croghan, 1959
Aeschna sp. (larva)	135	5.4	7.5	6.0	120	—	—	—	Duchâteau, Florkin & Leclerq, 1953
Periplaneta sp.	156	7.7	4.2	5.4	144	—	—	—	Van Asperen & Esch, 1956
Bombyx mori (larva)	3.4	41.8	12.3	40.4	14	—	—	—	Duchâteau, Florkin & Leclerq, 1953
Helix pomatia.........	113	4	11	13.4	—	24.2	—	—	Jullien et al.,1955; Florkin&Duchâteau, 1950
Rana temporaria......	104	2.5	2	1.2	74.3	30	0.7	3	Conway, 1945
Rattus rattus	140	6.4	3.4	1.6	119	24.3	3	2.3	Conway & Hingerty, 1946

anion deficit is probably made up by organic acids. Croghan
(1959) has pointed out that soils are cation exchange materials
of considerable capacity, and the concentration of available
anions in the interstitial water will be very small compared with that of the cations. The low concentration of
chloride in earthworm blood may be an adaptation to the
low concentrations of chloride available in the surrounding
medium.

The composition of insect blood is peculiar in several
respects (Table VI.2). Many insects, particularly herbivorous
forms, have very high concentrations of potassium in the
blood, while at the same time, the concentration of sodium
is low, so that the Na/K ratio may be less than unity (see
extensive collection of data by Duchâteau, Florkin and Leclerq,
1953). The Na/K ratio appears to be related to the diet:
omnivorous and carnivorous forms contain higher concentrations of sodium than herbivores, and in *Periplaneta* the Na/K
ratio varies with the diet (Tobias, 1948 a), although in *Tenebrio*
it is independent (Boné, 1944). Insect blood is notable for
a high concentration of magnesium (probably bound) and for
a low concentration of chloride, but the blood of the morphologically primitive insects, e.g. the Odonata and *Petrobius*,
have relatively high concentrations of chloride (Table VI.2).
This high chloride concentration is probably a physiologically
primitive character, and is not in accord with Croghan's suggestion that the low chloride content relates to the evolution
of the group in the interstitial fauna (see above, p.226). In
those insects with a low chloride content, the mineral anion
deficit is made good by a high concentration of amino and
other organic acids. Florkin and his associates have shown
that the individual amino acids present, and their total concentrations, vary from species to species, and even between
individuals of the same species reared on different diets, or
in different environments (Florkin in Levenbook, 1958;
Schoffeniels, 1960 a). Insect blood also contains large quantities
of phosphate compounds.

16*

Water Loss

General

Land animals lose water continuously by evaporation, unless the air is saturated and at the same temperature as the animal. Death by desiccation is avoided by adaptations of three kinds: first, many land animals reduce or avoid water loss by restricting their activities to damp habitats; secondly, land animals are usually more resistant to the effects of desiccation than are aquatic ones; and thirdly, land animals reduce evaporative and urinary losses by physiological adaptations.

Any crack or crevice, such as the space under a fallen leaf, may retain a higher humidity than the surrounding air, while air in the interstices of even apparently dry soil is usually saturated. By remaining in such microclimates, except in periods of high humidity, animals may avoid dry air altogether. This is true not only of small invertebrates, but also of some mammals. The kangaroo rat, *Dipodomys merriami*, can survive on a dry vegetable diet, provided the humidity does not fall below 20% (Schmidt-Nielsen and Schmidt-Nielsen, 1951). During the day, this animal lives in burrows where the humidity is high and where the low temperature obviates the need for thermoregulation by evaporation. Some anurans, such as *Heleioporus*, *Neobatrachus* and *Scaphiopus*, survive in arid regions by burrowing into the earth and remaining quiescent during dry periods (Bentley, Lee and Main, 1958; Thorson, 1955).

All land animals are fairly tolerant of the effects of desiccation, but this ability is best developed in those animals which are least able to avoid water loss, such as snails or land crustaceans, or in desert animals which may have limited access to water. When man is desiccated, the volume of blood becomes reduced and the increasing viscosity of the blood slows the circulation. At high temperatures, this interferes with the removal of heat from the body, and death through excessive overheating ensues when only about 10% of the body water has been lost. At lower temperatures, man and most other mammals may survive the loss of up to 20% of the body water, but then death follows from lowered plasma volume and the subsequent circulatory failure, and from uraemia with phosphate retention. In contrast to other mammals, the camel can survive the loss of up to one third of its body water, even at high temperatures (Schmidt-Nielsen, 1959). Even when the camel is desiccated, its blood volume is not significantly reduced, e.g. a camel which lost 50 litres of water had a blood volume reduced by only 1 litre. It is not known how the blood volume is maintained in these circumstances, but either solutes must be added to the blood, or solutes extracted from the tissues. Among the birds, the mourning dove, *Zenaida*, can tolerate a 24% water loss (Bartholomew and Dawson, 1954).* Among the amphibians, the vital limit of water loss is highest in the more terrestrial species. For example, *Scaphiopus holbrookii*, which inhabits semi-desert regions, may lose 60% of the body water before death, while the terrestrial *Hyla regilla* has a vital limit of 50% of its body water, and the aquatic *Rana grylio* one of only 38% (Thorson and Svikla, 1943). It is not clear if it is the water loss *per se* which is the cause of death in amphibians, or the concomitant increase in the blood concentration, or some other indirect effect. However, the tissues of *Scaphiopus* must be tolerant of the large changes in blood concentration. Some lizards are similarly tolerant of changes in concentration. The plasma sodium of *Trachysaurus rugosus* may increase from 152 mM/l. in the fully hydrated animal, to 196 mM/l. in the dry season, or even to 233 mM/l. in an animal which has been drinking saline water. These increases have apparently no ill effects (Bentley, 1959).

Terrestrial crustaceans can also tolerate a high degree of desiccation. The land crab, *Gecarcinus lateralis*, dies only when the water loss is equal to 22% of the body weight, equivalent to perhaps 30% of the body water (Bliss, quoted by Edney, 1957). As desiccation proceeds, the salt concentration in the blood must increase, and the tissues must be able to function

* The Savannah sparrow *Passerculus* can survive serum concentrations as high as 490-610 mOsm/1. (Paulson and Bartholomew, 1962).

in a wide range of concentration. The shore isopod, *Ligia oceanica*, can survive with a blood concentration as low as 775 mOsm/kg water, or as high as 1870 mOsm/kg water (Parry, G., 1953), and the blood concentration of the snail, *Helix aspersa*, is similarly variable from 97 mOsm/kg water after rain, to 330 mOsm/kg water in dry weather (Potts, unpublished). Some animals can tolerate extreme desiccation; for example, the freshwater leech *Ozobranchus* can lose 4/5 of its weight during exposure to dry air and rehydrate within 5 hours (Oka 1922).

In addition to the water lost by evaporation, there is a further loss in the urine and in the faeces. In the mammals and birds, the development of a high body temperature and its concomitant regulation by evaporative cooling, has aggravated their problems of water conservation. These animals have curtailed water losses in many different ways.

Respiration and Evaporation

Most of the evaporative water loss takes place through the respiratory surfaces. The rate of diffusion of oxygen through dry protein, or dry chitin, is very small compared with that through hydrated protein or chitin, and respiratory surfaces are usually kept moist while the rest of the body surface is relatively water-proof. Water loss from the respiratory surfaces may be reduced by the development of internal respiratory systems with controlled openings, so that the circulation of air over the respiratory surfaces may be reduced to a minimum. In those insects whose spiracles can be closed, the spiracles are opened only for short intervals (Wigglesworth, 1953, p.434). Increased activity, by increasing the time during which the spiracles are kept open, also increases the rate of water loss. In amphibians, reptiles and pulmonate snails breathing is discontinuous, while mammals and birds restrict losses during respiration by keeping the depth of ventilation to a minimum. Carbon dioxide accumulates in the semi-stagnant respiratory organs of terrestrial animals and the high concentration of bicarbonate in their blood can be correlated with this (Table VI.2).

In the kangaroo rat *Dipodomys*, the loss from the lungs is five times the loss from the skin, while in the rattlesnake it is only two and a half times the loss from the skin (Chew, 1961). Homoiothermic animals lose more water than poikilotherms during respiration, because the vapour pressure of water increases rapidly with temperature. The kangaroo rat *Dipodomys* may possibly recover some of the water vapour lost from its lungs, by condensation on the nasal mucosa, which has a temperature of only 24°C when the ambient temperature is the same (Chew, 1961). It is not clear how this low temperature is maintained, but some form of heat exchange with the surrounding air is conceivable.

Water loss through the rest of the body surface may still be significant, although the permeability is low compared with that of the respiratory surfaces. In insects, spiders and ticks, the permeability of the exoskeleton is reduced by the presence of a wax or lipoid layer in the epicuticle and if this layer is damaged, the permeability of the cuticle is greatly increased. In many species, the permeability of the cuticle increases rapidly above a certain critical temperature, probably as the result of a change of state of the waterproofing layer (Ramsay, 1935; Beament, 1945). No such wax or lipoid layer has been found in the cuticle of terrestrial crustaceans where the rate of water loss is always much greater (Fig. VI.1). In land vertebrates the skin is waterproofed by a layer of keratin. Among the amphibians, the more terrestrial species have less permeable skins than the more aquatic ones (Thorson, 1956.) The permeability of the skin of amphibians is closely controlled through the agency of hormones (Chap. IX, p.346). In the reptiles, total water loss varies from about 0.2% body weight/hr* in the arid zone snake *Masticophis flagellum*, to 2%/hr* in the skink *Eumices inexpectatus*, which is normally

* At 37°C and 37% relative humidity.

confined to damp habitats. Immediately prior to ecdysis, when
the skin structure is presumably damaged, water loss in snakes
doubles (Bogert and Cowles, 1947). The protective function of
the keratinised layer of the skin is summarised by Gray's gener-

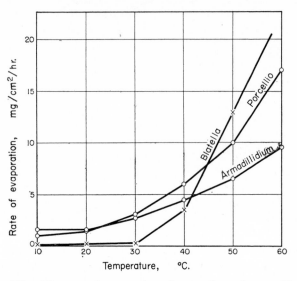

Fig. VI.1. The rate of evaporation of water from the woodlice
Armadillidium and *Porcellio* and the cockroach *Blatella* at temperatures from 10° to 60°C in dry air. The animals were exposed for
one hour periods. From Edney, 1957.

alisation that an intact newt loses water as rapidly as a skin-
ned lizard (Gray, J., 1928). In mammals and birds, the permeability of the surface is very low indeed (Trolle, 1937). The
total water loss (including respiratory loss) from desert
reptiles, rodents and amphibians is in the ratio 1:10:40 (Chew,
1961).

Nitrogen Excretion

Aquatic animals generally eliminate waste nitrogen as ammonia, but ammonia is toxic at even moderate concentrations. Terrestrial animals usually convert their waste nitrogen into a more harmless compound which can be excreted in a concentrated form, although some terrestrial isopods lose ammonia gaseously. Amphibians and mammals excrete mainly urea; insects, pulmonate snails, birds and most reptiles, uric acid; and spiders excrete guanine. The alligator excretes considerable amounts of ammonia, and the chelonians a mixture of ammonia, urea and uric acid. It is significant that in the alligator, dehydration reduces ammonia excretion, and within the chelonians, there is a transition from a predominantly ammonia and urea excretion in aquatic forms, to a predominantly uric acid excretion in the more terrestrial ones. For example, a semi-aquatic species, *Emys orbicularis*, excretes 47% of its waste nitrogen in the form of urea and only 2.5% as uric acid, while *Testudo graeca*, living in semi-arid conditions, excretes 52% as uric acid and 22% as urea (Coulson and Hernandez, 1955; Moyle, 1948).

Amphibians cannot form a hyperosmotic urine (Chap. II. p.48) and so the concentration of urea in the urine could not exceed *ca.* 250 mM/l. (1.5% solution); and probably rarely reaches this level; nitrogen excretion therefore requires a considerable volume of water. Mammals can produce a hyperosmotic urine containing up to 1.3 M/l. (8% solution) in man, or 3.6 M/l. (20% solution) in the kangaroo rat (Schmidt-Nielsen and Schmidt-Nielsen, 1951), and can therefore excrete more nitrogen per volume of water, but the water loss is still important. Further water economies are made by the camel in times of stress, apparently by the reconversion of urea to protein by the gut flora. When the camel is fed on dry vegetable matter, the urine flow can be as small as 500 ml/day. In these circumstances, the urea output is greatly reduced. Even ingested urea fails to appear in the urine but it is not known whether the kidney resorbs the urea from the urine or whether the filtration rate is reduced. The maximum concentration of urea in camel urine is not known (Schmidt-Nielsen *et al.*, 1937).

Uric acid is much more insoluble than urea, and when concentrated, precipitates out before it can exert any considerable osmotic pressure. Reptiles and birds usually resorb most of the water in the urine and eliminate a semi-solid mass of uric acid crystals, and the insects often excrete quite dry uric acid, thus eliminating nitrogen without the loss of any water. Terrestrial isopods excrete considerably less nitrogen than aquatic isopods or amphipods in comparable conditions, and this reduction in nitrogen metabolism may be an adaptation to terrestrial conditions, but it is not clear whether it is brought about by a change in diet or by a reduction in protein assimilation. The land isopods are peculiar in that they excrete 50–80% of their nitrogen as gaseous ammonia, although uric acid is found in the tissues (Dresel and Moyle, 1950).

Terrestrial animals usually have a low rate of urine production compared with freshwater ones. This is a consequence of these modifications of the nitrogen metabolism, combined with the absence of a problem of endosmosis. For example, the toad *Bufo bufo* on land, has a rate of urine production of 0.1 ml/kg/hr, only 1% of the rate when it is immersed in water (Jørgensen, Wingstrand and Rosenkilde, 1956). This antidiuresis may be the result both of a reduction of the filtration rate and an increase in the rate of tubular resorption (Chap. IX, p.345) (Heller, 1956; Sawyer, 1956). Further resorption of water can take place from the bladder, which acts as a reservoir (Dawson, 1951; Bentley, 1958 b). The rate of urine production is low in terrestrial reptiles even when they have access to water, and urine production may almost stop in dehydrated animals. For example, Bentley (1959) found that the lizard, *Trachysaurus rugosus*, produced urine at a rate of 0.57% body weight/hr when hydrated, but at only 0.024%/hr when deprived of water. Antidiuresis in reptiles is brought about by a reduction in filtration rate, and some further resorption of water may take place in the cloaca. In the fowl, the rate of urine production is about 3% body weight/hr (Dixon, 1958). Antidiuresis may be brought about by a reduction in filtration rate and increased tubular resorption, but there is no cloacal resorption in birds (Korr, 1939).

Faeces

Although the gut contents of most terrestrial animals are quite fluid, water resorption takes place in the hind end of the intestine and rectum. Many insects produce quite dry faeces as the result of water uptake by the rectal glands. In land isopods, the faecal pellets are usually moist, but the water content is less in the more terrestrial forms (Edney, 1957). In man, water loss in the faeces is between 50 and 200 ml/day, about one tenth the water loss in the urine.

Thermoregulation

Mammals and birds lose a great deal of water in controlling body temperature. The water may be lost either from the sweat glands, or by forced ventilation from the respiratory system. In man, loss from sweat may vary from 50 ml to 4 litres/day, at higher levels exceeding losses from all other sources (Adolph, 1947).

Unlike the kangaroo rat, the camel is unable to avoid the full heat of the day, but it does reduce its water loss in various ways. Although camels regulate temperature by sweating when adequate water is available, if they are dehydrated, the body temperature may be allowed to rise as high as 41°C (105°F) during the day, and to fall as low as 34°C (93°F) at night. The tolerance of the higher temperature during the day conserves a considerable amount of water and also reduces further heat gain from the environment and the low temperature at night delays the onset of sweating the following day. Thick hair on the back of the camel reduces solar heating, but the thin hair below aids heat loss. In the same way, the concentration of dermal fat into a dorsal hump facilitates thermoregulation. These adaptations are very effective in reducing the need to sweat, but the camel must still lose a lot of water in thermoregulation when air temperatures rise above 43°C (110°F). As a result of all these adaptations, the camel can go without water indefinitely in winter, and survive for at least 17 days in the summer without drinking (Schmidt–Nielsen, 1959). It is worth emphasising that the camel does not store water, and that its water reserves are similar to those of other ruminants, neither does it store proportionately larger amounts of fat, in spite of the hump.

The rate of water loss in birds is even higher than in mammals, because the body temperature is higher (38–44°C), and the rate of respiration is also higher. There are no sweat glands, but thermoregulation in some species is achieved by panting (Chew, 1961). As in the camel, water may be saved by allowing some rise in body temperature; for example, some passerines can tolerate a 3°C rise above their normal temperatures (Dawson, 1954).

Summary

The relative importance of the different routes of water loss are very variable. It has been estimated that a 70 kg man may lose each day 300–400 ml from the lungs, 350–700 ml by direct loss from the skin, 600–2000 ml through the kidneys, 50–200 ml in the faeces, and 50–4000 ml in the sweat (Adolph, 1947). In cool conditions, the losses through kidneys, lungs and skin are all of the same order of size, and other losses are negligible; but in hot conditions, the sweat loss is of overwhelming importance. In comparison, it has been estimated that in both the adult grass-hopper, *Gastrimargus*, and in the pupa of the moth, *Bombyx mori*, about two thirds of the water loss takes place through the spiracle and one third through the body wall, mainly at the intersegmental membranes (Koidsumi, K., 1935); water loss in the faeces in these insects is probably very small.

Water Uptake

Animals may gain water by eating and drinking, by the oxidation of foodstuffs, or by uptake through the body wall.

Even apparently dry food, such as grain, may contain as much as 20–30% water. Many insects and the kangaroo rat *Dipodomys* are entirely dependent on this and on the water produced by the oxidation of food. Food materials contribute different amounts of water: e.g. one gram of fat yields 1.07 g of water on oxidation, 1 g of carbohydrate, 0.60 g water. On the other hand, protein produces ammonia as well as water on oxidation, and the excretion of the ammonia as urea or uric acid may consume more water than the protein produces.

Some terrestrial animals take up water through the body wall. Frogs with access to water do not drink, but rely entirely on water taken up through the skin. The rate of water uptake is dependent on the degree of dehydration and is controlled through pituitary hormones. Immersion in water is not essential, for example, *Rana* can take up water or salts from wet paper (Adolph, 1932, 1933) and *Bufo* from damp moss (Sawyer, 1956). However, actual contact with water seems to be necessary, since dehydrated amphibians cannot take up water even in high humidities (Adolph, 1932; Thorson, 1956), but the rate of water uptake appears to be almost independent of the area of skin exposed to the water (Adolph, 1927). The Australian lizard, *Moloch horridus*, is said to take in water directly through the skin after rain (Buxton, 1923).* Some reptiles take up water from moist soil (Chew, 1961), but most have to depend on drinking (Adolph, 1943; Bogert and Cowles, 1947).

Many terrestrial crabs visit the sea periodically for drinking or to wet their gills. *Birgus latro* exercises some choice of drinking water, in that when presented with sea water or fresh water, it shows a preference for fresh water when its blood concentration is high, and for sea water when it is

* Water is taken up from the skin by capillarity along fine open channels which run over the skin towards the lips; if the mouth is closed water uptake is prevented (Bentley and Blumer, 1962).

low (Gross, 1955). If a partially desiccated *Pachygrapsus* is allowed to drink hyperosmotic sea water, the blood concentration is reduced (Gross, 1957). This is probably the result of drinking the water and excreting the salt, rather than by taking up water alone against a concentration gradient.

Spiders and woodlice have the ability to suck up water from a moist surface against the capillary attraction of the substrate; for example, lycosid spiders are able to drink against pressures of up to 600 mm mercury (Parry, D. A., 1954) and terrestrial woodlice can drink water from a surface of moist plaster of Paris (Spencer and Edney, 1954). In *Ligia*, most of the drinking is anal, rather than oral (Edney, 1957). Woodlice have capillary channels on their uropods which enable them to transfer water from a wet surface to the respiratory surfaces, thus conserving their own water reserves.

Some insects, for example *Tenebrio* (Mellanby, 1932), and ticks, *Ixodes*, (Lees, 1946) can take up water from air which is not fully saturated. In most cases, this faculty is feebly developed but the rat flea, *Xenopsylla brasiliensis*, can take up water from air of only 50% relative humidity (Edney, 1947). The mechanism for taking up water from unsaturated air is not known. The vapour pressure of an aqueous solution is less than that of water, and a solution will therefore take up water vapour from saturated or nearly saturated air. However, a 1% solution of sodium chloride is in equilibrium with a relative humidity of 99%, and such a process would be insufficient to account for the hygroscopic powers of some insects and ticks. Beament (1954) has proposed a static mechanism to account for this, but the process must be energy consuming, and the phenomenon is as yet unexplained (Edney, 1957, p.65).

Salt Gain and Loss

Terrestrial animals are generally dependent on their food to replace lost salts. Most land plants do not accumulate sodium and chloride ions to any extent, although they do accumulate potassium. For this reason, herbivores tend to be chronically short of sodium and chloride. The low concentration of sodium in the blood of herbivorous insects reduces their sodium requirements and also indirectly helps to reduce sodium loss in the urine. On the other hand, herbivorous tetrapods retain a high concentration of sodium and chloride in the blood, and they must reduce sodium and chloride losses from the sweat and urine to a minimum in order to conserve these ions. To replace lost salt, many herbivorous animals will eat or lick rock salt if it is available.

Mammals can produce a urine containing a high concentration of salts in addition to urea, and can thus eliminate excess electrolytes with little water loss. The concentration of chloride in the urine of the kangaroo rat may reach 900 mM/l. (Schmidt-Nielsen and Schmidt-Nielsen, 1951), or even 1900 mM/l. in the urine of the North American "desert rat", *Psammomys* (Schmidt-Nielsen, 1960 a). Many birds and reptiles can secrete very concentrated solutions of salt from specialised head glands (Chap. VII, p.303) but this faculty is more or less confined to some marine species, although the domestic duck retains the glands and can secrete a solution containing 640 mM Cl/l. from the nasal glands (Scothorne, 1959 a).

Some Other Body Fluids

In addition to the principal extracellular fluid, blood plasma and its associated lymph, the vertebrate body elaborates several other fluids, such as the cerebrospinal fluid around and inside the central nervous system, the perilymph and endolymph in the ear, and the humours of the eye.

Cerebrospinal Fluid

The origin and composition of the cerebrospinal fluid has been described in detail by Davson (1956). It contains almost no protein (0.25 mg/g), in contrast to plasma (65 mg/g), but

TABLE VI.3. — THE RELATIVE CONCENTRATIONS OF VARIOUS IONS IN A
DIALYSATE OF THE BLOOD PLASMA, THE CEREBROSPINAL FLUID, AND THE
AQUEOUS HUMOUR OF THE RABBIT. THE CONCENTRATION OF EACH ION IN
THE PLASMA IS TAKEN AS UNITY

(Davson, 1956 p.67)

Ion	Dialysate of plasma	Cerebrospinal fluid	Aqueous humour
Sodium	0.945 ± 0.003	1.03 ± 0.005	0.96 ± 0.01
Potassium	0.96 ± 0.005	0.52 ± 0.04	0.95 ± 0.02
Calcium	0.65 ± 0.02	0.33 ± 0.01	0.58 ± 0.005
Magnesium	0.80 ± 0.02	1.21 ± 0.05	1.015 ± 0.04
Chloride	1.04 ± 0.01	1.21 ± 0.007	1.015 ± 0.01
Bicarbonate	—	0.97 ± 0.04	1.26 ± 0.03

it differs significantly from a plasma ultrafiltrate or dialysate
(Table VI.3). In particular, the concentrations of sodium and
chloride are greater than in plasma, but the potassium concentration is less. The differences are therefore not the result of a
Donnan equilibrium, but must be actively maintained. The
cerebrospinal fluid is secreted by the choroid plexi into the
ventricles, and is then passed through foramina to the outside
of the brain where it is absorbed in the subarachnoid spaces.
The rate of production and resorption is considerable. In man,
the cat and the dog, the fluid is secreted and resorbed at a
rate between 0.2% and 0.4% of the total volume/minute. In
man, ^{24}Na injected into the blood accumulates in the cerebrospinal fluid at a rate corresponding to 0.41%/minute. In
contrast, potassium turnover is only about 0.2%/minute; either
potassium penetrates more slowly, or some of it is lost by
exchange with the surrounding tissues. It is difficult to compare the osmotic concentration of the cerebrospinal fluid directly
with that of the blood because of their very different protein
contents, but it is 3% hyperosmotic to the aqueous humour,
which is itself slightly hyperosmotic to the plasma (Davson
and Purvis, 1954; Auricchio and Bavany, 1959). It seems probable that the ions are actively secreted and that the water
enters down an osmotic gradient.

The Eye Fluids

The aqueous humour is thought to be secreted by the ciliary body lying around the circumference of the lens just behind the iris. The aqueous humour drains into the venous system by the canal of Schlemm, which lies in front of the iris at the corner of the anterior chamber. The rate of secretion—absorption is about 1%/minute in a variety of animals. The aqueous humour is only about 5 mOsm/l. hyperosmotic to the plasma (Auricchio and Bavany, 1959), but the permeability of the blood–aqueous humour barrier is very low, and it is not certain if the concentration difference is sufficient to explain the water movement. Like the cerebrospinal fluid, the aqueous humour contains very little protein (0.31 mg/g) but differs from a plasma ultrafiltrate (Davson, Duke-Elder and Maurice, 1949). Its composition depends on a dynamic equilibrium between the rate of secretion of ions into the posterior chamber, and the rates of diffusion into the other parts of the eye. The freshly secreted aqueous humour in the posterior chamber has a different composition to the bulk in the anterior chamber; Kinsey (1960) has suggested that the initial secretion in the rabbit may contain 93 mM HCO_3/l. and only 53 mM Cl/l., although the fluid in the anterior chamber contains 34 mM HCO_3/l. and 100 mM Cl/l. The fluid in the anterior chamber approximates to an ultrafiltrate of the blood,* but the differences are still significant (Table VI.3). In general, animals with small eyes have a smaller concentration of chloride and a greater concentration of bicarbonate in the aqueous humour, than those with large eyes (Davson, Matchett and Roberts, 1952). Davson points out that in small eyes, the relative volume of aqueous humour to lens is smaller, and therefore the buffering required against the lactic acid produced by the lens is greater (Davson, 1956).

The vitreous humour is similar to the aqueous humour in electrolyte composition, except that it has a higher potassium concentration (9 mM/l.) (Kinsey, 1960). In contrast to the eye fluids, the lens has the composition of a giant cell. The

* Because it is approaching Donnan equilibrium with the plasma.

17

frog lens contains 116.9 mM K/kg water, 17.3 mM Cl/kg water and 23.9 mM Na/kg water. The interior of the lens is 75 mV negative to the aqueous humour (Andrée, 1958 a and b). The potassium and chloride are approximately in a Donnan equilibrium with the aqueous humour, but the sodium must be actively extruded.

Perilymph and Endolymph

The perilymph in the ear is very similar to the cerebrospinal fluid in ion and protein content. As in the central nervous system, some of the ions must be transported against an electrochemical gradient.

TABLE VI.4. — SODIUM, POTASSIUM AND CHLORIDE CONTENT OF THE CEREBROSPINAL FLUID, PERILYMPH AND ENDOLYMPH OF THE GUINEA PIG (Expressed as mM/l. Smith *et al.*, 1954)

Fluid	Sodium	Potassium	Chloride
Cerebrospinal fluid	152	4.2	1.22
Perilymph	150	4.8	121.5
Endolymph	16	144	107

In marked contrast to the perilymph, endolymph contains a very high concentration of potassium and a correspondingly smaller amount of sodium (Table VI.4). This is a most unusual composition for an extracellular fluid. The functional significance of the high potassium in the endolymph is unknown, but the concentration differences between endolymph and perilymph are accompanied by a potential difference of 50-80 mV, endolymph positive (Bekesy, 1952). The only ion which could be in equilibrium between the two fluids is sodium, and chloride and potassium must be maintained against electrochemical gradients. The potential difference is probably the result of active transport of potassium into the endolymph. This active transport of potassium has been related to the high level of carbonic anhydrase present in the inner ear (Erulkar and Maren, 1961).

Secretions

Tears, sweat, saliva, bile and the pancreatic and gastric juices all have certain features in common. In each case, the primary secretion of the gland appears to be almost isosmotic with the blood but of a significantly different composition. This primary secretion may be modified later by back diffusion or by resorption, so the composition of the definitive fluid may vary with the rate of its secretion.

Tears

Human tears are approximately isosmotic with the blood, but the ionic composition is significantly different from serum (Fig. VI.2). While sodium concentration is similar to that of plasma, the potassium concentration is three times greater. The composition of the tears is almost independent of the rate of flow. The urea content is slightly lower than that of the serum (Thaysen and Thorn, 1954), but the glucose content

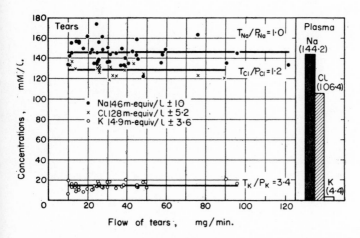

Fig. VI.2. The composition of human tears at different rates of secretion. The mean values of the concentrations of sodium, potassium and chloride in the plasma are included for comparison.
From Thaysen and Thorn, 1954.

is very much smaller (2.6 mg/100 ml. compared with 100 mg/100 ml.) (Giardini and Roberts, 1950). Both glucose and urea probably enter by diffusion.

Pancreatic juice

The exocrine secretions of the pancreas are a small volume of enzyme juice, and a larger volume of an alkaline solution. The information available always relates to the mixed secretions, but except at very low rates of secretion, the electrolyte composition is dominated by the alkaline component.

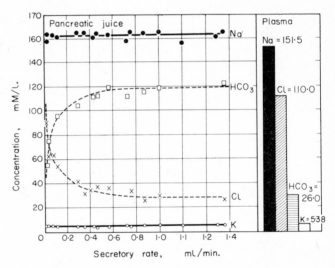

Fig. VI. 3. The variation of the composition of the dog's pancreatic juice with the rate of secretion. For comparison the sodium, potassium and chloride content of the plasma are included. From Bro-Rasmussen, Killman and Thaysen, 1956.

Most of our knowledge of mammalian pancreatic juice is based on investigations in the dog. The concentration of sodium is similar to that in plasma (Fig. VI.3), and is independent of the rate of secretion; the concentration of potassium is similar, but a little higher. On the other hand, the concentrations of chloride and bicarbonate vary considerably with the rate of secretion. At very low rates, the concentrations of chloride and bicarbonate are similar to serum concentrations, but at high rates, the chloride concentration is only one third that of the blood, while the bicarbonate concentration is four times as high (Fig. VI.3). It is suggested that sodium in the primary secretion is similar to serum, but bicarbonate is high and chloride low. At high rates of secretion, the juice passes through the ducts so rapidly that little exchange of chloride and bicarbonate takes place, and the juice approximates to the primary secretion. At low rates, chloride diffuses in and bicarbonate diffuses out, so that the secretion becomes similar to the plasma (Thaysen *et al.*, 1954). The main function of the bicarbonate is to neutralise the gastric acid but very little is known about the mechanism of this bicarbonate secretion.

The concentration of urea in the pancreatic juice is only slightly lower than in the blood (Bro-Rasmussen, Killmans and Thaysen, 1956) but the concentration of sugars in the juice is much lower, as in tears.

Saliva

The saliva is produced by a number of pairs of glands which show considerable differences in their secretion. Saliva may be isosmotic with the blood, as in the rat parotid, or hypo-osmotic, as in the rat sub-maxillary (Schneyer and Schneyer, 1961). Human parotid saliva (Thaysen, Thorn and Schwartz, 1954) resembles both sheep submaxillary saliva (Kay, 1960) and dog submaxillary saliva (Gregerson and Ingalls, 1931), and may be taken as typical of a common type of salivary secretion.

The composition of human parotid saliva varies with the rate of flow. It is always hypo-osmotic to the serum, and its sodium and chloride content are always less (Fig. VI.4), but the concentrations increase with increasing rates of secretion, approaching those of the serum. In contrast, potassium, which is always about five times higher than in the blood, is almost independent of the rate of secretion. The bicarbonate concentration increases with the rate of secretion and at the max-

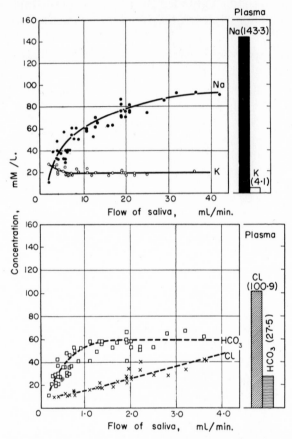

Fig. VI.4. The variation of the composition of human parotid saliva with the rate of flow. For comparison the sodium, potassium and chloride concentrations in the plasma are included. From Thaysen, Thorn and Schwartz, 1954.

imum rate is considerably higher than in the serum (Fig. VI.4).

The variation of sodium and chloride content of saliva with the rate of secretion is explicable on the hypothesis that they are resorbed from the primary secretion by a system of strictly limited capacity. If the rate of sodium secretion of the tear gland is plotted against the rate of fluid secretion, the result is necessarily a straight line passing through the origin (Fig. VI.5a) because the concentration of sodium in tears is constant. If the rate of sodium secretion in saliva is plotted against the rate of secretion, a straight line is obtained, but

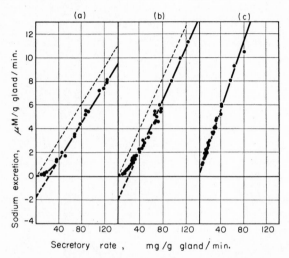

Fig. VI.5. Sodium secretion (μM/g/min) as a function of the secretory rate (mg secretion/g/min) in (a), the parotid salivary gland, (b) the sweat gland and (c) the human lachrymal gland From Bro-Rasmussen, Killman and Thaysen, 1956.

when this is extrapolated, it cuts the y-axis below the origin (Fig. VI.5a). It is probable that the primary secretion contains a constant concentration of sodium, and therefore the rate of sodium secretion is proportional to the rate of secretion of saliva (dotted line in Fig. VI.5a), but that sodium is resorbed from the primary secretion at a constant rate independent of the rate of flow. The intercept of the straight line with the y-axis is thus a measure of the rate of sodium resorption. The deviation of the line at low rates of secretion can reasonably be explained, either by the inability of the resorbing mechanism to function against very steep concentration gradients, and/or as the result of the back diffusion of sodium into the saliva. The primary secretion contains a high concentration of both bicarbonate and chloride ions, but both are abstracted by the resorbing mechanism along with the sodium (Fig. VI. 4). Chloride is resorbed first in preference to bicarbonate, but when the chloride level has fallen, bicarbonate is also taken up. It is possible that both these ions follow the sodium ions passively. The chloride ion is smaller than the bicarbonate, and so might be expected to move more rapidly.

When the ducts of the dog sub-maxillary gland are poisoned by a retrograde injection of mercuric chloride, sodium resorption is stopped, and the saliva resembles the plasma in composition. The potassium content is lower than that of the normal saliva, indicating that the sodium resorption is associated with some secretion of potassium (Henriques, 1961).

By using a very delicate technique of stopping and suddenly restarting the salivary secretion, Brasilow and Cooke (1959) have shown that the concentration of sodium depends on the time it spends in the duct. When the secretion was restarted, the first drops were of fluid which had been lying in the duct; the longer it had been there, the lower was its concentration. Resorption may take place in the striated or interlobular ducts of the glands (Bro-Rasmussen *et al.*, 1956). Striated ducts are absent, or almost so, in the rabbit parotid salivary gland, the canine sublingual salivary gland, both of which produce isosmotic saliva, and in the pancreatic and lachrymal glands which also produce isosmotic secretions.

Further evidence in favour of the resorption theory is provided by the observation of Albrectson and Thaysen (1955) that at moderate and high rates of secretion, the concentration of urea in the saliva is about two thirds that in the serum, but at low rates, the concentration in the saliva rises above that in serum. Urea probably enters by diffusion, hence the concentration in saliva is usually less than in serum, as in tears and pancreatic fluid, but at low rates of secretion, when the hypo-osmotic saliva lingers in the ducts, water will be lost by osmosis and inert constituents concentrated.

It is argued from the rate of appearance of injected ^{24}Na and ^{42}K in saliva, that potassium secretion is a primary process in saliva formation, and that a considerable influx of ions takes place in the ducts (Burgen, Terroux and Donger, 1959). It is not clear how this hypothesis can be correlated with Thaysen's picture of salivary secretion.

Although acinar secretion followed by resorption in the ducts explains most observations, glands lacking acini, as in the juvenile rat, can secrete saliva at almost the rate of glands of the adult rat. This saliva is hypo-osmotic to the blood but contains a high concentration of potassium (Schneyer and Schneyer, 1961).

The interior of the cells of the resting sublingual gland of the cat are about 30 mV negative to the outside medium, and about 55 mV negative when the gland is stimulated. The lumen of the gland in the resting stage is a few mV positive to the medium, but on stimulation, it becomes negative, the direction and magnitude of the change of potential in the lumen and inside the cells being similar (Lundberg, 1956). These glands produce an isosmotic saliva and the results are not complicated by resorption from the ducts. Lumberg suggests that chloride ions are actively transported into the cells, and thence into the lumen, and that cations follow passively. Secretion stops if nitrate is substituted for chloride in the medium, but it takes place normally if only half the chloride is replaced. This favours his theory that the primary secretion is formed by the active transport of chloride.

Sweat

The secretion of sweat shows many similarities to the secretion of saliva. At low rates of secretion, the sweat is very hypo-osmotic to the blood, but at high rates the sodium and chloride concentrations in the sweat approach that of the blood. This can be interpreted as the result of secretion, followed by resorption of sodium and chloride by a mechanism of limited capacity (Fig. VI.5c). As in salivary secretion, the primary secretion is rich in sodium but contains much more potassium than the serum (Fig. VI.6). The level of urea in sweat is

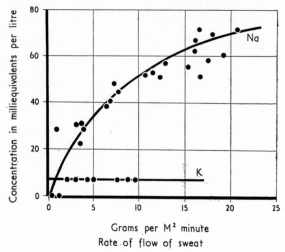

Fig. VI.6. The variation of the composition of human sweat with the rate of secretion. From Schwartz and Thaysen, 1956.

usually similar to that in serum but sometimes may be more concentrated, probably as the result of diffusion of water from the hypo-osmotic sweat back into the blood (Schwartz, Thaysen and Dale, 1953). The rate of sweat production in man is estimated to vary from 50 to 4000 ml/day (Adolph, 1947). It is curious that the resorptive capacity of the sweat glands should be so limited, because at high rates of secretion, the salt loss can be serious, even though at low rates all the salt is carefully recovered.

Gastric Juice

The stomach produces two secretions: an acid secretion from the oxyntic cells, and a smaller volume of an enzyme solution

from the parietal cells. The electrolyte content of the latter
is similar to that of the blood. The gastric secretion resembles
pancreatic secretion in that the composition varies with
the rate of production, although it remains almost isosmotic with the blood (Fig. VI.7) (Lifson, Varco and Vis-

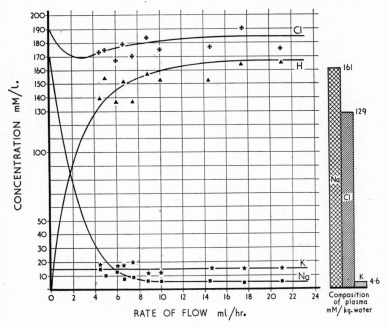

Fig. VI.7. The variation of the composition of cat gastric juice
with the rate of secretion. The lines adapted from Teorell, 1947
to fit the data of Gudiksen, 1943.

scher, 1941). At high rates of secretion, the gastric juice
approximates to 0.15 N hydrochloric acid. Teorell (1939,
1940, 1947) has suggested that the primary secretion is
strongly acid, but after it is formed the back diffusion
of hydrogen ions in exchange for sodium substantially reduces the acidity at low rates of secretion. In confirmation
of this hypothesis, he showed (1939) that when hydrochloric
acid was placed in the stomach, a considerable exchange of

sodium ions for hydrogen ions occurred, and the rate of loss of acidity was proportional to the concentration of hydrogen ions. This exchange of sodium for hydrogen in gastric juice (Fig. VI.7) is analogous to the exchange of bicarbonate for chloride in pancreatic juice (Fig. VI.3). Teorell's hypothesis predicts that the chloride concentration would be minimal at moderate rates of secretion. At very high rates, the gastric juice would approximate to the primary secretion, slightly hyperosmotic to the blood, while at very low rates, it would be osmotically equilibrated. At moderate rates, the inward diffusion of hydrogen ions proceeds more rapidly than the outward diffusion of sodium ions, and would remove some of the chloride from the gastric secretion, making it slightly hypo-osmotic both to the serum and to the primary secretion. The osmotic concentration is, in fact, minimal at moderate rates of secretion (Lifson et al., 1941). The low acidity at minimal rates of acid secretion is also due, in part, to dilution by the non-acid secretion of the stomach.

The problem of the origin of the secreted hydrogen ions has attracted a great deal of attention. The acid is secreted by the parietal cells and histochemical work has shown that the interior of the cells is not acid. Secretion into the stomach is accompanied by the liberation of an equivalent quantity of bicarbonate on the outer, serosal side, of the stomach (Davies, 1951).

Davenport (1939) and Davies (1948) have shown that the parietal cells contain a very large concentration of carbonic anhydrase, several times as high as the concentration in the erythrocytes. It has therefore been suggested that the acid originates from the dissociation of carbonic acid, the bicarbonate being passed back into the blood in exchange for chloride which accompanies the hydrogen ions. Carbonic anhydrase by itself, however, could not produce a 0.15 N solution of acid so that some ions must be actively transported.

More recently, Davies (1951) has suggested that the hydrogen ions are formed from the ionisation of water within the cells. The hydrogen ions might then be secreted into the stomach, while the hydroxyl ions are passed back into the blood to be neutralised by hydrogen ions formed from the ionisation of carbonic acid. The net effect would be the formation of bicarbonate ions on the serosal side of the stomach. On this view, the function of the carbonic anhydrase is the production of carbonic acid at a sufficient rate to mop up the hydroxyl ions produced by the cells.

It has often been suggested that the hydrogen ions might be derived from an organic acid produced by metabolism, but at least two, and perhaps as many as twelve equivalents of hydrochloric acid, are produced for each equivalent of oxygen consumed (Davies, 1948), so that sufficient hydrogen ions could not be produced in this way.

Conway (1953) and others (e.g. Patterson and Stetton, 1949) have suggested that hydrogen ions are derived from the hydrogen atoms removed in the dehydrogenation of metabolites and are secreted into the lumen of the stomach by a redox pump (see Chap. I, p.35).

The gastric potentials suggest that chloride is actively transported into the stomach in advance of the hydrogen ions, which are then transported down the diminished electrochemical gradient. In the dog, the mucosa (toward the stomach lumen) is about 70 mV negative to the serosa (toward the blood), but during secretion the potential difference is reduced to about 55 mV (Rehm, 1945). When the stomach wall is short-circuited, the current flowing in the external circuit is proportional to the net flux of chloride ions minus the net flux of hydrogen ions. The high potential recorded when there is no secretion, suggests that the chloride pump is continuously active, but secretion may be negligible because the permeability of the stomach wall is low to cations. Only when the hydrogen pump comes into action can secretion take place. Any activity of the hydrogen pump will tend to reduce the potential across the stomach wall, although Rehm, Hokin, Graffenried, Bajandas and Coy (1951) suggest that the fall in potential during secretion may be due to the greater rate of diffusion of hydrogen ions back from the lumen, compared with the rate for chloride ions. The flux ratios of sodium and potassium across the gastric mucosa are proportional to their electrochemical potentials (Hogben, 1955); in other words, the sodium and potassium enter the gastric juïce by diffusion, but the small potassium ion diffuses more easily than the larger sodium ion, and so it will become concentrated relative to the blood. Although the potential produced by the chloride pump will attract hydrogen ions into the stomach, it is far too small to account for the acidity produced, since a potential of 58 mV could not produce a difference of more than 1 pH across the stomach wall. The relation between oxygen consumption and the production of gastric acid is discussed in Chap. VIII, p.339.

Bile

The electrolyte composition of the bile has attracted little attention, but the few analyses available show that it is similar in composition to the pancreatic juice. Recently, Wheeler, Ramos and Whitlock (1960) have shown that the concentration of bicarbonate in bile increases with increasing rates of secretion, while the concentration of chloride declines. This suggests that the primary secretion is rich in bicarbonate, but that this ion is exchanged for chloride after secretion. A further exchange of bicarbonate for chloride takes place in the gall bladder during storage of the bile (Herman, Wilson and Kazyak, 1957). The bile is quite alkaline, but the volume produced in man is only one fifth that of the equally alkaline pancreatic juice, so it is not so important as a neutraliser of the gastric juice. Other intestinal secretions are produced by the duodenal glands, and the crypts of Lieberkuhn. Little is known of their composition but they appear to be similar to plasma in electrolyte composition.

Discussion

The salivary, lachrymal, sweat and gastric glands, and the pancreas have many features in common. In each case, the primary secretion of the gland is almost isosmotic with the serum. The lachrymal, salivary, pancreatic and sudoric secretions all contain large amounts of sodium and smaller amounts of potassium. Maximum rates of secretion of tears, sweat, saliva and pancreatic juice are all about 0.1 ml/g/minute (Bro-Rasmussen, Killmans and Thaysen, 1956); the rate of gastric secretion has not been accurately determined in terms of weight of secreting cells. The only electrical measurements available, for salivary and gastric glands, suggest that it is the anions which are actively transported, while the cations either follow passively or, in the case of the gastric hydrogen ions, are lifted over the energy barrier by some accessory mechanism. Potassium is usually more concentrated in the secretions than in the serum, while sodium has a similar or lower concentration. This may be due to the smaller size and greater rate of diffusion of the potassium ion. The very low concentration of sodium in gastric juice shows that the mucosa must be relatively impermeable to it, but in spite of this, a considerable exchange of hydrogen ions for sodium ions takes place after the secretion has been elaborated. Sodium and chloride are resorbed from the primary secretion in both sweat glands and salivary glands, producing a hypo-osmotic definitive solution.

The secreted ions are accompanied in each case by a large movement of water due either to osmosis or electrosmosis. The active transport of ions may create minute osmotic gradients which might be sufficient to account for the flow of water. At high rates of secretion, the gastric juice is slightly but significantly hyperosmotic to the serum, supporting the osmotic hypothesis (Lifson *et al.*, 1941). However, it is difficult to reconcile the osmotic theory with the observation that very moderate hydrostatic pressures will prevent gastric secretion, although it is possible that the hydrostatic pressure could produce a balancing back flow through pores in non-secretory parts of the mucosa (Öbrink, 1956). Alternatively, water may accompany the passage of ions by a process of electrosmosis. Urea and sugars enter the secretion by diffusion, but may be concentrated when water is lost by exosmosis from hypo-osmotic secretions such as saliva or sweat.

Milk

Milk is almost isosmotic with the blood, but differs considerably in composition. Both electrolytes and organic substances vary from species to species, within a single species, and in any individual during the process of lactation. The colostrum produced early in lactation differs from the later milk secretion in having a higher concentration of electrolytes and higher globulin content, but less lactose. Both colostrum and milk contain less electrolytes than the serum (Table VI.5).

TABLE VI.5. — ELECTROLYTE COMPOSITION OF HUMAN COLOSTRUM AND MILK. EXPRESSED AS mM/KG WATER
(Macie, 1949)

Fluid	Sodium	Potassium	Calcium	Magnesium	Chloride
Colostrum	24.2	21.1	13.3	1.9	18.3
Milk	8.3	14.5	9.6	1.5	11.7
Plasma*	142	5	5	3	103

*From Smith, 1956

Some of the osmotic difference is made up by organic compounds, particularly sugars. In human milk, these organic compounds amount to 12% of the total weight. The high concentration of calcium in human milk, much of it organically bound, must be brought about by some specific calcium transport system, but the concentration of other ions in milk is similar to that in sweat. Physiologists have been more interested in the origin of the organic components of milk (see Kon and Cowie, 1961) and there has been little speculation on the process of electrolyte secretion. The non-protein nitrogen in milk and blood are almost the same, and it is suggested that it might be formed by direct filtration and later modified in the ducts. The similarity to sweat suggests that it may be formed by a secretion resorption process. If water is not freely available to the lactating mammal, the composition quickly changes due to body dehydration (Ling, Kon and Porter, 1961).

The Internal Salt and Water Balance

Water Absorption in the Gut

The salivary glands, the gastric mucosa, liver and pancreas pour a torrent of secretion into the gut, but practically all these liquids, together with all the water and salts in the food and drink, are resorbed in the intestine. In man, the total quantity of liquid passing into the gut probably amounts to 10 litres a day (Table VI. 6), of which all but about 100 ml are resorbed.

Water and salts exchange rapidly across the intestinal mucosa. If distilled water is placed in the gut, sodium, chloride and bicarbonate ions pass through into the gut, while water passes into the blood, until the fluid in the gut becomes almost isosmotic. Hyperosmotic solutions of sodium chloride tend to become isosmotic by the movement of salt into the blood and the movement of water into the solution. Isosmotic solutions of autogenous sera are absorbed, but become slightly hypo-osmotic in the process (Visscher, Raepke and Lifson, 1945). These results suggest that while the gut wall is permeable to both water and salts in either direction, ions are actively transported in one direction only, from the gut to the blood. When a mixture of sodium chloride and sodium sulphate, or sodium chloride and mannitol, isosmotic with the blood, is placed in the gut, chloride and an equivalent amount of sodium is resorbed while the sulphate or mannitol remains in the gut. As the gut contents become depleted of chloride, concentration gradients of as much as 100:1 may be established (Ingraham and Visscher, 1936). As the chloride concentration falls, the flux decreases

18

and the rate of water resorption is correspondingly reduced. The gut wall is relatively impermeable to magnesium, although active uptake can take place to a small degree (Ross, 1961). The inability of the gut to absorb large quantities of sulphate or magnesium ions or to remove water from their solutions is one of the explanations of the fame of Epsom salts (magnesium sulphate).*

Most of the observations of salt and water movement in the gut are explicable on the hypothesis that ions are actively transported, while water moves passively down the osmotic gradients. However, when a hyperosmotic solution is introduced into the gut, water uptake begins before the solution becomes hypo-osmotic (Visscher et al., 1945), and water absorption can occur in the rat when the gut contents are as much as 90 mM/l. hyperosmotic to the blood (Parsons and Wingate, 1958). It has been suggested that the active uptake of ions produces local increases in the concentration of the plasma, sufficient to draw in water by osmosis (Durbin, Curran and Solomon, 1958). The uptake of water seems always to be linked with the uptake of ions, so that water cannot be taken up from hyperosmotic solutions of sodium sulphate.

Visscher et al. (1945) measured the fluxes of sodium and chloride in both directions across the dog ileum, and found that the fluxes were not proportional to the concentrations (Chap. I. p. 19, Equation 1), but their conclusion that chloride transport was active and sodium transport passive was unsound in the absence of simultaneous measurements of the potential difference across the gut wall (cf. Chap. I, p.20, Equation 2). More recently, it was shown that in the guinea pig, sodium is actively transported, but as the sodium transport exceeds the short circuit current, it is probable that chloride is actively transported as well (Ussing and Andersen, 1955).

In the mammal, the contents of the gut remain roughly isosmotic to the blood, although in the colon, where uptake of salt and water is most active, the contents may be slightly

* It also affects the muscle activity of the intestine.

hypo-osmotic. The rectum contents appear to be about isosmotic with the blood (Dempsey, Carroll, Albright and Henneman,
1958).

Less is known of the electrolyte metabolism of other vertebrates. The active uptake of sodium from the gut lumen has
been demonstrated in the turtle, the toad and the frog (Ballien
and Schoffeniels, 1961; Ussing and Andersen, 1955; Cooperstein,
Chalfin and Hogben, 1957).

Other Internal Salt and Water Movements in Animals

The internal movements of salt and water are known only in
the mammals and one insect, and in both of these quantities
of water and salt secreted and resorbed internally are vastly
greater than the net exchange with the environment.

It is interesting to try to assess the osmotic and ionic activity
which takes place. A man weighing 76 kg (12 stones) may
contain 50 l. of water, of which about 3.5 l. will be in the
plasma (Smith, 1956). The salivary secretion may exceed 2 l./
day, the gastric secretion is about $1\frac{1}{2}$ l./day, the pancreatic
secretion 1 l./ day, and the bile 200 ml/day (Table VI.6). All but
100 ml lost in the faeces are resorbed in the lower part of the
intestine. Along with the water, about one third of a mole of
sodium chloride is secreted and resorbed, together with smaller
amounts of potassium. The quantity of bicarbonate secreted
exceeds the amount of acid, and the neutralisation of the two
must make the mixture slightly hypo-osmotic to the blood.

The quantity of fluid and electrolytes secreted and resorbed
by the gut is much less than that resorbed in the kidney, where
the clearance rate of inulin in man is of the order of 183 l./day
(Smith, 1956). Of this, 181.5 l. are resorbed by the kidney,
mostly while the ultrafiltrate is similar in its composition to
the blood. The totals of ionic work performed by the gut and
by the kidney are probably similar. In man, about 5% of the
total sodium intake is lost in the faeces, about 15% of the
potassium, 50% of the magnesium, 30% of the phosphate and
18*

TABLE VI.6. — SECRETION AND RESORPTION OF ELECTROLYTES
IN THE ADULT HUMAN GUT

Volume l./day	Concentrations, mM/l.					Total quantity, mM					Author
	H^+	Na^+	K^+	Cl^-	$HCO_3^=$	H^+	Na^+	K^+	Cl^-	$HCO_3^=$	
Saliva 2	—	30	20	20	30	—	60	40	40	60	Schneyer,1956
Gastric juice 1½	100	50	10	160	—	150	75	15	240	—	Hirschowitz et al., 1957
Pancreatic juice......... 1	—	150	5	25	130	—	150	5	25	130	Kepcs et al., 1956
Bile .... 0·2	—	150	5	70	85	—	30	—	14	17	Kepcs et al., 1956
Total after neutralisation 4·7						315	60	319	57		
Lost in faeces 0·1	—	50	50	50	50	—	5	5	5	5	Dempsey et
Resorbed...... 4·6						310	55	314	52		al., 1958

most of the calcium, the rest being excreted by the kidneys (Dempsey *et al.*, 1958). The proportions of calcium, magnesium and phosphate excreted by the gut are independent of the amount eaten, so the gut plays an important part in ionic balance.

The large flux of water and salt in the mammalian gut and kidney is analogous to that of *Carausius*, where the malpighian tubes secrete and resorb the equivalent of all the potassium in the blood every three hours, and all the body water each day (Ramsay, 1955 b) (Chap. II, p.86).

The Composition of the Tissues

The tissues of land vertebrates are similar in composition to those of their freshwater relatives; most of the osmotic pressure is contributed by potassium ions and phosphate compounds, while free amino acids are present only in small amounts. The few analyses of insect muscle available present a similar picture, in spite of the fact that insect blood may contain high concentrations of potassium and amino acids. Nothing is known about the tissues of animals which have body fluids of high osmotic pressures, such as woodlice or scorpions and which might be expected to contain more free amino acids than other land animals.

Vertebrate Tissues

Striated muscle — Vertebrate striated muscle has been analysed more extensively than any other tissue. The concentrations of practically all the osmotically effective constituents have been assayed, and the proportion of extracellular fluid determined (Table VI.7). Conway and McCormack (1953) showed, by extrapolation back to zero time, that the osmotic pressure of mammalian muscle was the same in life as that of the plasma, although after death autolysis caused the osmotic pressure to rise. The autolysis could be prevented by 0.1% mercuric chloride. Maffly and Leaf (1959) showed that the muscle remained isosmotic with the serum if it was frozen rapidly. The assayed constituents of rat muscle would produce an osmotic pressure slightly greater than that of the plasma (Table VI.7, col. 4), but most of the calcium and magnesium are un-ionised (Chap. I, p.42). The potassium and chloride are evidently in a Donnan equilibrium, and the Donnan ratio is about 24:1, corresponding to a resting potential of 80 mV, in good agreement with a measured potential of 83 mV (Paul, 1960). The ionisation of the constituents varies with pH, and cations and anions are in electrical equilibrium at a pH of about 6.5 (Conway, 1950).

Heart muscle and smooth muscle — Whole heart muscle contains considerably larger amounts of sodium and chloride than whole striated muscle, but the two muscles are difficult to compare since analyses of heart muscle are rarely accompanied by estimates of the extracellular space. In cat heart muscle, the sodium space is larger than in striated muscle and is equi-

TABLE VI. 7. — COMPOSITION OF THE PLASMA AND MUSCLES OF
THE RAT AND FROG

(Expressed as mM/kg water)

Ion	Rat			Frog		
	Serum[1]	Whole striated muscle[1]	Intracellular striated muscle[1]	Serum[2]	Intracellular striated muscle[2]	Intracettular smooth muscle[3] (stomach)
Sodium	150	35.3	16	109	15.5	66
Potassium	6.4	132	152	2.6	126	129
Calcium	3.4	2.1	1.9	2.1	3.3	—
Magnesium	1.6	14.3	16.1	1.3	16.7	—
Chloride	119	21.1	5.0	77.9	1.2	14
Carbonate	24.3	3.3	1.2	26.6	0.4	—
ATP	—	8.5	9.8	—	4.8	—
Phosphocreatine	—	31.8	36.9	—	38.5	—
Other acid sol. P. cpds.	2.3	22.4	26	3.2	—	—
Anserine	—	26.4	30.7	—	—	—
Carnosine	—	11.4	2.1	—	16.4	—
Urea	7	7	7	—	—	—

1. Conway & Hingerty, 1946
2. Conway, 1945
3. Botzler & Levine, 1958

valent to 37% of the water content, and the chloride space to
38%, while in dog heart muscle, the comparable figures are
24% and 22% (Darrow, Harrison and Taffel, 1939). The extracellular space in human heart muscle is also larger (20-24%)
than in striated muscle, where it is only 10% of the water
content (Harris, 1960 p.176). If the potassium and chloride in heart
muscle are in a Donnan equilibrium, the sodium content must
be very small (Table VI.8). For example, if it is assumed that
the extracellular space in cat heart muscle is 36% of the water
content, then the potassium and chloride concentrations inside
the muscle cells are 152 and 4 mM/kg water, respectively (in
Donnan equilibrium with the plasma), while the sodium concentration is only 2 mM/kg water (Table VI.8). It is more likely
that the extracellular space is less than this, in which case the

TABLE VI.8. — THE SODIUM, POTASSIUM AND CHLORIDE CONTENT
OF SOME MAMMALIAN TISSUES
(Expressed as mM/kg water)

Ion	Cat serum[1]	Whole heart[1]	Intracell. heart conc.[2]	Cat nerve, sheath water[3]	Cat nerve, fibre water[3]	Ox, whole A/V bundle[4]
Sodium ...	161·7	59·4	1·8	245	41	198
Potassium	4·6	94·3	145	5–7	181–3	114
Chloride...	128·7	48·7	3·6	190–210	17·5–0	—

1. Darrow *et al.*, 1939
2. Calculated from columns 2 and 3, assuming 36% of water is extracellular.
3. Krnjevic, 1955
4. Davies *et al.*, 1952.

intracellular sodium and chloride concentrations will be larger,
but the potassium then cannot be in a Donnan equilibrium.

Smooth muscle contains high concentrations of sodium and
chloride. The potassium and chloride ions in this muscle are
not in a Donnan equilibrium; for example, in the muscle of
frog stomach, the intracellular concentration of chloride is
several times higher than the equilibrium concentration (Table
VI.7). After treatment with calcium chloride solutions, the
muscle of frog's stomach becomes permeable to inulin, but
the cells retain a considerable concentration of potassium; it
is suggested that the potassium is mainly bound, but this raises
osmotic problems, unless most of the water is bound as well
(Botzler and Levine, 1958). If this were also the case, the similarity in composition of striated and smooth muscle would
depend on two entirely different mechanisms. Whole smooth
muscle of mammals also contains a very high concentration of
sodium and chloride (Daniel and Singh, 1958; Table VI.8).
Simultaneous measurements of the potassium content of rabbit
uterus smooth muscle and of the resting potential of the muscle
fibres, show that the potassium is not in electrochemical equilibrium (Daniel and Robinson, 1960). When the external solution
contains 4.5 mM K/kg water and 145 mM Na/kg water, the
smooth muscle of the uterus contains 139 mM K/kg water

and 8.5 mM Na/kg water. If the potassium were in electro-chemical equilibrium, the resting potential should be about 90 mV negative but the measured potential is only 50 mV. This implies either that some of the potassium is bound, or that potassium is actively accumulated by the muscle fibres.

In the muscle of rabbit intestine, the chloride space is 48% of the water content (Manery and Bale, 1941), and in the cat, 64% (Prosser and Sperelakis, 1958). The inulin space of guinea pig taenia coli muscle was 36% of the total volume, or about 45% of the water content (Bulbring and Born, quoted by Holman, 1957).

Nerve — The sodium, potassium and chloride concentrations inside cat nerve fibres, and in the liquid surrounding the fibres but inside the nerve sheath, have been estimated by Krnjevic (1955). His results are compatible with a Donnan equilibrium between the potassium and chloride inside the fibres and in the extracellular fluid, but they raise several osmotic problems (Table VI.8, col. 6). The sum of the concentrations of sod-ium, potassium and chloride in the fluid inside the nerve sheath amounts to 450 mM/kg water, compared with about 320 mM/kg water in the plasma. The sum of these ions in the axoplasm amounts to only 230 mM/kg water, but allowance must be made for organic anions which will balance the high concentration of potassium. Krnjevic's results are based on indirect calculations involving a number of assumptions; the results are so unexpected that direct measurements of the osmotic pressure of mammalian nerve fibres and the surround-ing fluid would be of particular interest. A high concentration of ions in the nerve and inside the nerve sheath would allow the nerve to conduct more impulses without fatigue.

The auricular-ventricular bundle of the heart, a group of modified muscle fibres with some of the properties of nerves, are also possibly hyperosmotic to the blood. In the ox, the sum of sodium and potassium in the whole bundle amounts to 312 mM/kg water (Davies, Davies, Francis and Whittam, 1952) and if allowance could be made for an unknown amount of extracellular fluid, the intracellular concentrations would be even higher. It is just possible that the cell contents might be isosmotic with the blood if the cations were balanced by polyvalent anions of negligible osmotic effect.

Erythrocytes — Excepting carnivores and most artiodactyls, the erythrocytes in mammals resemble other cells in containing a high concentration of potassium and a correspondingly low concentration of sodium, but they also contain a high concentration of chloride (Table VI.9). In the carnivores and artiodactyls, the concentration of sodium is higher than that of potassium (Table VI.9, col. 5), so the erythrocytes approach the extracellular fluid in composition. The low concentration of sodium inside most erythrocytes is maintained by active extrusion, This, combined with the presence of about 50 mM/kg water of indiffusible anions (mostly phosphate compounds and haemoglobin), produces a resting potential of about 7 mV, inside negative, in normal physiological conditions. The chloride and bicarbonate are in equilibrium with this potential, but the potassium is not. A potential of -7 mV is sufficient to concentrate potassium in the cell to about 150% of its concentration in the blood. The higher concentration is maintained by the active transport of potassium into the cells (Glynn, 1957). In artiodactyls, where potassium is lower than in most mammals, it must still be actively accumulated, whereas in the dog and the cat, it is possible that the potassium is in a passive equilibrium.

TABLE VI.9. — SODIUM, POTASSIUM AND CHLORIDE CONTENT OF ERYTHROCYTES AND PLASMA OF THE RAT AND CAT
(Expressed as mM/kg water; Bernstein, 1954)

Ion	Rat		Cat	
	plasma	erythrocytes	plasma	erythrocytes
Sodium	152	28	158	142
Potassium	5.9	135	4.6	8
Chloride	118	82	112	84

The degree of ionisation of the haemoglobin in the cell, and hence the concentration of indiffusible anions, depends on the pH of the contents. The isoelectric point of haemoglobin is at about pH 6.5, when the concentration of indiffusible anions in the cell is very low. At this pH, the membrane potential is very small, and the concentrations of bicarbonate and chloride on either side of the cell membrane are almost equal. For this reason, the addition of carbon dioxide to the blood, by lowering the pH from the normal value of 7.4, causes a movement of chloride ions into the cell (the "Hamburger shift") and a corresponding movement of water to maintain isosmoticity.

Kidney — The concentrations of electrolytes in kidney cells are of particular interest, because of the ability of the kidney to produce a urine hyperosmotic or hypo-osmotic to the blood. Unfortunately, the exact concentrations are in doubt, particularly because it is difficult to measure accurately the volume of extracellular fluid. However, it is probable that the cells of the cortex are approximately isosmotic with the blood, while the cells of the medulla are hyperosmotic to normal plasma, but isosmotic with the fluids in the loop of Henle and the vasa recta (Chap. II, p.56). It is difficult to estimate the volume of the extracellular fluid because the kidney may concentrate in the tubules, inulin and other substances used for determining extracellular spaces. The inulin space in the dog kidney is estimated at 33.6% of the total water content in the cortex, and 33–61% in the various zones of the medulla (Ullrich, Drenkhahn and Jarausch, 1955). Another estimate of the volume of extracellular fluid can be made from the observation that 70% of the sodium in the guinea pig kidney cortex is exchanged very rapidly, while the remainder exchanges very slowly (Whittam and Davies, 1952). If it is assumed that the more rapidly exchanging fraction is extracellular and that the sodium concentration in this fluid is the same as normal plasma, then the volume of extracellular fluid must be 40% of the total water content.

There is a very significant difference between the composition of the cortex and of the medulla (Table VI.10, col. 3

and 4). Both contain the usual high concentration of potassium, but the medulla contains, in addition, about the same concentrations of sodium and chloride as plasma. If the extracellular fluid amounts to 40% of the water content of the cortex (Table VI.10, col. 5), then the intracellular potassium and chloride are not in a Donnan equilibrium, and it is probable that the cortex actively transports both sodium and potassium; the chloride could be in a passive equilibrium as it is in the erythrocyte. An intracellular concentration of 51 mM Cl/kg water (Table VI.10, col. 5) would be in equilibrium with a resting potential of about 20 mV (cell negative to plasma) and values similar to this have been recorded for kidney cells (Harris, 1960, p.195).

TABLE VI.10. — COMPOSITION OF SOME TISSUES OF THE DOG AND RAT
(Expressed as mM/kg water)

Ion	Dog	Dog kidney				Rat	
	Plasma[1]	Cortex[2] whole	Medulla whole[2]	Intracell. conc. cortex[3]	Intracell. conc. medulla[4]	Serum[5]	Liver Intracell. conc.[6]
Sodium ...	150	91	151·6	52	52	166	59
Potassium	3·86	79·6	60	129	95	5·97	120
Calcium...	2·56	1·68	1·8	—	—	—	—
Chloride	117	77·7	139·7	51	77	144	37

1. Eichelberger & Maclean, 1942.
2. Eichelberger & Bibler, 1949.
3. Calculated assuming 40% cortex water is extracellular.
4. Calculated assuming 40% medulla water is extracellular and twice as concentrated as the blood.
5. Harrison, 1953.
6. Bernstein, 1954.

The electrolyte balance in the medulla is more complex than in the cortex. It is clear (Table VI.10, col. 4) that the medulla, as a whole, is hyperosmotic to the plasma, but this could be due to the highly concentrated fluids in the tubules and vasa recta, while the cells themselves might be isosmotic with the rest of the body tissues. If we assume that extracellular fluids amount to 40% of the total water content as in the cortex, and that these fluids contain just twice as much sodium, potassium and chloride as the plasma, then the intracellular concentrations would be as in Table VI.10, col. 6. It is just possible, on these figures, that the cells are isosmotic with the rest of the body, but it is much more likely that they are isosmotic with the contents of the loop of Henle and the vasa recta. Maffly and Leaf (1959), using a cryoscopic technique, found that the medulla of the rat kidney was hyperosmotic to the blood although the kidney cortex and liver, heart and brain were all isosmotic. Once again, this could have been caused by the presence of concentrated extracellular fluids.

The concentrations of electrolytes in medullary tissue shown in Table VI.10, col. 4 are average values for the whole medulla, but this is a simplification because the medulla consists of a series of concentric zones, increasing in concentration towards the papillae (Chap. II. p.58, Fig. 5.)

When kidney slices are cooled or deprived of metabolites, they gain sodium, take up water, and lose potassium. The restoration of normal conditions reverses these changes. A theory has been put forward (Robinson, 1960) that the cells of the kidney cortex are hyperosmotic to the plasma, and that water is continually entering and being removed. If the cells are cooled to near $0°C$, or poisoned, they swell in media of similar ionic composition to the plasma, but this swelling is reversible. On the other hand, when the sodium extrusion mechanism fails in other tissues isosmotic with the medium, sodium will accumulate, the membrane potential will fall, and chloride and water will enter (Whittam and Davies, 1952; Harris 1960). If the urine is concentrated by a counter current mechanism (Chap. II, p.57), the cells need not be significantly hyperosmotic to the media, and each cell need be capable of producing only a minute concentration difference.

Liver — Harrison (1953) has calculated by devious means the electrolyte concentrations in liver cells. His results (Table VI.10, col. 6) show that the potassium must be actively accumulated.

Invertebrate Tissues

Little is known of the electrolyte composition of the tissues of land invertebrates. Incomplete analyses of *Periplaneta* muscle (Tobias, 1948 a) show that it contains large quantities of potassium, moderate amounts of sodium, and low magnesium (Table VI.11. col. 3). No doubt, much of the sodium is not in the cells but in the extracellular space. Nothing is known about the chloride content, but by analogy with the striated muscles of other animals, it is probably in a Donnan equilibrium. However, the ionic equilibrium of the striated muscle

TABLE VI.11. — ELECTROLYTE CONTENT OF SOME INVERTEBRATE TISSUES AND EXTRACELLULAR FLUIDS

	Periplaneta[1]			Romalea[1]			Hydrophilus[2]		Helix[2]	
	serum	muscle	nerve	serum	muscle	nerve	serum	muscle[1]	plasma	muscle
Sodium ...	107	45.6	83	64	15	89	—	—	—	—
Potassium	17.3	112	140	18	101	57	4.3	160	4.2	128.9
Calcium...	—	—	—	—	—	—	12.2	18	10.3	117.8
Magnesium...	1.7	7.4	4.0	—	—	—	23.4	45.3	13.2	33.2

1. Tobias, 1948 a.
2. Florkin & Duchâteau, 1950. Muscle concentrations calculated on the assumption that all chloride is extracellular.

of those herbivorous insects which contain only small quantities of sodium in the blood must be different from that of other animals. Total sodium in the whole adult of the silk moth, *Bombyx mori*, is less than 0.16 mM/l. (Tobias, 1948 b), so that the concentration of sodium in the blood can be only a few millimoles, at most, and the tissue concentration will be negligible. A Donnan equilibrium can still be maintained between the potassium and chloride, provided other solutes are present in the blood to maintain the osmotic pressure. If the concentration of potassium in the blood is very high, the resting potential of the muscle fibres will be correspondingly low, and the mechanical response weakened, but rapid contraction will not become impossible, because insect muscle does not depend on a propagated action potential to initiate contraction (Hoyle, 1953, 1954). In *Locusta*, the concentration of potassium in the blood rises shortly before a moult, and the consequent reduction of the power of muscular contraction probably protects the soft new exoskeleton from damage (Hoyle, 1954).

In *Helix* muscle, the potassium concentration is similar to that in vertebrates or insects. Magnesium is larger than in other animals, and the concentration of calcium is enormous. This high level of calcium is probably due to concretions of calcium carbonate present in the muscle. An even higher concentration of calcium has been reported for *Lymnaea* (Florkin and Duchâteau, 1950).*

Periplaneta nerve cord, together with its sheath, contains a very high concentration of potassium and a fairly high concentration of sodium (Table VI.11, col. 4). Recent work (Treherne, 1962 a and b) has shown that sodium and potassium ions are held in the sheath in a much higher concentration than in the surrounding blood. The ions are probably maintained in a Donnan equilibrium by a high concentration of bound anions in the nerve sheath. In accord with this, the concentration of chloride ions in the sheath is much lower. The ions in the sheath are freely exchangeable with those in the blood (Treherne, 1961). Nothing is known of the composition of the nerves in those insects where the body fluids contain only small amounts of sodium. A conducted action potential depends on the presence of a reasonable concentration of sodium in the extracellular fluid, so the fluid in the nerve sheath of these insects may be expected to contain more sodium than the blood.

---

* Florkin and Duchâteau's figures were calculated on the assumption that all the chloride was extracellular. The real concentration must be rather smaller.

Ion Fluxes through the Tissues

In all the tissues examined, the low concentration of sodium inside the cells is a consequence of the active extrusion of sodium against an electrochemical gradient. In striated muscle and in nerves, the potassium and chloride are in a Donnan equilibrium; but in the erythrocytes, and probably in most other tissues as well, the potassium is not in electrochemical equilibrium and must be actively concentrated, unless some of it is bound.

It is possible to calculate the energy required to maintain the ionic concentrations inside the cells in cases where the rate of exchange has been measured with radioactive tracers, assuming that exchange diffusion does not occur. For example, in rat diaphragm muscle, although the cells *in vivo* contain only 18 mM Na/kg cell water, *in vitro* they contain 60 mM Na/kg water (and 1 kg diaphragm tissue contains 522 gm of cell water). The rate constant for the exchange of intracellular sodium *in vitro* is 3.75 h^{-1} (Creese, 1954). The efflux of sodium is therefore $60 \times 3.75 \times 0.522$ mM Na/kg/hr. This takes place against an electrochemical gradient of

$$\frac{RT}{F} \left[\ln \frac{Na_o}{Na_i} + \ln \frac{K_i}{K_o} \right] \quad \text{(Chap. I, pp. 27 and 31)}.$$

Hence it can be calculated that the sodium extrusion requires at least 300 cal/kg/hr or 0.3 cal/g/hr. In frog muscle, the concentrations and the rate of exchange are lower (Table VI. 12, col. 6) and the energy required is about 0.025 cal/g/hr. This is still equivalent to 6–11% of the energy available to the muscle (Harris, 1960, p.195).

The potassium in rat diaphragm cells is in electrochemical equilibrium with the potassium outside, with a half-time of exchange equal to 46 minutes (38°C) (Creese, 1954). In frog muscle, potassium does not exchange as a single fraction (Carey and Conway, 1954) but whether this is due to the existence of several compartments inside the muscle fibres, or to the

TABLE VI.12. THE SODIUM AND POTASSIUM FLUXES THROUGH THE TISSUES
OF SOME LAND ANIMALS

Tissue	Ion	Temp.° C.	Extracell. conc. mM/kg water	Intracell. conc. mM/kg water	Rate const. h^{-1}	Efflux mM/kg/hr	Author
Frog muscle	Na	0	117	13	0·61	8	Harris, 1950
Frog muscle	Na	18	117	15·5	1·35	21	Harris, 1950
Rat muscle............	Na	38	145	60	3·75	225	Creese, 1954
Human erythrocyte	Na	38	155	19	0·35	7	Harris, 1960 p.157
Cat nerve	Na	37	149	41	1·57	64	Dainty & Krnjevic, 1955
Rat muscle............	K	37	5·9	149	2·5	372	Creese, 1954
Human erythrocyte	K	38	5·0	136	0·012	2·3	Harris, 1960 p.157

mechanics of exchange through long pores (Chap. I, p.20), is
not clear. The rate constant for turnover of most of the potassium is about 0.1 h^{-1}.

In the erythrocyte, both sodium and potassium are transported against electrochemical gradients. In human erythrocytes,
sodium exchanges in three fractions; a small rapid exchange
probably associated with the cell membrane, a main part which
exchanges with a time constant of 0.3 h^{-1}, and another small
very slow fraction. The energy required to transport both the
potassium and sodium ions is equivalent to about 0.01 cals g/hr,
about 10% of the energy liberated by cell metabolism (Harris
and Maizels, 1952).

The rate constants of the exchange of sodium and potassium
in a number of tissues are given in Table VI.12. In all tissues,
the ion fluxes are considerable and approximately, the energy
required to maintain dynamic equilibrium is about one tenth
that of the total energy available. This figure is probably an
upper limit, for it does not allow for that fraction of the sodium
efflux which is due to passive diffusion, or for the possibility
of exchange diffusion. A problem which remains, is the significance of the multiple fractions of potassium which have
been reported, not only in frog muscle (above), but also in

mammalian kidney (Whittam and Davies, 1952) and in some other tissues* (Chap. III, p.114).

In spite of the complications of the subject and the gaps in our knowledge there emerges a pattern of almost fantastic activity. Inorganic ions and water molecules are the most mobile of all the components of the living body because of their small size, yet the body concentrates and manipulates them in innumerable ways. Ions and water diffuse so readily down electrochemical gradients that a living organism has to devote a large part of its available energy to putting them back in their places; the greater part of this work is performed at the cell surface. The total area of all the cells of the body is enormous, yet a considerable concentration difference is maintained between each cell and its environment. The surface area of the cells of a 12 stone man is at least 150 million cm^2, about twice the area of a Rugby pitch.[†] It is hardly surprising that the work done in maintaining a dynamic equilibrium across this area takes a large part of the whole metabolic energy. In addition to this enormous flux of ions, the body also elaborates a host of secretions and fluids of various compositions and osmotic concentrations.

Terrestrial Eggs and Embryos

Most terrestrial eggs are cleidoic but their isolation from their environment is a matter of degree and chelonian eggs and some snake and insect eggs take up water after they have been laid (Needham, 1931, p.899).

The cleidoic egg of the domestic fowl has been studied extensively, and the information reviewed by Needham (1931, 1950). When first laid, the egg white is markedly hypo-osmotic to the yolk, and both are hypo-osmotic to adult serum(Table VI. 13). The concentration of ions in the white is very different from that in the yolk. There is evidence that, as in the am-

* The muscle of *Nephrops*, the marine decapod, also appears to have some bound potassium (Robertson, 1961).

† It is estimated that 1 ml of striated muscle cells has a surface of 2000 cm^2 (Creese, 1954).

19

TABLE VI.13. — ELECTROLYTE COMPOSITION OF HEN EGG YOLK AND
WHITE (*Gallus gallus*). CONCENTRATIONS EXPRESSED AS mM/KG WATER
(Needham, 1950, Table 3)

Ion	Yolk	White	Plasma
Sodium	93	26·1	—
Potassium	58·1	37·3	—
Chloride	78·9	51·5	—
Total, mOsm/kg water	298	236	344

phibian egg (Chap. V. p.223), sodium is more concentrated in
the granules than in the intracellular fluid (Bialascewicz, 1929).
Although at one time it was thought that the osmotic concentration difference between yolk and white was actively
maintained, it now seems that this is not the case. Osmotic
equilibrium is reached only after 70 days in stored eggs, although
yolk and white separated by a piece of vitelline membrane
reach equilibrium much more rapidly. Needham (1950, p.13)
has suggested that the lipoids and lipoproteins of the intact
egg are highly orientated, and that the physical organisation
of the egg somehow retards diffusion.

During the early development of the embryo, there is movement of salt and water from the yolk to the embryo, and from
the white to the yolk. In the first week of development, there
is a net increase in the electrolyte content of the yolk, while
that of the white declines rapidly. The amniotic and allantoic
fluids are generally similar to plasma in composition (Table
VI.14) but the amniotic fluid is first hyperosmotic, then
isosmotic, and finally hypo-osmotic to the embryo, as development proceeds. The allantoic fluid is always strongly hypo-osmotic to the amniotic fluid. This is probably the result of the
production of hypo-osmotic urine by the kidneys of the embryo.

In the eggs of the turtle, *Caretta caretta* the difference
in electrolyte composition between the white and the yolk is
more marked than in the hen's egg; the yolk contains almost
equivalent quantities of sodium and potassium, while the

TABLE VI.14. INORGANIC COMPOSITION OF CHICK EMBRYONIC FLUIDS ON
THE 11TH. DAY OF DEVELOPMENT. EXPRESSED AS mM/L.*
(Smoczkiewiczowa, 1959)

	Sodium	Potassium	Calcium	Chloride
Amniotic fluid......................	134	4.5	1.05	141
Allantoic fluid......................	115	12	1.75	68

*Originally expressed as "milliequivalents", volume not stated, but evidently l. not kg water.

white contains a lot of sodium but little potassium and much
less chloride than the yolk.

Although some mammalian embryos have been reported to
be hyperosmotic to the maternal circulation, they are generally
isosmotic (see Needham, 1931, Table 244, p.1533).* This is to
be expected in view of the area and permeability of the placental
barrier. The allantoic fluid is produced by the kidneys of the
embryo. Filtration begins before tubular resorption, so the
first urine is isosmotic with the blood, but it becomes hypo-
osmotic when tubular resorption develops. The area of contact
between the allantois and the amnion is extensive and the
amniotic fluid also becomes hypo-osmotic to the embryonic and
maternal circulations. Late in development the urine becomes
hyperosmotic to the embryo (Alexander and Nixon, 1961).

During development, the tissues and body fluids of the
mammalian foetus have a relatively high potassium, and low
protein, sodium and chloride content, and it is not until
some time after birth that the foetus attains full "chemical
maturity" (Widdowson and McCance, 1956). This is not achieved until 6 weeks after birth in the pig and 7 months after
birth in the human infant. The change is associated with a
fall in the total body water and extracellular sodium and chloride, and an increase in the protein and intracellular potassium and phosphorus, and can be interpreted as a progressive
decrease in the volume of extracellular fluid and an increase in
the cell mass; this change has been observed histologically
as well as chemically (Dickerson and Widdowson, 1960).

* See also Winkler, Theil and Goetze, 1962.

19*

CHAPTER VII

HYPO-OSMOTIC REGULATORS

Introduction

Animals which can maintain the salt concentrations of their body fluids below that of the environment live both in the sea and in inland waters of high salinity. All these animals appear to be descended from freshwater, or at least brackish water, ancestors.

The geological evidence suggests that the vertebrates had entered fresh water by the Silurian period (Robertson, 1957), but independently, they have returned many times to the sea; in every case (lampreys, sturgeons, teleosts, selachians, a few amphibians, turtles, snakes, whales and seals) the salt content of the blood is maintained lower than that of sea water. The elasmobranchs maintain a low salt content in the blood, but they are slightly hyperosmotic to sea water by virtue of a high concentration of urea and a moderate concentration of trimethylamine oxide in the body fluids. A number of frogs are found in marine and brackish water environments, and one of these, *Rana cancrivora*, like the selachians, maintains a high concentration of urea in the blood (Gordon, Schmidt-Nielsen and Kelly, 1961).*

Many grapsoid and ocypodid crabs, the palaemonid prawns, and some sphaeromid isopods amongst the marine crustaceans,

---

* On the other hand, *Bufo viridis* survives high salinities by a high degree of tissue tolerance of increased plasma concentration, and the urea content rises only a little between fresh water and $19^0/_{00}$ salinity (Gordon, 1962.)

also maintain their blood concentrations hypo-osmotic to sea water. Although each of these families contains some fresh-water members, they are predominantly brackish or marine. The occurrence of free-living larval stages in the marine species of palaemonid prawns, but not in the freshwater ones, indicates that this family at least is not primitively a freshwater one, but it is possible that both the marine and the fresh-water members of the family are descended from brackish water ancestors.

Inland saline waters, such as the Dead Sea, Salt Lake, Utah, or the North African Shotts, contain a diverse fauna which survives by virtue of exceptional powers of osmotic regulation. Saline waters are derived from several sources: salt springs, the concentration of sea water, or even by the concentration of fresh waters in desert regions, and they therefore differ widely in salinity and ionic composition. Sodium and chloride are usually the most abundant ions, but the relative amounts of the other ions may be very different from those in sea water. The fauna of inland saline waters, apart from stragglers from fresh water, may be divided into two groups (Beadle, 1943): (1) those animals which are typically found in brackish water of moderate salinity, though they may be found occasionally in very low salinities, or even in fresh water, e.g. the crusta-ceans *Palaemonetes varians*, *Cyclops bicuspidata*, the gastropod *Hydrobia brondeli*, the teleost *Cyprinodon fasciatus*; and (2) animals which can survive in the very highest salinities, including even saturated solutions, e.g. the brine shrimp *Artemia salina* and *Aedes detritus*, the brackish water mosquito. Members of the second group and most members of the first are able to survive only by their ability to osmoregulate in hyperosmotic solutions, but it is probable that a few members of the first group, such as *Hydrobia*, are incapable of hypo-osmotic regulation and merely tolerate the high salinities. While most saline water insects osmoregulate, a few, e.g. the caddis larvae, *Limnephilus stigma* and *Anabolia nervosa*, are almost isosmotic with the medium, but maintain a low salt concentration. As in elasmobranchs, the osmotic pressure of the blood is made up by non-electrolytes (Sutcliffe, 1961 a and b).

Practically all the inhabitants of inland saline waters belong to predominantly freshwater groups, e.g. rotifers, branchiopods, Cyclopidae, insects and cyprinodont fishes, and normally they maintain blood concentrations similar to those of their freshwater relatives, even when living in solutions more concentrated than sea water (Fig. VII.1).

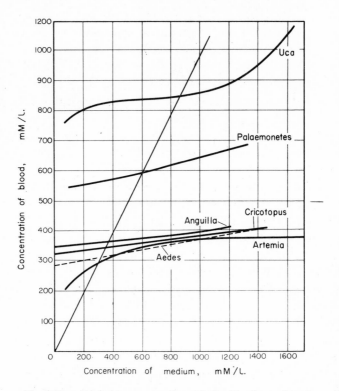

Fig. VII.1. Osmotic concentration of the blood as a function of the osmotic concentration of the medium. To the left of the diagonal isosmotic line the animals are hyperosmotic to the medium, to the right of the line they are hypo-osmotic. *Cricotopus* from Sutcliffe, 1960, *Artemia* from Croghan, 1918 a and b; *Palaemonetes* from Panikkar, 1941; *Aedes* from Beadle, 1939; *Anguilla* from Duval, 1925, *Uca* from Jones, 1941.

Osmotic Pressure and Composition of the Blood

Concentration

To some extent, the composition of the body fluids of animals which practise hypo-osmotic regulation varies with the concentration of the medium. This variation is hardly significant in marine animals, where the environment is relatively constant, but it may be of considerable importance in animals living in brackish water or in salt lakes (Fig. VII.1).

Vertebrates — The salt content of the blood of marine vertebrates is usually less than half that of sea water (Table VII.1), and only slightly higher than that of related freshwater or terrestrial animals. For example, the marine turtle, *Caretta caretta*, has a blood concentration of 509 mOsm/l., while the land tortoise, *Testudo graeca*, has a concentration of 321 mOsm/l.; the marine fulmar, *Fulmarus glacialis*, has a concentration of 360 mOsm/l., and the domestic fowl, *Gallus*, a concentration of 290 mOsm/l.

Euryhaline fishes maintain a remarkably constant blood composition and concentration in all salinities (Fig. VII.1). Strictly stenohaline fishes regulate the osmotic pressure of the blood at a fairly constant level. In freshwater fishes, the range of concentration is from *ca.* 280 to 360 mOsm/l., independent of the hardness or softness of the water. In most marine fishes, the blood concentration is 10–20% higher than this, and ranges from *ca.* 340 to 460 mOsm/l. In a few fish it is higher, e.g. in the herring, *Clupea harengus*, 512 mOsm/l. (Holliday and Blaxter, 1960), but even these fish are markedly hypo-osmotic to sea water (*ca.* 1000 mOsm/l.). Most marine species can tolerate dilutions of sea water down to isosmoticity with the blood without much change in concentration of the body fluids, but no lower. Thus, this concentration of about one third sea water constitutes an osmotic barrier for such stenohaline forms. Euryhaline species which pass this barrier in either direction have arisen from both freshwater and marine forms, e.g. the stickleback, *Gasterosteus*, and the salmon, *Salmo salar* are derived from freshwater forms, the eel, *Anguilla*, and *Fundulus*,

TABLE VII.1. — OSMOTIC CONCENTRATION OF THE BLOOD OF SOME
MARINE VERTEBRATES
(Concentrations as mOsm/kg water)

Animal	Medium	Blood	Author
Agnatha : *Petromyzon marinus* *Lampetra fluviatilis*	1237 522	312 308	Burian, 1910 Morris, 1958
Elasmobranchiata: *Raja ocellata*	995	1035 (Cl) 272 (urea) 357	Smith, 1931 b
Scyliorhinus stellaris	1222	1264	Botazzi, 1906
Chondrostei : *Acipenser stellatus* ...	"Sea water"	339	Kalashnikov and Skadov- skii, 1948
Teleostei : *Conger conger*	1145	552	Burian, 1910
Gadus morhua	"Sea water"	479	Woodhead and Woodhead, 1959
Lophius piscatorius...	1012	431	Botazzi 1906
Clupea harengus	1033	512	Holliday and Blaxter, 1961
Reptilia : *Caretta caretta*.........	985	409	Smith, 1932
Aves : *Fulmarus glacialis*	"Sea water"	360	Portier, 1910
Mammalia : *Physeter catodon*	"Sea water"	355–387	Sudzuki, 1924
Phoca foetida	"Sea water"	379	Portier, 1910

from sea water forms (Pickford and Atz, 1957, p. 168).
The degree of independence from the environment varies;
in some fish such as the salmon and the eel, the osmotic
pressure of the body fluids fluctuates by 10–15% on transfer

from one medium to another, while in others such as the sticklebacks and *Fundulus* and other cyprinodonts, the osmotic pressure of the body fluids is kept at a more constant level.

Invertebrates — Invertebrates that can regulate hypo-osmotically usually maintain a blood concentration equivalent to about two thirds sea water when living in the sea (Fig. VII.1), but insects such as *Aedes detritus* or *Cricotopus vitripinnis* have much lower blood concentrations. *Artemia salina* is remarkable in surviving in saturated solutions of sodium chloride, *ca.* 300‰ salinity, while maintaining the blood less concentrated than sea water (Fig. VII.2). In caddis larvae surviving in sea water, about half the osmotic concentration of the blood is due to electrolytes (Sutcliffe, 1961 a and b).

It is significant of the brackish or freshwater origin of hypo-osmotic regulators that many of them are also capable of hyperosmotic regulation in fresh water, or in solutions of low salinity (Fig. VII.1).

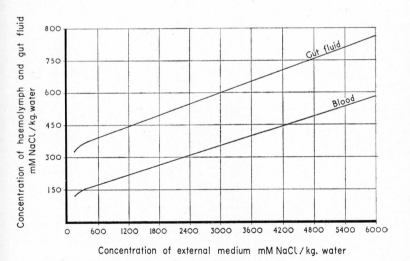

Fig. VII.2. *Artemia.* The osmotic concentrations of the blood and gut fluid as a function of the osmotic concentration of the medium. From Croghan, 1958 a.

Composition

In composition, the blood of hypo-osmotic regulators resembles that of their freshwater or terrestrial relatives (Table VII.2). The greater part of the osmotic pressure of the blood is due to sodium and chloride ions. The concentration of other ions is generally low, especially of magnesium and sulphate, but the prawn, *Palaemon*, and the crab, *Uca*, which are probably of brackish water origin, contain larger concentrations of these ions (Table VII.2).

The variation of the concentration of individual ions with external concentration has been examined in the brine shrimp, *Artemia*, (Croghan, 1958 b), the crab, *Pachygrapsus*, (Prosser,

TABLE VII.2. — COMPOSITION OF THE BODY FLUIDS OF SOME ANIMALS WHEN IN EQUILIBRIUM WITH SEA WATER

Animal	Na	K	Ca	Mg	Cl	SO₄	HCO₃	Author
Artemia salina......... (blood, mM/l.)	207	8	—	2	179	—	—	Croghan, 1958 b
Uca pugnax .... (blood, mM/l.)	328	11	16	23*	537	42	—	Green, Harsch, Barr & Prosser, 1959
Palaemon serratus...... (blood mM/kg water)	394	7·7	—	25·2	430	5·2	—	Parry, G., 1955
Physeter catodon ...... (serum. mM/l.)	170	2·6	0·2	2·35	120	—	—	Brull & Nizet, 1953
Lophius piscatorius... (plasma, mM/l.)	185	5·1	3·2	2·5	153	—	—	Robertson, 1954
Muraena helena ...... (plasma mM/kg water)	212	1·9	3·86	2·42	188	6·2	8·03	Sudzuki, 1924
Raja laevis .... (plasma, mM/l.)	255	4·9	3·75	2·77	241	0·2 Urea 452	6·1	Smith, 1929 a

*Given as 46, evidently mE/l.

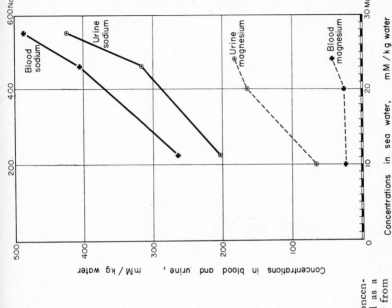

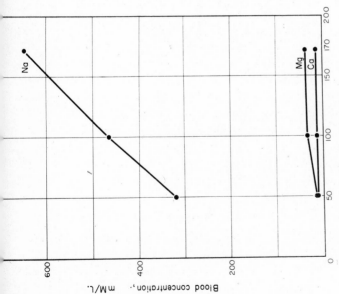

Fig. VII.3. *Pachygrapsus* (left) and *Palaemon* (right). The concentrations of sodium, calcium and magnesium in the blood as a function of the concentration of the medium. *Pachygrapsus* from Prosser, Green and Chow 1955; *Palaemon* from Parry 1954.

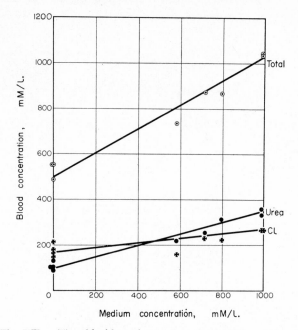

Fig. VII.4. The chloride and urea content (mM/l.) and the total osmotic concentration (mOsm/l.) of the blood of several species of selachians as functions of the concentration of the medium. From Smith, 1931 a.

Green and Chow, 1955), and the prawn, *Palaemon*, (Parry, G., 1954). The concentrations of the minor ions in these animals, particularly of calcium, remain remarkably constant and changes in the osmotic pressure are brought about by changes in the sodium and chloride concentrations (Fig. VII.3). In selachians, on the other hand, the chloride concentration of the blood remains almost constant, and changes in total concentration are brought about mainly by changes in the urea (Fig. VII.4).

Salt and Water Balance

In a hyperosmotic medium an animal loses water by exosmosis and gains salt by diffusion, and in order to maintain osmotic equilibrium, the salt must be excreted and the water replaced. Although the information available about hypo-osmotic regulators is incomplete, it is clear that these animals remove excess salt in two different ways. Teleosts, and probably also the brine shrimp, secrete salt directly into the medium, without losing any significant quantities of water in the process. Selachians, reptiles, birds, mammals, and insects, eliminate the salts as concentrated solutions, losing small but significant quantities of water in the course of salt excretion. The animals which adopt this latter method are mainly of terrestrial origin and have therefore developed very impermeable body walls, perhaps thereby losing the opportunity to secrete ions directly into the surrounding water.

Water lost by exosmosis, together with any water lost in the course of salt secretion, nitrogen excretion, or in respiration, is either replaced from the food or by drinking the medium. In the latter instance, the animals absorb both water and salts and excrete the salts, thus gaining free water. Marine mammals may rely entirely on water derived from the food, but most other hypo-osmotic regulators probably drink the medium to some extent. The tissues of all marine animals, especially those of hypo-osmotic regulators, contain less salt than sea water (Table VII.12), so that marine carnivores benefit from the lower salt content of their prey. The metabolism of food also provides additional supplies of water.

Marine Teleosts

The mechanisms used by the marine teleosts for hypo-osmotic regulation are, (1) the relative impermeability of the surface; (2) the swallowing of sea water with the subsequent absorption in the gut of water and monovalent ions; (3) the active excretion of monovalent ions by the gill epithelium; and (4) the production of a minimal quantity of urine, excreting divalent ions and some nitrogenous waste. The urine is never hyperosmotic to the blood.

Permeability — The low permeability of the skin, excepting the respiratory epithelium, is attained by the thickening of the dermis, by the presence of mucous glands, and by the growth of scales. The skin may be thickened considerably: for example, in the eel, the skin may be 10% of the total weight. Mucus produced by the skin glands is not impermeable to salt and water exchanges, in itself, but may assist in maintaining an osmotic difference simply by reducing water flow at the body surface (Van Oosten, 1957), thus increasing the layer through which exchange takes place by diffusion and not by mixing. Non-scaly fishes generally have leathery and mucoid surfaces. Removal of scales or mucus often leads to osmotic imbalance: for instance, removal of mucus from the surface of an eel quickly brings loss of regulation, and descaling of herring is followed by increases in blood concentration (Holliday and Blaxter, 1961). Handling, with associated skin damage, induces a state of physiological shock in fishes, which causes diuresis and the loss of considerable quantities of both water and salts (Grafflin, 1931; Forster and Berglund, 1953).

The more permeable respiratory epithelium of the gills represents a large but variable proportion of the surface area of a fish; the variation between different species may be as much as nine-fold (Gray, I. E., 1954; Fry, 1957).

Water balance — The ability of hypo-osmotic regulators to drink and absorb sea water was first demonstrated by Smith (1930 b), who observed that when teleosts were kept in sea water containing phenol red, the dye became strongly concentrated in the gut. In a typical experiment, the gut of an eel was first carefully emptied and the anus ligatured to prevent the loss of any fluid. After 20 hours in the tinctured sea water, the gut was found to contain 2.3 ml of fluid, but contained phenol red equivalent to 12.3 ml of sea water. Hence, the eel had drunk at least 12.3 ml of water and absorbed 10 ml from the gut. If any dye had been absorbed as well, the volumes would have been larger. In the same period, the fish produced 2.3 ml of urine and lost 1.3 g of weight, most probably as water. The fish had therefore lost $10 - 2.3 + 1.3 = 9$ ml of water extrarenally, as well as 2.3 ml through the kidneys.

In a series of experiments with eels (*Anguilla*) and sculpins (*Myoxocephalus*), Smith found that in sea water (970 mOsm/kg water), the fish drank 50–200 ml/kg/day, three quarters of which were absorbed. The extrarenal water loss was about twice as great as the renal loss (Table VII.3) and was probably due to exosmosis. In Smith's experiments, this was just over 4% body weight/day, and the osmotic gradient between the body fluids and sea water was about 500 mOsm/kg water. In freshwater fishes, the rate of urine production, corresponding to the osmotic inflow of water, amounts to 4–8% body weight/day when the osmotic gradient between the fish and the medium is about 300 mOsm/kg water.

TABLE VII.3. — WATER DRINKING ABSORPTION AND EXCRETION BY TWO MARINE TELEOSTS, mM/kg/day

Fish	Swallowed	Absorbed	Urine Loss	Extrarenal Loss
Anguilla	66·4	53	9·7	43.3
Myoxocephalus ...	115·9	71·8	29·8	42·0

The absorption of water in the gut is accompanied by the uptake of monovalent ions. The residual fluid is isosmotic or even hypo-osmotic to the blood (Table VII.4), but contains a higher concentration of magnesium and sulphate than sea water. The relative degree of concentration of magnesium and

TABLE VII.4. — COMPOSITION OF THE GUT CONTENTS OF *Lophius* IN SEA WATER

(Concentrations expressed as mM/kg water; from Smith, 1930 b)

Sample	Total ions	Na	K	Ca	Mg	Cl	SO_4	HCO_3
Sea water	629	235	8·0	6·9	29	275	18	2·5
Gastric fluid...................	516	237	6·6	6·1	18	235	17	8
Anterior intestinal fluid	478	127	24	20·6	94	90	125	45
Posterior intestinal fluid	382	56	5·5	21·5	98	41	116	64

calcium ions is even greater than Table VII.4 suggests, because basic carbonates are precipitated in the gut.

Although magnesium and sulphate ions are preferentially excluded, small amounts of these ions do penetrate the gut wall and are excreted in the urine (Table VII.5). Most of the

TABLE VII.5. — COMPOSITION OF THE BLOOD AND URINE OF *Lophius*
(Expressed as mM/l.: Brull and Nizet, 1953)

Sample	Total ions mOsm/kg water	Na	K	Ca	Mg	Cl	SO₄	Urea	NH₃	TMO	Creatinine
Blood	452	185	5·1	3·2	2·5	153	—	0·3	0·2	8·1	0·1
Urine	406	11	1·8	7·2	137	132	42	0·6	13·7	20·3	18·3

magnesium and about half the sulphate in the urine must be derived from the gut contents, for when eels were kept in 0.05 N solution of magnesium sulphate, the excretion of magnesium was reduced by 90% and the excretion of sulphate was halved. The 0.05 N solution contained about as much magnesium and sulphate as the rather dilute sea water used in the other experiments, but the eels did not drink it, as it was hypo-osmotic to the blood. Most of the sulphate excreted in these circumstances was probably of metabolic origin. The urine in the eel was slightly hypo-osmotic, in spite of its high concentration of magnesium and sulphate, and contained only a moderate concentration of chloride, very little sodium and various nitrogenous waste products.

In general, the urine of marine teleosts is almost isosmotic with the blood, even in aglomerular species. Very few analyses are available for the inorganic constituents of the urine of marine fishes (Table VII.5), but it is clear that the volume of urine is so small that the kidney cannot play an important part in the regulation of monovalent ions. Some nitrogen is excreted by the kidneys, but because of the low urine flow, the ammonia produced as the principal nitrogenous endproduct mostly diffuses out through the permeable gills, and only small amounts of ammonia, urea and trimethylamine oxide are found in the urine. The ability of the aglomerular kidney to secrete nitrogenous end-products was demonstrated by Brull, Nizet and Verney (1953) (Chap. II, p.52).

Salt uptake and loss — The very large quantities of sodium and chloride absorbed from the gut must be excreted elsewhere. Smith (1930 b) believed that fish excreted a hyperosmotic solution of salt, thus accounting for the extrarenal loss of both water and salt, but water loss may reasonably be attributed by exosmosis (see above), and it is probable that the salt is excreted directly into sea water. Sodium and chloride must be excreted in this way, and also potassium, as the concentration of potassium in the urine is very low, even in the carnivorous angler fish (*Lophius*).

The gills of teleosts, which are the most permeable parts of the surface, are almost certainly the sites of extrarenal excretion in marine fish. The localisation of salt secretion in the head region of fish was demonstrated by Keys (1931) and Krogh (1937 b). Keys perfused the buccal cavity of the eel, and was able to demonstrate the active excretion of chloride from the blood through the gills and/or buccal epithelium. The rate of chloride secretion was governed by its concentration in the internal medium (Fig. VII.5). The maximum rate of secretion of chloride is nearly 1 mM/kg/hr. Keys thought that the passage of some water was associated with the chloride movement, because the volume of fluid bathing the gills increased during the experiment; but later experiments (Schlieper, 1933 a and b) showed that, if the solutions inside and outside the gill were identical, but more concentrated than normal plasma, chloride transport took place without any movement of water. The ionic work performed by the gills amounts to 0.1–0.3 cal/g gill/hr (Bateman and Keys, 1932). The demonstration of active secretion of ions (especially cations) by the gills of teleost fishes is badly in need of further confirmation with more modern techniques.

20

The uptake of sodium, potassium, bromide and phosphate by the stickleback, *Gasterosteus aculeatus* (? var. *trachura*), has been examined by Mullins (1950) using radiotracers. Unfortunately, the experiments in hyperosmotic solutions were made in Baltic sea water containing only 267 mM Cl/kg water. In fresh water, the sodium influx was 0.625 mM/kg/hr, and

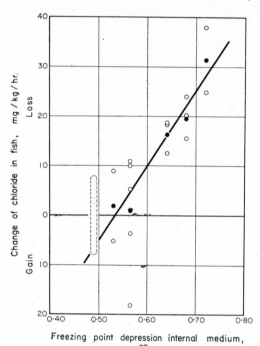

Fig. VII.5. The net excretion of chloride into sea water by the gills of the eel as a function of the concentration of the blood. From Keys, 1931.

the potassium influx 0.15 mM/kg/hr. In the sea water, the rates of uptake of sodium, potassium, bromide and phosphate were all very similar in terms of activity/g animal: activity/g solution (Fig. VII.6), i.e. virtually all the uptake could be accounted for by supposing that the animal was swallowing sea water at a rate of 4% body weight/hr, and absorbing all the ions. The extracellular space in the fish was only 30% of the body volume, so that the rate of turnover of sodium was rapid, and a graph of the concentration of labelled sodium in the fish begins to level off after a few hours (Fig. VII.7). On the other hand, potassium taken up exchanges rapidly with the large pool of potassium in the tissues, so that potassium only reaches equilibrium after several days.

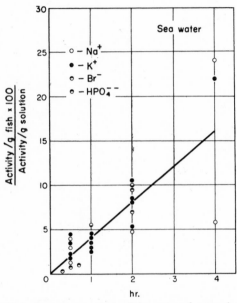

Fig. VII.6. *Gasterosteus aculeatus.* The entry of several ions in sea water expressed in terms of $\dfrac{activity/g\ animal \times 100}{activity/g\ solution}$
From Mullins, 1950.

The rate of sodium turnover in sea water, 10.7 mM Na/kg/hr, is 15 times greater than the rate in fresh water, but the ionic work performed is only 2.5 times as great (assuming that the blood concentration is the same in both media). The potassium flux is 0.40 mM K/kg/hr in sea water (5.9 mM K/kg water) and 0.15 mM K/kg/hr in fresh water (2 mM K/kg water) (Fig. VII.8).

20*

In the stickleback, the calculated rate of drinking is 4%
body weight/hr, while in the eel it was only 0.25% body
weight/hr. However, the eels weighed 250 times as much as
the sticklebacks and the temperatures of Smith's (1930 b) and

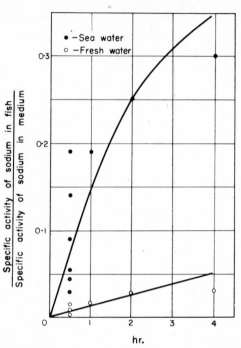

Fig. VII.7. *Gaasterosteus aculetus*. Entry of sodium in sea water and
fresh water expressed in terms of $\dfrac{\textit{specific activity of Na in fish}}{\textit{specific activity of Na in medium}}$
From Mullins, 1950.

Mullins' (1950) experiments were different (10° and 15–20°C,
respectively). When allowance is made for these differences
the results are quite comparable. In another euryhaline teleost, the flounder *Platichthys flesus*, the exchange of sodium in
sea water is 18–27/%hr of the total, while in fresh water the
exchange is only 0.6–0.9%/hr. Adaptation to the new medium
is complete within a few hours (Motais, 1961).

"Chloride-secretory" cells of the gills – The site of excretion of excess monovalent ions in marine fish, and of active uptake in freshwater fish, is probably in the gills, and some workers have followed Keys and Willmer's (1932) suggestions that

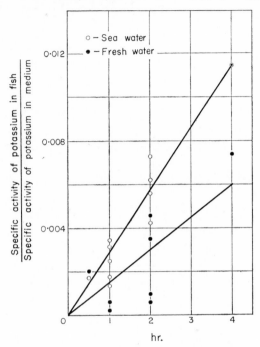

Fig. VII.8. *Gasterosteus aculeatus.* Entry of potassium in sea water and fresh water expressed in terms of $\dfrac{\text{specific activity of K in fish}}{\text{specific activity of K in medium}}$

From Mullins, 1950.

in the eel and other teleosts, acidophil cells in the gill epithelium perform these functions. Both marine and freshwater fish usually possess these cells in the gills and also in the pseudobranch and sometimes in the buccal epithelium. Similar cells are reported in marine and freshwater lampreys (Morris, 1957) and recently, in the elasmobrachs (Doyle and Gorecki, 1961) although earlier accounts denied their existence in elasmobranchs. They are said to be absent in the diadromous sturgeons (Acrivo, 1938), but are present in *Amia* and *Lepisosteus* (Bertin, in Grassé, 1958). The ability of these acidophil cells to excrete or absorb salts has been accepted by many workers, but there are criticisms of the theory. The evidence has been reviewed recently (Parry, Holliday and Blaxter, 1959; Houston and Threadgold, 1961).

The experimental evidence for a salt-regulating function is that their development in goldfish is favoured by a gradually increasing salt concentration (Liu, 1942, 1944; Vickers, 1961). Morris (1957) estimated that their numbers declined in the gills of lampreys with decreasing environmental salinity. Some histological changes have been related to a secretory phase, or an absorptive phase in the mud-skipper, *Fundulus* (Pettengill, 1947; Copeland, 1950), in the salmon (Threadgold and Houston, 1961) and in the eel (Getman, 1950). However, similar changes have been observed in the cells in the catfish after a number of different stress reagents (Enami, 1959), and in the flounder after long exposure to light (Holliday and Parry, 1962). Enzymic activity has been localised within the cells (Pettengill and Copeland, 1948; Maetz, 1953) providing a possible mechanism for the physiological processes of chloride exchange. The acidophil cells in the cod, *Gadus morhua*, increase below $2°C$, when the fish are not able to osmoregulate, and this increase has been interpreted as a response to the higher blood salt concentration consequent on the osmoregulatory failure (Woodhead and Woodhead, 1959).

Krogh (1939) was sceptical of a chloride secretory function for the cells in the absence of any direct evidence. Their absence in some fish, and in fish larvae which can regulate before the gills are developed (Holliday and Blaxter, 1960) and their presence in elasmobranchs (Doyle and Gorecki, 1961), has created some doubts as to the general validity of the theory. Bevelander (1935) made a comparative study of many fish, and suggested that the cells were mucous cells, a conclusion which is interesting in the light of Vicker's more recent conclusion that the cells represent a metaplastic form of

mucous cells. A recent study of the function of the pseudobranch in some teleosts has indicated that this organ is not
directly concerned with osmoregulation, although it is composed almost entirely of acidophil cells (Parry and Holliday,
1960). Electron microscopy of both gills and pseudobranch
in the same fish (the flounder, *Platichthys flesus*) indicates that
the cells from these two sites are identical (Holliday and
Parry, 1961).

True cholinesterase (acetylcholinesterase) is absent from
the gills of two freshwater species of *Fundulus*, but present
in the gill tissue of seven brackish water species of the genus.
Eserine, which inhibits cholinesterase, blocks sodium extrusion, but has no effect on sodium uptake (Fleming, Scheffel
and Linton, 1962). Histochemical studies show that the enzyme is found in the epithelium of the gill leaflets but not
within "chloride cells", nor in the pseudobranch (Fleming,
pers. comm.).

Many factors can influence osmoregulation in fish. Matura-
tion, especially in diadromous species, affects their ability to
osmoregulate and may well be a deciding factor in inducing
migrations to water of a different salinity (Fontaine, 1956,
1960). This points to osmotic control through the agency of
hormones, and thyroid, adrenals, and pituitary probably all
play a part in an inter-related fashion (Chap. VIII, p.349).
There is a breakdown of the regulatory processes in the cod
in cold arctic water at less than 2°C, which determines the
distribution of the fish (Woodhead and Woodhead, 1959).
Some arctic teleosts show a particular adaptation to their
environment. The blood concentration of some deep water
arctic fishes in summer is about 485 mOsm/kg water (Δ 0.9°C),
while the water in which they were caught was at a temperature of -1.73°C. Thus these fishes were living in water which
was about 0.85°C below the freezing-point of their blood
but as they never came into contact with ice in the deep
water, no freezing occurred, though their body fluids and
tissues were supercooled. However, in winter when the water

was at the same temperature but when they were in greater danger of coming into contact with ice, the same fish, as well as the sculpin, *Myoxocephalus* and some shallow water fish, had blood freezing-points much nearer to the temperature of the water (810–860 mOsm/kg water = Δ 1.5—1.6°C) (Fig. VII.9) (Scholander, van Dam, Kanwisher, Hammel and

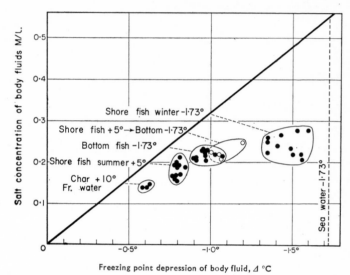

Fig. VII.9. Freezing point depression and salt content (M/l.) of the blood of some arctic marine teleosts in summer and winter. From Scholander *et al.*, 1957.

Gordon, 1957). In a *Myoxocephalus* with a blood concentration of 860 mOsm/kg water, salts accounted for 430 mOsm (Δ0.8°C) leaving about half of the osmotic concentration due to some other constituents. A further investigation of the problem failed to discover the nature of the "antifreeze" responsible, although common electrolytes, glucose, glycerol, proteins, urea and ammonia were all considered (Gordon, Amdur and Scholander, 1959).

Elasmobranchs

Elasmobranchs maintain the characteristic low salt of the body fluids of other fishes but the presence of urea and trimethylamine oxide makes them slightly hyperosmotic to sea water (Table VII.2) (Norris and Benoit, 1945). The osmotic concentration of the blood as determined by freezing-point techniques, is 10–50 mOsm/kg water greater than that of sea water (Smith, 1931 b) (Table VII.1) so that water could enter by osmosis and be removed as urine. In this respect, the elasmobranchs resemble freshwater teleosts rather than marine ones, but in contrast, salt also enters the fish by diffusion and must be removed by secretion against a concentration gradient as in the marine teleosts. As the fish are only very slightly hyperosmotic to sea water, the rate of urine production is low, 5–20 ml/kg/day, but the glomerular filtrate is about 80 ml/kg/day (Smith, 1936 a), so considerable water resorption must take place in the kidney. The urine is hypo-osmotic to the blood, and generally contains less chloride and urea than the plasma (Table VII.12). Elasmobranch gills are relatively impermeable to urea, so that the high concentration of urea in the plasma can be maintained, but even so, more urea is lost through the gills than in the urine.

Elasmobranchs do not drink sea water (Smith, 1931 a) although small quantities are probably ingested with the food. In starved animals, the gut contents are slightly hyperosmotic to the body fluids (Smith, 1931 b), and contain considerable quantities of urea which have entered by diffusion, or in the digestive juices. As in the teleosts, the contents of the intestine contain relatively larger concentrations of magnesium and sulphate ions and smaller concentrations of monovalent ions than the stomach, but the flux of water and salt through the gut is much smaller than in teleosts and not so important to the salt and water balance.

The salt which enters by diffusion through the gills and body wall and the (probably) smaller quantities which enter from the gut, must be excreted against a concentration gradient. Of this salt, sodium and chloride are removed by the rectal gland, while calcium, magnesium and sulphate are removed by the kidneys. The secretion of the rectal gland is isosmotic with the blood, but consists almost entirely of sodium chloride, with only small quantities of urea and other ions (Table VII.6). The rate of secretion averaged 1.9 ml/kg/hr in a number of the dogfish, *Squalus acanthias*, and is similar to the rate of urine production, and the combined products of the rectal gland and the kidneys is roughly equivalent to sea water in ionic composition (Burger and Hess, 1960).

TABLE VII.6. — COMPOSITION OF THE SECRETION OF THE RECTAL GLAND OF *Squalus acanthias* COMPARED WITH THAT OF THE URINE AND PLASMA (From Burger and Hess, 1960). Expressed as mM/l. (8 animals).

Fluid sample	Total mOsm/kg water	Na	K	Ca	Mg	Cl
Sea water ...	925–935	440	9.1	10	51	492–500
Plasma	1001–1036	254–320	4.4–7.0	2.6	3.9	239–250
Rectal gland	1001–1036	502–580	5.6–8.4	1	1	490–562
Urine.........	754–780	327–352	2	4	50	170–286

When elasmobranchs are adapted to dilute sea water, the chloride concentration in the blood remains relatively constant, while the urea content declines (Fig. VII.4), although in very dilute sea water, the chloride may also fall. On transfer to dilute sea water, the diuresis produced by the osmotic inflow of water will lead to an increased loss of urea and a new equilibrium level is established; on transfer to more concentrated sea water, the urine flow will be reduced and urea will accumulate until the fish is once again hyperosmotic to the medium.

A few elasmobranchs live in fresh water (Smith, 1931 a), but still retain a considerable concentration of urea in the body fluids (Table VII.5), and must therefore be descended from marine ancestors. The urine flow is similar to that of freshwater fish, 150–460 ml/kg/day (cf. Table V.4) and the urine is considerably hypo-osmotic to the blood, containing only about one tenth the concentrations of chloride and urea. Urea resorption must occur in the kidneys, as in marine forms, but the rate of urine production is so large that the concentration of urea in the blood cannot be maintained as high as in marine species.

In the freshwater *Pristis*, 77% of the urea and 76% of the chloride (of a total of 9.2 mM Cl/kg/day) were lost extrarenally (Smith, 1931 a). This chloride loss was probably underestimated because no allowance was made for the concurrent uptake.

Lampreys

Both the marine lamprey, *Petromyzon marinus*, and the river lamprey, *Lampetra fluviatilis*, living in brackish water, maintain their blood concentrations hypo-osmotic to the medium. Both migrate into fresh water to spawn. Fresh-run *Lampetra fluviatilis* can still adapt to 50% sea water (552 mOsm/kg water) while maintaining the blood at a concentration of 324 mOsm/kg water (Morris, 1958). Like the teleosts, the lampreys swallow considerable amounts of sea water (142 ml/kg/day) absorbing 76% of the water and 87% of the chloride. The urine output in 50% sea water is negligible, so the chloride must be excreted extrarenally (Morris, 1957). Chloride excretion in three lampreys was estimated at 41 ml/kg/day. According to Morris (1958), ingested sea water becomes diluted in the gut, but remains hyperosmotic to the body fluids and contains a higher concentration of chloride than the blood. This need not necessarily imply that water is actively transported (cf. Chap. I, p.40, Chap. VI, p.260). The ability of *Lampetra* to survive in hyperosmotic solutions is lost soon after migration into fresh water when the fish reach sexual maturity (Morris, 1957).

The permeability of the lamprey to water is similar in both sea water and fresh water. The rate of urine production in fresh water was 160 ml/kg/day and the osmotic concentration difference about 260 mOsm/kg water. In 50% sea water, with a similar osmotic gradient, water absorption in the gut was about 110 ml/kg/day.

Amphibians

The brackish water frog, *Rana cancrivora*, can live in brackish water of 28% salinity, and its tadpoles have an even greater range. Even at the highest concentrations, the blood is slightly hyperosmotic to the medium. In fresh water, the plasma contains about 40 mM/l. urea, and at the highest concentration as much as 300 mM/l., while the electrolyte content has only doubled. The urine is always strongly hypoosmotic to the plasma. At the highest external concentrations, its urea content is less than that of the plasma, and the electrolyte content is only about a tenth that of the plasma. The urea and electrolytes together account for only a half of the osmotic pressure of the urine; the remainder is unidentified.

Although the high uraemia solves the problem of water balance in these frogs, the mechanism of salt balance remains obscure. Measurements of the electrical potential across the skin and the short-circuited current indicate that active salt transport continues at high external concentrations. In most cases, the inside of the skin is positive with respect to the outside in high salinities (Gordon, Schmidt-Nielsen and Kelly, 1961). Since the loss of salt in the urine is so small, salt must be removed extra-renally. The electrical measurements seem to indicate that at high concentrations, active chloride extrusion maintains the salt balance.

Reptiles, Birds and Mammals

The osmotic problems of marine tetrapods are essentially the same as those of fishes. Although they lack the exposed respiratory surfaces where most salt and water is exchanged in fishes, their osmotic problems are aggravated because they lose considerable amounts of water by evaporation and in the excretion of nitrogenous waste. No marine tetrapod appears to be able to excrete salt directly into the sea, but all can produce extremely concentrated solutions of salt, hyperosmotic even to sea water. The mammalian kidney can secrete a strongly hyperosmotic urine, but the avian kidney is less effective in this respect* and the reptile is unable to produce a hyperosmotic urine at all. However, both birds and reptiles can secrete very concentrated solutions of salt extrarenally.

Marine reptiles and birds — Marine reptiles and birds have a serious osmotic problem, but the inadequacies of their kidneys are compensated by the development of "salt glands". In birds, the glands are usually nasal in origin, but are often situated elsewhere. In most marine birds, they lie at the top of the head (Fig. VII.10), but open into the nasal cavity. In the marine turtle, the glands are of different embryological origin, and open into the posterior of the orbit. They are probably modified lachrymal glands, although their histological structure is very similar to that of the avian glands (Schmidt-Nielsen, 1960 b). Terrestrial birds and reptiles often possess homologous but less well developed glands, but their function is unknown and usually they cannot secrete salt solutions hyperosmotic to the blood.

Only a few reptiles are marine, but they represent four distinct orders: turtles, snakes, lizards and crocodiles. Many marine turtles go on land only to lay their eggs, and as the eggs are deposited they have been observed to shed tears; but this is an outward sign of osmoregulation rather than pain. Some sea snakes are completely marine but their powers of osmoregulation are quite unknown, perhaps understandably, since they are reputed to be the most poisonous of all snakes. However, they do possess well-developed salt glands, either

* Salt glands are absent in the passerine Savannah sparrow, which survives in the arid areas of North America by drinking from saline lagoons. It can maintain its weight on a solution as concentrated as 0.7 mM NaCl/l. by producing a urine containing 960 mM Cl/l. See footnote on p.231.

orbital or nasal. Marine crocodiles *(Crocodylus porosus)* have been found far out to sea, although they are normally estuarine in habit. They have both orbital and nasal glands, but the single specimen examined did not respond to an osmotic load, and "crocodile tears must still be classed as one of the mysteries of biology" (Schmidt-Nielsen, 1960 b). The marine iguana *(Amblyrhynchus cristatus)*, which feeds on seaweed, can secrete a solution containing as much as 840 mM Na/l. from its nasal glands (Schmidt-Nielsen and Fänge, 1958). The secretion is eliminated as a fine spray from the nostrils. The brackish water terrapin *(Malaclemys terrapin)* can produce tears containing 616–784 mM Na/l., and the marine loggerhead turtle *(Caretta caretta)* can produce tears containing 810–922 mM Na/l. and 18–31 mM K/l. (Schmidt-Nielsen and Fänge, 1958). These concentrations are higher than that of sea water, so the animals could obtain free water by drinking sea water and excreting the salt in the tears, but there is no evidence that

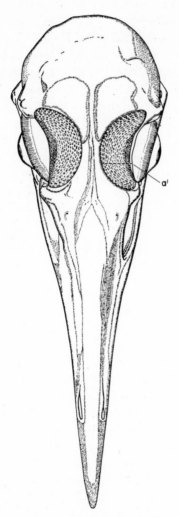

Fig. VII.10. The nasal salt gland of the sea gull *Larus.*. Section of the gland at "a" illustrated in next figure. From Schmidt–Nielsen, 1960 b.

they do deliberately drink sea water. Marine turtles produce a urine slightly hypo-osmotic to the plasma (Burian, 1910) and as the urine contains some urea, the salt concentration in the urine must be low.

Marine birds belong also to several different orders; most, if not all, can secrete hyperosmotic salt solutions from the nasal glands. Leach's petrel, which lives mainly on crustacean plankton and comes to land only to breed, can secrete a solution containing 900–1100 mM Na/l. (Schmidt-Nielsen, 1960 b). Most other marine birds produce a solution less concentrated than this but still hyperosmotic to sea water. For example, the cormorant *Phalacrocorax* and the mallard duck can secrete a solution containing *ca.* 550 mM Na/l.; the penguin, *Spheniscus humboldti*, 726–840 mM Na/l. Other marine birds which can produce hyperosmotic nasal secretions include the herring gull, *Larus argentatus;* the pelican, *Pelicanis occidentalis;* the albatrosses, *Diomedea immutabilis* and *D. nigripes;* and the gannet, *Sula bassana* (Schmidt-Nielsen and Sladen, 1958; Macfarland, 1959; Scothorne, 1958). The domestic duck retains the ability to secrete a solution containing up to 640 mM Cl/l. (Scothorne, 1959 a).

The nasal glands are far more effective than the kidneys in excreting salt. When a 5.8 kg Humboldt penguin was fed 5 g of solid sodium chloride, the nasal gland excreted 3.5 g in 4 hours, in about 60 ml of solution. The nasal secretion contained 726–840 mM Na/l., 635–805 mM Cl/l. and 21–29 mM K/l. During the same period, the cloaca eliminated between 20 and 40 ml. of liquid derived from both gut and kidneys, but this contained only 40–209 mM Na/l., 32–280 mM Cl/l. and 23–173 mM K/l. The nasal secretion continued for a further 7 hours.

Swallowed sea water does not seem to play an important part in the osmoregulation of sea birds. Albatrosses will drink water voluntarily, but the cormorant does not drink sea water when fed on fish.

In the herring gull, the nasal gland consists of many long tubular lobes, each with a central canal (Fig. VII.11 a). Each lobe consists of many "tubulous glands" (Fig. VII.11 c) which drain by secretory tubules into the central canal. The tubulous glands are supplied with capillaries in which the blood flows in a direction opposite to that of the secreted fluid (Fänge, Schmidt-Nielsen and Osaki, 1958). The cells of the gland are characterised by an eosinophilic cytoplasm and many mitochondria (Scothorne, 1959 b). A simple counter current system of this kind (not a "hairpin counter current") would seem more likely to equilibrate the blood and the secretion, than to build up a concentrated solution, yet the glands are remarkably efficient. Although they amount to about 0.05% of the body weight (cf. mammalian kidney, 1% body weight), their maximum rate of secretion, *ca.* 0.5 ml/kg/min, compares favourably with the maximum rate of urine secretion in a mammal, *ca.* 1.5 ml/kg/min (Schmidt-Nielsen, 1960 a). The secretion is probably formed by the active transport of ions into the lumen of the gland, while the primary function of the mammalian kidney, on the other hand, is not the production of a concentrated salt solution, but of a concentrated urea solution as the indirect result of ion transport. Although the secretion consists mainly of a solution of sodium and chloride ions, significant quantities of other ions are found. For example, the normal secretion of the glands of the herring gull contains 718 mM Na/l., 24 mM K/l., 1.0 mM Ca + Mg/l., 720 mM Cl/l., 13 mM HCO_3/l. and 0.34 mM SO_4/l. The high concentration of potassium, five times greater than that of the blood, implies either that there is a specific potassium transport system, or alternatively, that chloride is actively secreted and the other ions enter by diffusion down the electrochemical gradient. The latter seems the more probable (cf. p.257). The composition of the nasal gland secretion is similar to the secretion of the rectal gland in selachians (Table VII.6).

Mammals — Marine mammals probably do not drink sea water to any extent and must therefore rely wholly on their food as a source of water. The gut contents and urine of the

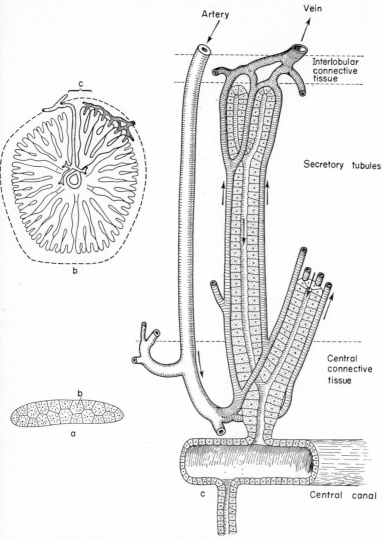

Fig. VII.11. The structure of the salt gland of the sea gull. *Larus*.
(a) Section of the gland shown in Fig. VII.10, showing
the tubular lobes in section.
(b) Section of a single tubular lobe showing central canal.
Artery (on left) and vein (on right).
(c) Enlarged view of a single tubular gland forming small
part of the tubular lobe shown in Fig. (b).
From Schmidt-Nielsen 1960 b.

common seal contain only traces of magnesium and sulphate (Smith, 1936 b), and Geiling and Roberts (quoted in Fetcher, 1939) reported that the contents of whales' stomachs are almost dry. The water requirements of marine mammals will be rather smaller than those of land mammals because no water is required for thermoregulation, and water loss from the lungs will also be proportionately smaller because of the higher extraction of oxygen from the air. Their body fluids are rather more concentrated (350–390 mOsm/l.) than those of land mammals (290–320 mOsm/l. (cf. Table VII.6 and Table VI.1). The urine is strongly hyperosmotic to the blood and even to sea water, but the sodium and chloride content of the urine is usually less than that of sea water (Table VII.6), although Lovenback (quoted in Krogh, 1939, p.165) reported that the urine of the whale, *Megaptera novaengliae*, contained as much as 820 mM Cl/l. One advantage of the slightly higher blood concentration in marine mammals was illustrated by the calculations of Fetcher (1939). The kidneys of land mammals perform about 1.8 kcal osmotic work/l. urine, and those of marine mammals about 2.5 kcal/l. urine, but if the blood concentrations of marine mammals were the same as those of land mammals, the osmotic work would have to be 2.9 kcal/l. urine.

An assessment of the water balance of the seal, *Phoca vitulina*, (Irving, Fisher and McIntosh, 1935) showed that it could maintain osmotic equilibrium on a diet of fish, without access to fresh water and without extrarenal salt secretion. It was calculated that 1250 g of fish contain 1000 g of water and would give a further 120 g of water on metabolism. This 1120 g of water is sufficient to provide for urine formation, and to replace the water lost in the faeces and by evaporation from the lungs. The metabolism of the fish was estimated to require 236 l. of oxygen. If the oxygen extraction rate were assumed to be 6 volumes/100 volumes of inspired air, the total volume of air breathed would be 236/0.06 or 3937 l. If the inspired air were assumed to be saturated and at 15°C, and the expired air saturated at 35°C, 106 g of water would be lost by evaporation from the lungs. If the air were cold and dry, the water loss would be greater, but if the oxygen extraction rate were more than 6 volumes %, less air would be used. The faeces from 1250 g of fish were estimated to contain 200 g water, so that just over 800 g of water would be left for the urine. The oxidation of the fish would give 48 g of urea, or 1000 mM urea/l. in 800 ml and the salt from the fish would amount to about 240 mM NaCl/l. in the same volume of urine. Even though no allowance has been made for the salt lost in the faeces, both the urea and salt concentration are within the range found in seal urine (Table VII.7). Fetcher (1939) maintains that fish contain more salt than Irving, Fisher and McIntosh estimated, and that the urine should contain 340 mM NaCl/l., but this is still in the recorded range (Table VII.7).

Mammals feeding on teleosts have the advantage of osmotic work already done by the fish. If the diet were invertebrate, the salt concentrations would be much higher. Fetcher (1939) calculates that a seal on a diet of oysters would have to produce urine containing 600 mM Cl/l. to remain in osmotic equilibrium, and if it were fed on lobsters, the urine would have to contain 700 mM Cl/l. This is considerably higher than the usual chloride content of seal urine, but still within the limit of a mammalian kidney. To check these calculations, Smith (1936 b) fed a seal on clams *(Mya)*, but found that the urine contained only 510 mM Cl/l., and even after 10 hours the seal had not eliminated all the ingested salts. Krogh (1939, p. 167) modified the calculations of Irving, Fisher and McIntosh, and concluded that whales could survive on an invertebrate diet without any other source of water. After making allowances for the salt and water lost in the faeces and reducing the allowance for water lost from the lungs by assuming a higher oxygen extraction rate, he concluded that a whale could remain in water balance if the urine contained 800 mM urea/l. and 565 mM Cl/l., both higher than the concentrations nor-

21*

mally found in whale urine (Table VII.7), but possibly still within the capacity of a whale's kidney.

TABLE VII.7. — COMPOSITION OF WHALE AND SEAL URINE
(Expressed as mM/l.; Fetcher, 1939)

	Total ions mOsm/kg water	Na	K	Ca	Mg	Cl	SO$_4$	Urea
Balaenoptera borealis	1320	240– 290	36– 92	0·3– 2·0	1·6– 4·1	180– 370	33– 43	380– 530
Phoca vitulina	925– 2150	—	—	1·3– 5·5	0·8– 30	200– 420	6—97	120– 1050

Few experiments have been made on the cetaceans. Fetcher and Fetcher (1942) examined the osmoregulatory ability of two specimens of the dolphin, *Tursiops truncatus*. The animals (70 and 140 kg) were each given 2 l. of 0.5 M NaCl (approx. isosmotic with sea water) and the urine, saliva, and faeces were collected for several hours. The saliva was slightly hyperosmotic to the blood (120–170 mM Cl/l.) unlike that of other mammals, but can play no significant part in the osmotic regulation. The rectal fluids were generally hypo-osmotic to the blood (60–230 mM Cl/l.), indicating that preferential salt uptake had occurred in the gut. The concentration of the urine rose rapidly to nearly 600 mM Cl/l. and remained high, but after 9 hours, 84% of the water and only 53% of the salt had been excreted. Although the urine was more concentrated than sea water, the net fluid absorbed from the gut was much more concentrated than sea water, because a considerable volume of faecal solution was produced, isosmotic or even hypo-osmotic to the blood. At the end of the experiment, the concentration of the blood (121.2 mM Cl/l.) was higher than at the beginning (115.3 mM Cl/l.) but the increase in the chloride content of the blood (assuming blood volume to be constant) was smaller than the net increase in the chloride content of the whole animal. The authors conclude that there was either a slight net shift of water from the tissues to the blood, or possibly some extrarenal secretion of salt.

Neither in Smith's nor in Fetchers' experiments had the animals returned to osmotic equilibrium by the end of the experiment. Although the kidneys of marine mammals are able to produce urine containing more salt than sea water, they are not so effective as the salt excreting glands of marine reptiles and birds. The possibility of extrarenal salt secretion in marine mammals cannot be excluded.

Whale and seal milk both contain a high concentration of solids (Eichelberger, Fetcher, Geiling and Vos, 1940; Schmidt-Nielsen, quoted by Krogh, 1939, p. 168) (Table VII.8). The

TABLE VII.8. — COMPOSITION OF MILK OF THE DOLPHIN (Expressed as mM/kg water; Eichelberger *et al.*, 1940)
FOR COMPARISON, THE PLASMA OF THE SPERM WHALE IS INCLUDED IN THE TABLE (Sudzuki, 1924)

Sample	Total ions mOsm/kg water	Na	K	Ca	Mg	Cl
Tursiops milk	330–389	81–117	21·2–43·7	23·1–29·1	3·74–5·05	81·1–98·5
Physeter plasma (mM/l.)	355–387	170	4·6	0·2	2·3	120

milk of the dolphin, *Tursiops truncatus*, contains about 100 g/l. protein and 108–167 g/l. fat, compared with 20 g/l. and 40 g/l., respectively, in human milk. Eichelberger, Fetcher, Geiling and Vos correlated the richness of the milk with the rapid growth of the calves, but Krogh points out that a rich milk will place less strain on the water economy of the mother. However, although whale milk is very rich compared with human or cow's milk, there is a similar high concentration of solids in rabbit or dog's milk. The total salt content of whale milk is rather lower than that of the blood, but much higher than that of human milk (Table VI.5).

Insects

The larvae of several insects, e.g. the mosquito, *Aedes detritus*, (Beadle, 1939), the chironomid, *Cricotopus vitripinnis*, the flies, *Coelopa frigida* and *Ephydra* spp. (Sutcliffe, 1960; Nemenz, 1960 b and c) can live in concentrated saline waters. *Aedes detritus* will develop in a solution of 1.2 M NaCl/kg water, while

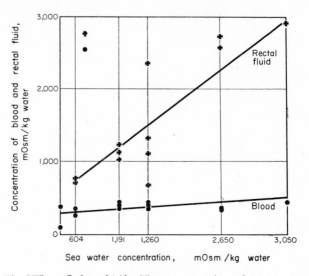

Fig. VII.12. *Coelopa frigida*. The concentration of the blood and rectal fluid as a function of the concentration of the medium. From Sutcliffe, 1960.

maintaining a blood concentration of only 260 mOsm/kg water (Beadle, 1939). *Coelopa* will develop in three times concentrated sea water (Fig. VII.12) and *Ephydra cinerea* in 10 molar sodium chloride (Nemenz, 1960 a). Although many of the details of hypo-osmotic regulation in the insects are still obscure, it is known to depend on their ability to produce a concentrated solution of salts in the rectum (Ramsay, 1950; Sutcliffe, 1960). The rectal fluids of *Aedes detritus* are hypo-osmotic to the blood when the larva is in fresh water, but hyperosmotic when it is in sea water (Table VII.9). Similarly, the rectal fluids of both *Ephydra* and *Coelopa* are less concentrated than the blood in dilute media, but more concentrated than either the blood or the medium in concentrated media (Nemenz, 1960 b). The ability of these insects to live in hyperosmotic media has arisen from the water conserving properties of the rectal glands in terrestrial insects.

TABLE VII.9. OSMOTIC CONCENTRATIONS OF THE BODY FLUIDS OF *Aedes detritus* IN SEA WATER AND FRESH WATER
(Expressed as mOsm/kg water; Ramsay, 1950)

Medium	Blood	Mid-gut fluid	Intestinal fluid	Rectal fluid
Fresh water	194	280	194	112
Sea water	322	354	432	1060

The intestinal and midgut fluids of *Aedes detritus* are only slightly hyperosmotic to the blood (Table VII.9). On average, the rectal fluid was about three times as concentrated as the other body fluids (Ramsay, 1950). Although the measured concentrations were not hyperosmotic to the medium in every case, it is probable that some samples included fluid from more anterior parts of the rectum where concentration was not complete. If the larva is to remain in osmotic equilibrium, the voided rectal fluid must be hyperosmotic to the medium.

The rectal fluid of *Aedes detritus* is derived mainly from the malpighian tubes, but as the malpighian tubes produce an isosmotic fluid, all the osmotic work is done in the rectum. *Aedes detritus* larvae can survive in isosmotic potassium chloride (Ramsay, 1953 a) but not in hyperosmotic potassium, calcium or magnesium chloride (Beadle, 1939). The ability to produce a hyperosmotic rectal fluid must depend not only on the active removal of water, but also, in some way, on the availability of sodium.

The permeability of the body wall of insects living in saline waters is similar to that of those living in fresh water. For example, the permeability in the saline dipterous larvae of

Ephydra cinerea is 0.04 μ sec^{-1} at 23°C (Nemenz, 1960 b) compared with 0.05 μ sec^{-1} at 20°C in the freshwater lacewing
larva, *Sialis lutaria* (Shaw, 1955 a).

The body wall of *Aedes detritus* larvae has a very low permeability to water, but larvae shrink and die within 24 hours
in sucrose isosmotic with sea water. It is suggested that the
gut is impermeable to sucrose and that the larvae are unable
to absorb water from a sucrose solution in the gut (Beadle,
1939). The chloride concentration of the body fluids falls
rapidly in the sucrose solution, possibly because the malpighian tube–rectum system excretes the body salts in an
attempt to correct the increasing osmotic pressure of the blood.
There is no certain evidence that the larvae drink the medium
like the teleosts, but Beadle's experiments suggest that this
is so. The anal gills, which in the freshwater species, *Aedes
aegypti*, are responsible for salt uptake, are almost vestigial
in *A. detritus*, but the latter species can osmoregulate in fresh
water apparently as well as the former.

A number of brackish water caddis larvae maintain a low salt
concentration in the body fluids, but only one, *Lymnephilus
affinus* is known to maintain its body fluid slightly hypo-osmotic to the medium and only this species can survive in full-
strength sea water. The salt content of the body fluid of these
larvae is low, and about half of the observed osmotic pressure
of the blood is due to unidentified non-electrolytes. The body
wall of *L. affinus* is about twice as permeable as that of *Sialis*.
The small quantity of water lost by exosmosis is made good
by drinking the medium and then excreting the salt in a hyperosmotic rectal fluid which may contain three times as much
chloride as the blood. The permeability of the body wall to
salts is low and most of the salt exchange takes place through
the gut (Sutcliffe, 1961 a and b). The mechanism of osmoregulation is thus fundamentally the same as in other saline insects,
but the higher permeability of the body wall is offset by a high
concentration of non-electrolytes in the blood which reduces
the osmotic gradient.

Artemia Salina

The brine shrimp, *Artemia salina*, has the most remarkable powers of osmotic regulation known. It can maintain the osmotic concentration of its body fluids below that of sea water, while living in a saturated solution of sodium chloride, *ca.* 30% salt. In very dilute solutions, it can maintain its body fluids hyperosmotic to the medium, although it cannot survive for long in completely fresh water (Croghan, 1958 a).

The permeability of its body wall to water is very low. Ussing (quoted in Krogh, 1939, p.98) found that the gross water flux measured by heavy water was equivalent to 25% of the total body water/hour (temperature and size of animals unspecified). The net water flux would therefore be 0.45% body water/molar concentration difference/hour (Chap. I, p. 23), a remarkably low permeability for such a small animal of complex shape (cf. Table V.5). Croghan (1958 a) found that *Artemia* ligatured around the neck and anus were not visibly dehydrated after 23 hours in sea water containing 2.5 M glycerol/kg water. If these had the same permeability as Ussing's animals, the net water loss would have been about 25% of the body water in this time. The ligatures, by preventing water exchange through the gut, may have reduced the permeability of the animals still further.

In hyperosmotic solutions, water balance is maintained by drinking the medium and excreting surplus salt. By keeping animals in sea water coloured with phenol red, Croghan (1958 c) demonstrated that *Artemia* drank the medium both orally and anally and subsequently absorbed the swallowed water. The maximum concentration of phenol red in the gut was seven times that in the medium. Sodium and chloride ions were taken up from the gut because the concentrations of these ions in the gut fluid were lower than in the blood; but the total osmotic concentration of the gut fluid is greater than that of the blood (Fig. VII.2) because the levels of potassium and divalent ions are high (Fig. VII.13). *Artemia*,

unlike the marine teleosts, must be able to take up water
against a concentration gradient. Croghan suggests that the
removal of sodium and chloride from the water in the gut
reduces the osmotic pressure of the fluid to a level that the

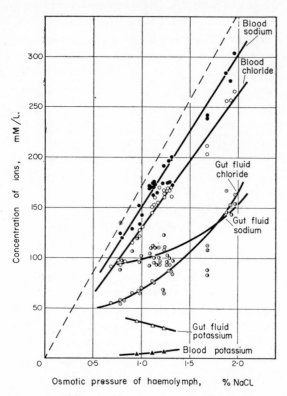

Fig. VII.13. *Artemia salina*. The concentrations of sodium, potassium and chloride in the blood and gut as functions of the osmotic pressure of the blood. From Croghan, 1958 a.

water pump can overcome. Alternatively, it may be suggested
that the uptake of water is somehow linked with the uptake
of these ions (cf. *Aedes detritus*, above). A curious feature is
that the gut contents remain hyperosmotic to the blood even
in hypo-osmotic media (Fig. VII.2). It is possible that the

active uptake of water is obligatory and continues even in conditions where it is no longer necessary.

Croghan (1958 b) was able to demonstrate fairly conclusively that the sodium chloride taken up from the gut was excreted by localised areas on the first ten pairs of branchiae. These areas are the only ones visibly affected by short treatment with silver nitrate, methylene blue or saturated potassium permanganate, and therefore the only areas of the cuticle reasonably permeable to these substances. The underlying epithelium was brown and distorted after treatment with potassium permanganate, and animals which survived such treatment were quite unable to osmoregulate, although they could live in a solution of sodium chloride or sea water isosmotic with the normal blood. Animals in which the ability to osmoregulate had been destroyed in this way still retained some powers of ionic regulation; for example, in a solution containing 4.8 mM Mg/l., the concentration of magnesium in the blood was only 1 mM/l. The silver staining of the branchiae took place in areas which were probably excreting sodium chloride, but it also occurred in dead animals and was only significant of a passive permeability to silver ions.

The flux of sodium through *Artemia* is roughly proportional to the concentration of sodium in the external medium (Fig. VII.14), and declines almost to zero in distilled water or in an erythritol solution isosmotic with sea water. Croghan does not estimate the efflux in sodium-free solutions, but from two of his figures (Croghan, 1958 d, Fig. VII.6 and 7) the calculated effluxes in three animals were 4.5, 8 and 8 mM Na/kg/hr, compared with fluxes of 50–250 mM Na/kg/hr in solutions containing sodium. This rough estimate of the efflux in distilled water agrees with Croghan's observations that the blood concentration of two groups of animals, each containing several individuals, declined from 170 to 75 mM Na/l. during 13 hours in distilled water. Experiments with [82]Br suggest that the chloride fluxes are similar to the sodium fluxes.

As the efflux is approximately proportional to the external

sodium concentration, Croghan concluded that the greater part
of the flux was due to exchange diffusion, which masked any
net exchange. The magnitude of the flux (50–250 mM Na/kg/hr)
compared with the fluxes of animals such as *Nereis diversicolor*
(12.6 mM/kg/hr in sea water at 12°C) (Chap. IV, p.145) or
Astacus (0.5 mM/kg/hr in ½ sea water at 19°C) (Chap. V, p.192)
supports this suggestion. Ligation of the mouth and rectum

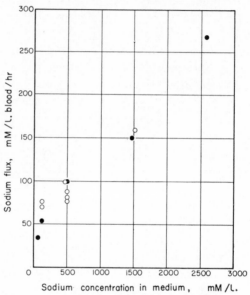

Fig. VII.14. *Artemia salina*. Sodium fluxes through *Artemia* in
various media. Influx ●, efflux ○. From Croghan, 1958 d.

had no apparent effect on the fluxes of sodium or bromide,
which suggests that exchange diffusion takes place through
the branchiae. Ligation would certainly affect active transport
of ions in *Artemia*, because swallowing is an essential part
of its regulation mechanism.

Potassium can substitute for sodium in the exchange system,
but the carrier has a lower affinity for potassium than sodium.
In a 550 mM/l. solution of potassium benzene sulphonate,
there was a 1:1 exchange of potassium for sodium in the

blood, but the influx of potassium was about 30 mM/kg/hr, only one third of the sodium influx from solutions containing 550 mM Na/l. If the affinity of the carrier for potassium were as high as for sodium, it would be difficult for the animals to maintain a Na/K ratio in the blood different from that of the medium.

It is possible to estimate the active fluxes of sodium through *Artemia*. If the water flux is 0.45% body water/molar concentration difference/hour, the water loss in 3000 mM Na/l. would be 1.4%/hr. If this were replaced by swallowing the water, and excreting the salt, the efflux would be 45 mM Na/kg water/hr. In addition, some salt will enter by diffusion and must be excreted. The observed efflux in 3000 mM Na/l. was 270 mM Na/kg/hr. The efflux into sodium-free solution was about 7 mM/kg/hr. but approximate calculations suggest that the permeability of the body wall to sodium is normally less than this. For example, if the net efflux from the blood (170 mM Na/l.) were 7 mM Na/kg/hr, the diffusion influx from 3000 mM Na/l. would be 120 mM Na/kg/hr, or almost half the observed efflux. It is possible that much of the efflux in sodium free solution took place from the gut. It is not known if the gut is still hyperosmotic in distilled water (Fig. VII.2), but this is probable. A study of the efflux from ligated animals in distilled water would elucidate this point. The maxillary excretory organs in *Artemia* may remove excess divalent ions in hyperosmotic media and water in hypo-osmotic media.

Palaemonid Prawns

Palaemon serratus and *Palaemonetes varians* are approximately isosmotic with 70% sea water, but are hypo-osmotic in more concentrated media. Like so many other animals which regulate hypo-osmotically, they are hyperosmotic in dilute solutions (Fig. VII.2). The urine of *Palaemon* is almost isosmotic with the blood in all media, although it has a different ionic composition (Fig. VII.3b). In *Palaemonetes varians*, the rate of urine production is minimal in isosmotic solutions but increases both in hyperosmotic and hypo-osmotic solutions (Fig. VII.15). Measurements of the permeability of *Palaemonetes* to heavy water (Parry, G., 1955) show that the total water flux averages 1.28 ml/ml body water/hr. This is equivalent to 2.3% body water/molar concentration difference/hr, or 1.5% body weight/hr in fresh water, in fair agreement with the observed

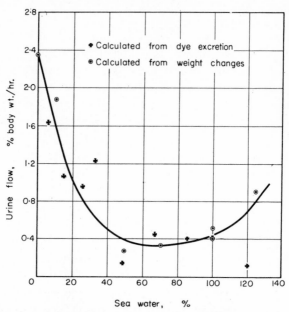

Fig. VII.15. *Palaemonetes varians.* Estimated rates of urine production in different salinities. From Parry, 1955.

rate of urine production in fresh water (Fig. VII.15). The increased rate of urine production in more concentrated solutions may be necessary for the maintenance of ionic regulation. If the composition of the urine of *Palaemonetes varians* were similar to that of *Palaemon* (Parry, G., 1954), then in 70% sea water, *Palaemonetes varians* will excrete 210 μM Mg/kg/hr, and in 120% sea water, 760 μM/kg/hr. This increase is not proportional to the increase in the concentration of magnesium in the medium, but may well be proportional to the increased concentration of magnesium in the gut. If the prawn absorbs water from the gut after swallowing the hyperosmotic solutions the concentration of magnesium there will increase steeply with increasing concentration of the medium and the passive influx of magnesium would increase in proportion. However, although both anal and oral swallowing are common to many crustaceans (Fox, 1953), it is not known if any water absorption takes place in the gut of *Palaemonetes*.

The sodium flux through *Palaemonetes* in 5%, 70% and 120% sea water is about 25 mM Na/kg/hr (cf. 5.3 mM/kg/hr for the freshwater *Palaemonetes antennarius*, (Chap. V, p.179). The preliminary observations were very variable (Parry, G., 1955), but later measurements (Parry and Potts, unpub.) show that the flux is higher in 120% sea water than in 70% or 5% sea water. These fluxes are not excessively large for such a small animal (0.1–0.2 g), and are not proportional to the external sodium concentration: they are therefore probably due to diffusion and active transport, not to exchange diffusion. The efflux in 5% sea water is about four times the rate of sodium loss in the urine, so most of the exchange probably takes place through the body wall.

Crabs

Many grapsoid and ocypodid crabs, e.g., *Uca pugnax* but not all (e.g. *Hemigrapsus nudus*, *H. oregonensis*, Jones, L., 1941) can regulate hypo-osmotically in sea water and concentrated sea water (Fig. VII.1). The urine may be almost isosmotic with the blood, as in *Pachygrapsus crassipes* (Prosser, Green and Chow, 1955; Jones, L., 1941), although of different ionic composition, or strongly hyperosmotic to the blood, as in *Ocypode albicans* (Flemister and Flemister, 1951). The mechanism of hypo-osmotic regulation in these crabs is still obscure. It is suspected that sea water is swallowed and the excess salt excreted by the gills as in the marine teleosts (Green, Harsch,

Barr and Prosser, 1959), but a suggestion has been made that the gills secrete not only magnesium but also absorb water (Green *et al.*, 1959).

The composition of the stomach fluid of *Uca* (Table VII.10) indicates that water and salt uptake occur in the gut. The gastric fluid contains less sodium and chloride than sea water, but six times as much sulphate, more than twice as much calcium, and more magnesium and potassium. Green *et al.* (1959) suggest that sulphate may be excreted into the gut, but this is unlikely, as the blood appears to contain a higher concentration of sulphate than sea water.* The gut fluid is hyperosmotic to the blood, so water uptake must take place against an osmotic gradient as in *Artemia* and the insects.

TABLE VII.10. — COMPOSITION OF BODY FLUIDS AND MEDIUM OF *Uca pugnax* (Expressed as mM/l.; Green, Harsch, Barr and Prosser, 1959)

Sample	Total osmotic concn. mOsm/kg water	Na	K	Ca	Mg[1]	Cl[2]	SO$_4$	NH$_4$
Sea water.........	1120	397	9	12	44	576	22	0
Stomach fluid...	1516	335	17	31	51	542	143	63
Serum	994	328	11	16	23	537	42	20
Urine	1166	276	16	17	54	622	47	75
Gill fluid (branchial chamber)	1012	314	10	12	32	569	36	18

1. In their original table, Green *et al.* give the magnesium content of sea water as 88 mM/l., evidently mE/l. All magnesium concentrations have therefore been halved.
2. The chloride content of the sea water does not accord with the concentration of the other ions. Sea water containing 397 mM Na/l. should contain 8.3 mM/K, 8.7 mM Ca, 45.2 mM Mg, 463 mM Cl and 23.9 mM SO$_4$/l. (Barnes, 1954)

The urine of these crabs contains less sodium than the serum, even in *Pachygrapsus* which produces a slightly hyperosmotic urine (Table VII.11), suggesting that the sodium is excreted extrarenally. It is possible that it is removed by the gill epithelium, but the fluid in the gill chamber contains a lower concentration of sodium than the bathing medium

* This may be due to confusion between the units of mE and mM on the part of Green *et al.*

(Table VII.10).* The cells of the gill epithelium of the related *Ocypode albicans*, another hypo-osmotic regulator, are rich in mitochondria, which could be a sign of actively secreting cells (Flemister, 1959). Magnesium is concentrated in the urine of *Pachygrapsus*. It may originate from the sea water in the gut, because although sulphate is strongly concentrated there, magnesium is not.

TABLE VII.11. — OSMOTIC COMPOSITION OF MEDIUM, SERUM AND URINE
IN *Pachygrapsus crassipes* IN 175% SEA WATER
(Expressed as mOsm/kg water; Prosser, Green and Chow, 1955)

Sample	Total ions mOsm/kg water	Na	K	Ca	Mg
Medium	1980	780	16·7	17·0	88·5
Serum	1780	668	17·4	12·3	33·1
Urine	1800	264	17·2	18·6	324·6

Flemister (1958) provides interesting evidence of the extra-renal excretion of thiocyanate in hyperosmotic solutions. The urine flow estimated from the inulin clearance in *Goniopsis cruentatis* is equivalent to about 10% body weight/day, and is independent of the concentration of the medium. The thiocyanate space amounts to 30.4% of the body weight, and so about one third of injected thiocyanate should be excreted by the antennary glands in 24 hours. In fact, a third of the thiocyanate is lost in only 12 hours in hypo-osmotic or isosmotic media; the rest is probably lost by diffusion; but in a hyperosmotic medium, one third of the thiocyanate is lost in as little as 2½ hours. This strongly suggests that it is actively excreted elsewhere in these conditions.

Summary

For comparison, the rates of excretion of sodium and chloride of a number of hypo-osmotic regulators are collected in Table

---

* The fluid in the gill chamber of *Uca* could be sampled because this animal keeps its gills wet but not immersed.

VII.12. Apart from an apparently very rapid rate in *Artemia* which is due to exchange diffusion, the rates of excretion are remarkably uniform.

TABLE VII.12. — EXCRETION INTO HYPEROSMOTIC SOLUTIONS

Animal	Ion measured	Rate mM/ kg/hr	Blood concentration mM/kg water	Medium concentration mM/kg water	Reference
Fish:					
Lampetra	Chloride	1·7	173	280	Morris, 1958
Anguilla	Chloride	0·56	*ca.* 170	530	Keys, 1931
Myoxocephalus	Chloride	0·81	*ca.* 170	457	Smith, 1930 b
Gasterosteus ...	Sodium	10·7	150	230	Mullins, 1950
Squalus acanthias	Sodium	1·0	*ca.* 300	440	Burger & Hess, 1960
Crustacea:*					
Artemia	Sodium	250[1]	330	2700	Croghan, 1958 d
Palaemonetes ...	Sodium	25	473[2]	600	Parry, 1955
Mammals:					
Tursiops	Chloride	0·43[3]	120	530	Fetcher & Fetcher, 1942
Phoca	Chloride	0·95[3]	*ca.* 120	390	Smith, 1936 b
Birds:					Schmidt-Nielsen &
Spheniscus	Sodium	2·7[3]	*ca.* 140	800	Sladen, 1958

1. Exchange diffusion
2. Assumed the same as *Palaemon*
3. Maximum rates.

* See also Dehnel, 1962.

Other Body Fluids

Analyses of body fluids other than blood, serum and urine are uncommon and are restricted mainly to the elasmobranchs and teleosts (Table VII.13). In the elasmobranchs, although there is no dura mater, the cranial fluid is homologous with the cerebrospinal fluid in other vertebrates, but it contains a clotting protein. In composition it is very similar to the plasma, whereas the perivisceral and pericardial fluids are remarkably different, notably in the high potassium concentration of the pericardial fluid, and the high magnesium and sulphate concentrations of the perivisceral fluid. It is interesting to note that the pericardial fluid of the Sei whale, *Balaenoptera borealis*, also contains a high concentration of potassium (15–18 mM/l.) and moderate amounts of sulphate (5–6 mM/l.) (Sudzuki, 1924). The composition of the ear fluids is of interest in that the perilymph in both elasmobranchs and teleosts is very similar to the plasma, but the endolymph contains a much greater concentration of potassium, as in other vertebrates (Tables VI.4 and VII.13).

TABLE VII.13. — COMPOSITION OF SOME FISH BODY FLUIDS
(Expressed as mM/l.)

1. *Raja laevis* (Smith, 1929 a and 1931 b)

Sample	Na	K	Ca	Mg	Cl	SO$_4$	HCO$_3$	Urea	pH
Plasma	262	5·0	3 8	1·7	232	trace	6·0	445	7·35
"Cerebrospinal fluid"	262	3·8	3·0	0·9	244	,,	5·5	443	7·64
Pericardial fluid	353	21	0·5	1·0	366	,,	0·3	321	6·86
Perivisceral fluid ...	299	5·2	9·7	21·7	332	13·9	0·4	467	6·15
Urine	—	46	64	182	200	192	—	103[1]	—

[1] This figure includes ammonia

2. *Raja clavata* (Murray and Potts, 1960)

Serum	Na	K			Cl			Urea	
Serum	289	3·98			311			444	
"Cerebrospinal fluid"	280	3·34			311			437	
Perilymph	281	3·54			321			447	
Endolymph	295	63·4			391			381	

3. *Gadus morhua* (Harden Jones and Woodhead, unpub.)

"Cerebrospinal fluid"	173	3·06	3·6						
Perilymph	173	3·25	3·7						
Endolymph	128	74·03	1·2						

22*

Tissues

Little is known about the composition of the tissues of hypo-osmotic regulators but, except for the selachians, they are probably similar to those of their freshwater and terrestrial relatives. A few marine teleosts analysed by Becker, Bird, Kelly, Schilling and Young (1958) (Table VII.14) indicate that the different tissues are similar to those of mammals (cf. Tables VI.8 and VI.10). When allowance is made for the extracellular fluid (*ca.* 20%), the intracellular concentration of sodium and chloride in the muscle will be quite small. On the other hand, heart muscle and kidney must contain higher intracellular concentrations of these ions.

The selachians are peculiar in that their tissues, like the blood plasma, all contain a high concentration of urea and

TABLE VII.14. — COMPOSITION OF SERUM AND TISSUES OF
TWO MARINE TELEOSTS
(Expressed as mM/kg water; Becker, Bird, Kelly, Schilling
and Young, 1958)

Scomberomorus maculatus (mackerel)

Sample	Na	K	Cl
Serum	198	10·3	176·0
Muscle	71·1	153·5	53·8
Heart	130·5	123·5	103·0
Liver	144	133·5	135·5
Kidney	137·5	127	153·5

Mycteroperca bonaci (grouper)

Sample	Na	K	Cl
Serum	237	8·2	217
Muscle	51·5	123·5	26·7
Heart...............................	96·9	91·2	65·8
Liver...............................	90·4	152·0	53·3
Kidney	146·0	89·2	106·0
Sea water	461	10·2	556

trimethylamine oxide (Table VII.15). The urea is uniformly distributed throughout the body, whereas trimethylamine oxide is most unequally distributed, probably because it has too large a molecule to diffuse across the cell walls. Marine teleosts have similar, or even larger, amounts of trimethylamine oxide in their tissues.

TABLE VII.15. — UREA AND TRIMETHYLAMINE OXIDE IN THE TISSUES OF ELASMOBRANCHS

Tissue	Urea mM/kg water[1]	Trimethylamine oxide mM/kg wet weight[2]
Plasma or serum...................	315	64
Blood cells	343	—
Muscle	321	135–88
Liver	350	8
Spleen	296	62
Kidney	—	42
Skin	393	—

1. Smith, 1929b: *Raja laevis*
2. Norris and Benoit, 1945 ; *Squalus acanthias*

The concentration of free amino acids in salmon tissues amounts to only 10mM/kg wet weight of muscle. In contrast to many invertebrates (Chap. IV, pp.159, 161), the levels of free amino acids do not change significantly when the fish migrates from one salinity to another (Cowey, Daisley and Parry, 1962) (Table VII.16.)

Eggs and Embryos

The eggs of marine teleosts are approximately isosmotic with the parental body fluids when spawned (e.g. *Platichthys flesus*, Krogh, 1939, p.178), and this low concentration, compared to sea water, is maintained throughout embryonic development, e.g. *Pleuronectes platessa* (Dakin, 1911) *Clupea harengus* (Holliday and Blaxter, 1960), *Nerophis ophidium* (Krogh, 1939, p.179), although the eggs are permeable to both salt and water. The perivitelline fluid *(in Clupea* and *Nerophis)* is almost

TABLE VII.16. COMPOSITION OF WHOLE MUSCLE OF THE SALMON, *Salmo salar* IN SEA WATER FRESH WATER (SPENT FISH).
(From Cowey, Daisley and Parry, 1962).

Constituent	Sea water mM/kg water	Fresh water mM/kg water	Composition expected in fresh water from change in water content
Sodium	28·1	45·5	25·8
Potassium	206	199	189
Taurine	2·70	1·86	2·48
Aspartic acid	0010	0·16	0·09
Threonine	0·86	0·80	0·79
Serine	0·64	0·60	0·59
Glutamic acid	1·49	1·50	1·34
Proline	0·70	0·75	0·64
Glycine	4·04	4·10	3·71
Alanine	4·90	5·41	4·50
Valine	0·80	0·70	0·73
Isoleucine	0·42	0·37	0·39
Methionine	0·81	0·71	0·74
Tyrosine	0·26	0·19	0·24
Phenylalanine	0·19	0·21	0·17
Lysine	0·23	0·18	0·21
Arginine	0·30	0·33	0·28
Anserine	0·41	0·39	0·38
β—alanine	34·34	35·77	31·56
Histidine	absent	absent	—
Total free amino acids	53·19	54·38	49·24
% Water	71·7	78·0	—

isosmotic with the medium, but the embryo maintains its low concentration until hatching (Holliday and Blaxter, 1960). It is difficult to understand how the embryo can regulate its water content before it is able to swallow and before the gills and kidney have developed. The greater part of the osmotic pressure of the new laid egg is due to chlorides, but during the course of development the chloride content of the embryo declines, as in freshwater or terrestrial animals, as the organic anions accumulate. For example, early embryos of *Nerophis*, taken from sea water of 412 mM Cl/l., contained 180 mM Cl/l., while later embryos contained only 97 mM Cl/l.

Selachian eggs contain little urea when first laid. The eggs are relatively impermeable to urea, and autogenous urea accumulates until by the time of hatching it has reached the adult level (Needham and Needham, 1930). The new laid eggs are about isosmotic with sea water, but contain a much lower concentration of salt (Bialascewicz, 1929); the solutes making up the osmotic pressure have not been identified.

CHAPTER VIII

RESPIRATION AND
ELECTROLYTE REGULATION

Since active transport requires energy, it may be related to oxygen consumption. The relation between the metabolic rate of animals and active transport has been studied both in isolated tissues and in whole animals. In some cases a correlation has been found between the rates of ion transport and the metabolic rate and in some of these experiments, the data are sufficiently precise to elucidate the thermodynamic efficiency of transport systems. However, many experiments, particularly those with whole animals, are very difficult to interpret.

There is an extensive literature on the relation between metabolism and salinity in brackish water animals. Curiously, the first of these observations were primarily ecological. In 1924, Roch noted that the coelenterate *Cordylophora* was found in fresh water only when the water was well oxygenated, although it was found also in poorly oxygenated brackish water. Similarly, Thienemann (1928) found that *Mysis relicta* was absent from stagnant water of low salinity, although it can live in sea water of low oxygen content. Thienemann suggested that oxygen uptake was easier in water of higher salinity. However, Schlieper (1929) measured the rate of respiration of several brackish water animals at various salinities, and found that oxygen consumption of *Carcinus* generally increased and that of *Nereis* temporarily increased as the salinity was reduced. This was confirmed later by Beadle

(1937) and Schwabe (1933) (Fig. VIII. 1). Schlieper noted that the salinity of the medium did not affect the activity of the animal (provided certain precautions were taken) and therefore concluded that the rate of respiration was directly related to the fall in salinity. Later observations on many euryhaline invertebrates have confirmed Schlieper's conclusions. In *Procerodes* (Gunda), the rate of respiration increases as the salinity of the medium falls (Beadle, 1931) and in

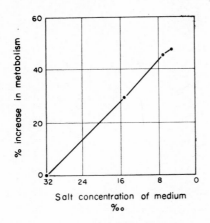

Fig. VIII.1. *Carcinus maenas.* The relation between respiratory rate and the salinity of the medium. From Schwabe, 1933.

Gammarus chevreuxii, the rate of respiration is about 20% higher in ¼ sea water than it is in full strength sea water. Within the gammarids, the brackish water *G. chevreuxii* has a higher rate of respiration than the marine *G. marinus* (*Marinogammarus*), while the freshwater *G. pulex* has a higher rate of respiration than either (Fig. VIII.2). In all these cases, it is tempting to correlate the changes in the respiratory rate with changes in the osmotic work of the animals.

A similar interpretation might be placed on the experiments of Peters (1935) who showed that the rate of respiration in the freshwater crayfish *Astacus* (*Potamobius*) was 40% lower in isosmotic sea water (15‰ salinity) than in fresh water. In the same way, many euryhaline animals which maintain the blood hypo-osmotic to concentrated media have a minimum respiration rate in isosmotic media, and the rate is increased both in hyperosmotic and hypo-osmotic media. The crabs, *Hemigrapsus oregonensis* and *H. nudus*, generally have a higher rate of respiration in 25% sea water, to which they are hyperosmotic, than in

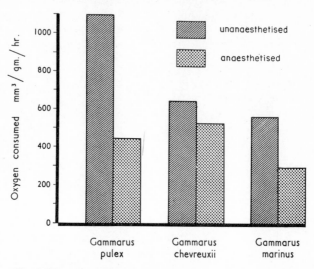

Fig. VIII.2. Comparison of the respiratory rates of three species of *Gammarus*. *G. pulex* in fresh water; *G. chevreuxii* in brackish water, and *G.* (*Marinogammarus*) *marinus* in sea water. From Löwenstein, 1935.

isosmotic 75% sea water (Dehnel, 1960). When it lives in brackish water, the Indian prawn, *Metapenaeus monoceros*, has a minimal rate of respiration in 50% sea water and the rate increases both in more concentrated and in more dilute media, although *Metapenaeus* taken from the sea has a minimal rate in sea water, and the rate is increased as the salinity is reduced (Rao, 1958) (Fig. VIII.3). Similarly, the brackish water prawn, *Palaemonetes varians*, has a minimal rate of respiration in brackish water and the rate increases both in more concentrated and in more dilute media, but a population from dilute brackish water had a minimal rate at 6‰ salinity, while a population from a more concentrated environment had a minimal rate at 26‰ (Lofts, 1956).

A comparison of the effects of salinity on the respiration rate of osmoregulating and non-regulating animals again suggests that an increase in osmotic gradient is associated with an increase in metabolic rate. While the respiratory rates of *Carcinus*

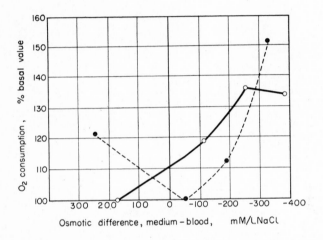

Fig. VIII.3. *Metapenaeus monoceros.* Oxygen consumption as a function of the concentration difference between the animal and the medium.
o——o prawns from sea water; ●----● prawns from brackish water. From Rao, 1956.

and *Eriphia*, both osmoregulating crabs, increase in dilute sea water, those of the non-regulating *Maia* and *Hyas* decline (Schlieper, in Remane and Schlieper, 1958, p.284). The rate of respiration of the starfish, *Asterias*, from sea water declines both in more concentrated and in more dilute media, and *Asterias* from the Baltic have lower respiration rates than those in the North Sea (Bock and Schlieper, 1953). The sea anemone, *Metridium*, responds in the same way to any change from its normal salinity, although it has been suggested that in this animal, the reduction could be caused by the anemone retracting in abnormal salinities (Shoup, 1932).

On the other hand, many teleosts do not respond in this way to salinity changes. The euryhaline stickleback, *Gasterosteus*, although it lives for long periods in fresh water, has a higher respiratory rate in fresh water than in isosmotic sea water (Graetz, 1931), whereas both elvers and the seaward migrating

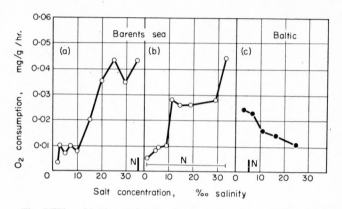

Fig. VIII.4. *Mytilus edulis*. Oxygen consumption as a function of the salinity of the medium in animals taken from the Barents Sea and the Baltic. N represents normal salinity. From Beliaev and Tschugunova in Remane and Schlieper, 1958.

adult eels (*Anguilla anguilla*) use less oxygen in fresh water than in sea water (Raffy, 1933; Raffy and Fontaine, 1930). The euryhaline and diadromous starry flounder, *Platichthys stellatus*, also decreases its oxygen consumption in fresh water below the level in isosmotic sea water (8‰ salinity). In the flounder, this decrease can be related to a reduction in thyroid activity when the fish migrates into fresh water (Hickman, 1959).

Excepting migratory animals in which hormones may override the basic metabolic pattern, most of those animals which osmoregulate increase their metabolic rates as the salinity falls.

Isolated tissues do not always show the same response to salinity changes as the whole animals. The gills of the lamellibranch *Mytilus*, like those of the crab, *Carcinus*, have a higher respiration rate in more dilute media (Schlieper, 1929). However, the rate of respiration of whole *Mytilus provincialis* adapted to sea water (32‰ salinity) remained approximately constant when they were transferred to more dilute sea water, down to 25‰ salinity, and then declined very rapidly at lower salinities. The rate also declined in more concentrated sea water (Bouxin, 1931). *Mytilus* from the Barents Sea (35‰ salinity) behaved in a similar fashion (Beliaev and Tschugunova, in Remane and Schlieper, 1958 p.283). Mussels from an area of variable salinity had an almost constant rate of respiration between 10‰ and 30‰ salinity (Fig. VIII.4). On the other hand, mussels from an area of low salinity had a maximum rate of respiration at 5‰ salinity, and the rate was less both in more concentrated and in less concentrated media. Therefore, it appears that these animals adjust their respiratory rate to a maximum in their normal environment and they respond to any sudden change by a reduction in the metabolic rate. Mussels often respond to environmental changes by closing the shell and Schlieper suggests that the changes in respiratory rate may be due to this. However, when the valves are kept open, the rate of respiration of whole *Mytilus* adapted to 36‰ salinity declines by a third, in sea water of 18‰ salinity and the respiration of isolated tissues is similarly reduced (Potts, unpub.).

In general, it may be concluded that many osmoregulating animals respond to a decrease in salinity with an increase in the respiratory rate, but many non-regulating animals, such as *Asterias*, *Eriphia*, *Hyas*, *Metridium* and *Mytilus*, respond to a change in salinity with a decrease in respiratory rate. Although experiments of this kind suggest a causal relation between the osmotic demand and the changes in metabolic rate, further consideration and experiment throw doubts on this simple hypothesis. First, the changes in metabolic rate are usually much too large to be attributed to osmotic regulation alone. In several cases, experiments have shown that an increase in metabolism in lower salinities is not confined to those tissues which might perform the osmotic work. Secondly, such large respiratory changes imply a very low efficiency for the transport system, whereas experiments with isolated tissues imply a high efficiency for biological transport systems. Thirdly, although in related animals in marine, brackish and freshwater media, the rates of respiration are higher in those from more dilute media, in some other groups of animals the reverse is true. Lastly, the respiratory rates are not affected by changes in salinity in many of the most competent regulators such as the crab *Eriocheir*, the shrimp *Artemia*, or the salmon *Salmo salar*.

The respiratory rate of the crab, *Carcinus*, increases by about 50% in dilute sea water, but the gills, which are probably the site of active uptake of ions, constitute less than 1% of the weight of the crab (Krogh, 1939, p.77). Thus, a hundred-fold increase in the activity of the gills would be required to account for the observed increase in respiration. Pieh (1936) has shown that the metabolic rate of isolated crab gills in dilute sea water is similar to that of the whole crab. It must be concluded that most of the increase in metabolic rate takes place in the other tissues of the body. Similarly, the epithelium of *Nereis* responsible for active uptake is too small to account for the large increase in respiratory rate when the worms are transferred to brackish water. Measurements of the rate of respiration of *Astacus* (*Potamobius*) tissues, including muscle and digestive gland, show that the decrease in metabolic rate, observed when the whole animal is adapted to 40% sea water, affects all the tissues (Peters, 1935).

A further objection to the hypothesis that the changes of metabolic rate are directly related to changes in ion transport, is that it implies a low overall efficiency for the transport system, at variance with the high efficiency of isolated transporting tissues (see below). The work done in ion transport by *Carcinus*, *Nereis* or *Gammarus* in brackish water is only equivalent to about 1% of the animal's total metabolism (Chap. IV, p.155), yet the metabolic rates of the whole animals increase by about 50% in brackish water. This would imply an overall efficiency of only 2%, whereas isolated frog skin or gastric mucosa have efficiencies of 20-80%. If the ion transport system of the whole animal were equally efficient, then the increase of metabolism consequent on the increased ion transport would not be detectable against the background of the metabolism of the whole animal.

Many of the most efficient regulators respire at the same rate within a wide range of salinities. The crab, *Eriocheir*, has the same metabolic rate in sea water (30‰ salinity) as in brackish water (15‰ salinity), or in fresh water (Schwabe, 1933). The rate of respiration of the brine shrimp, *Artemia*, is the same in media of 35‰ and 140‰ salinity (Gilchrist, 1956). *Artemia* has a very large surface: volume ratio and the osmotic stresses in the two media are very different. These results are of particular interest because Kuenen (1939) reported that the rate of respiration increased in higher salinities, while Eliassen (1953) found an increase in low salinities. However, when comparisons were made between individuals of similar size and the same sex, the apparent differences in respiratory rate disappeared (Gilchrist, 1956). Again, in the three gammarids, *Gammarus oceanicus*, *G. zaddachi*, and *G. duebeni*, there was no clear correlation between respiratory rate and salinity in the range 1‰-20‰ salinity (Suomalainen, 1956), and furthermore, *G. duebeni* which is found in Ireland and western Britain in fresh water, had a lower respiratory rate than either *G. zaddachi* or *G. oceanicus*. In the euryhaline teleosts, the brackish water *Fundulus heteroclitus* respires at the same rate both in fresh water and in isosmotic Ringer solutions (Maloeuf, 1938), and the mature eel, *Anguilla anguilla*, respires at the same rate in sea water and fresh water (Raffy, 1933), although the elvers showed some variation. The alevins of rainbow trout, *Salmo gairdnerii*, and salmon, *Salmo salar*, showed no change in respiratory rate after transfer to different salinities (Busnel, Drilhon and Raffy, 1946). A detailed study of the rate of respiration of some brackish and freshwater gastropods in a variety of salinities showed that when individuals of the same weight were compared, *Theodoxus* respired at the same rate both in brackish and fresh water, while *Potamopyrgus jenkinsi* consumed more oxygen in brackish water than in fresh (Lumbye, 1958) (Fig. VIII.4).

Although the relation between transport and respiration in whole animals has been found to be so complex, it is much less ambiguous in isolated tissues, particularly frog skin and gastric mucosa. Both these tissues respire at a basic rate, but when they are stimulated to transport ions, the rate of oxygen consumption increases; in frog skin the increase of rate of consumption of oxygen is said to be proportional to the active flux of ions. Each additional molecule of oxygen above the basic level is associated with the transport of 18 sodium ions (Zerahn, 1956 a). This relation is independent of the electrochemical gradient across which the ions are transported (Leaf and Renshaw, 1957). The efficiency of the transport system therefore increases with the electrochemical gradient, but active transport between similar sodium solutions cannot take place against an electrical gradient of more than 140 mV, where the efficiency will be at a maximum. In the experiments of Zerahn (1956 a, b), and Leaf and Renshaw (1957), the sodium concentration differences across the skin were such that the overall efficiency was about 10%, but assuming that only the incremental oxygen was significant, the efficiency would be 22%. No measurements were made of oxygen consumption when the skin was transporting against an electrical gradient of 140 mV, but if the ratio of incremental oxygen: ions transported remains constant, the efficiency must reach 50%.* According to Krogh (1939, p.159) frogs can take up sodium chloride from solutions containing as little as 0.01 mM NaCl/l. This corresponds to an efficiency of at least 80%, if the ratio remains unchanged (see Chap. I, p.38).

The gastric mucosa is also very efficient. Whole gastric

* 1 mole of oxygen oxidising carbohydrate liberates 11,600 calories. The movement of 1 gram-ion across a potential gradient of 1 volt requires 96,500 joules, or 23,000 calories. The transport of 18 gram moles against 140 mV will thus require 58,000 calories. This corresponds to an efficiency of 50% in optimum conditions.

mucosa produces about 2 moles of hydrochloric acid for each mole of oxygen consumed (Crane and Davies, 1951). This corresponds to an overall efficiency of about 20%, but the oxyntic cells make up only 10% of the weight of the whole mucosa. When acid secretion is stimulated by histamine, oxygen consumption also increases and the ratio of acid produced: increased oxygen consumption may reach as high as 12 moles/mole, corresponding to an efficiency of nearly 100%. However, the maximum rate of acid secretion cannot be maintained over long periods. It is possible that energy reserves in the cells are being used up, and the average efficiency is lower.

In nerve, muscle and erythrocyte (Chap. VI, p.273), the energies required to maintain ionic equilibria appear to be equivalent to 5–10% of the metabolism of the resting cells. It is most unlikely that all the cellular energy is devoted to ion transport even in the resting state, so the efficiency of the transport processes is probably greater than this. However, in most cases some fraction of the effluxes (on which these calculations were based) may be due to exchange diffusion, in which case the real energy requirements may be lower.

If the active transport systems of whole animals work at the same high efficiency as those of frog skin and gastric mucosa, the effects of salinity transfer on the total metabolism will be very difficult to detect. In this case, the large variation of respiration rate with salinity which is found in many animals remains unexplained. No single theory will explain the decrease in metabolism which occurs when the tissues of *Asterias* or *Mytilus* are subjected to a lower osmotic concentration and the increase in metabolism which takes place in the same circumstances in the tissues of *Carcinus* or *Astacus*. However, it is possible to suggest a number of reasons why the respiratory rate might vary with salinity in certain conditions.

It is often suggested that an adverse osmotic environment stimulates an animal to random movements or to escape movements (Gross, 1957). This may account for the increase in the metabolic rate which occurs in some brackish water animals

23

in both high and low salinities; it is the active crustaceans which respire most rapidly in these conditions rather than the more quiescent lamellibranchs or echinoderms. However, Schlieper (1929) was satisfied that the activity of the crabs in his experiments was not affected by changes in the salinity of the medium. Löwenstein (1935) found that the rate of respiration in *Gammarus chevreuxii* was 20% higher in ¼ sea water than in full strength sea water, and the relative difference was the same when the animals were anaesthetised. However, he does report that the anaesthesia was deeper in full strength sea water than in ¼ sea water, so presumably the animals were less quiescent in the more dilute medium.

Schlieper (in Remane and Schlieper, 1958, p.291) has suggested that the changes in respiration rate which occur in brackish water animals are a consequence of changes in the hydration of the tissues which may affect the activity of the enzymes. He cites as an example the close correlation between the volume of *Nereis* and its respiratory rate, after transfer to a more dilute medium, but Beadle (1937) has plausibly suggested that this increased respiration is due to an increased tension in the muscles of the body wall. Schlieper also correlates the increase in respiratory rate of *Carcinus* in brackish water with the increased hydration of the tissues (Pieh, 1936; Shaw, 1955 d). This does not explain, however, why an increase in muscle hydration following transfer to a dilute medium in *Mytilus* and *Asterias* is associated with a fall in the respiratory rate.

Although freshwater animals must do more ionic work than marine animals at the body surface, they probably do significantly less work at the cell surface. In most tissues, the greater part of the ionic work is the excretion of sodium ions from the cell against an electrochemical gradient. In this respect, freshwater animals are more fortunate than marine ones, as the sodium content of the blood is lower and the sodium influx into the cells correspondingly reduced. The freshwater mussel, *Anodonta cygnaea*, appears to expend proportionately less than one tenth as much energy as the marine species *Mytilus edulis* in ionic regulation of heart muscle, and this may explain why, in some cases at least, a freshwater form has a lower metabolic rate than a related marine form. It is difficult to predict, in any specific case, the effect of a change in the sodium concentration of the body fluids on the ionic activity of a tissue. A lowering of the blood sodium, by reducing the load on the sodium pump, might reduce its work, but the pump might respond by working faster, thus maintaining a proportionately lower intracellular sodium concentration.

CHAPTER IX

THE CONTROL OF ELECTROLYTE
METABOLISM

A living animal constitutes an open system: that is to say, the materials of which it is composed are in continual exchange with those of the environment. To some degree, homeostasis is an inherent property of such a system, just as a closed system conforms to Le Chatelier's principle* (Burton, 1939; Bertalanffy, 1950). Thus, any disturbance in an actively maintained open system is to some extent self-compensating; for example, any increase in the salt concentration of the blood will facilitate salt excretion and any decrease will facilitate salt conservation. When one open system exists inside another, such as a cell surrounded by extracellular fluid, the stability of the inner system is enhanced. However, automatic homeostasis of this kind is not very effective, even in such a double system. Another limitation of this type of system is that concentration differences between the animal and the environment can only be maintained in one direction. More accurate control of the composition and volume of the body is possible only if the transporting system is controlled by reference to the concentrations and volumes which it affects. Such a regulating system which includes a closed loop, or servo-system (concentration of body fluids $\rightleftharpoons$ transport mechanism), makes much more accurate control possible. With systems of this kind, the

---

* If a change occurs in one of the factors affecting an equilibrium, the equilibrium shifts in such a way as to annul the effects of the change.

composition of the body fluids may be kept remarkably constant even in the face of reversals of concentration gradient across the body walls.

The independence of the composition of the body depends on the characteristics of its control systems. In general, any control system will include a "misalignment detector" which is activated by displacement from normal, and which in turn activates the restoring forces, such as the rate of input or output of salt or water. In the simplest case, the rate of input or output would be proportional to the misalignment. The constant of proportionality is known as the "stiffness" of the system. If a small displacement results in a large change in the rate of input or output, the system will not be easily displaced far from the normal, i.e. it will be stiff. In many biological systems, both input and output are maintained actively and controlled under "normal" conditions; the steady state of the animal depends on the equilibrium between the two. In this case, any displacement results in a change in both input and output. Such a system is more stable than a simpler system in which either the input or the output alone is activated by a displacement from the normal. It is necessary for good stabilisation that the control system should respond rapidly to any misalignment, otherwise a large displacement may ensue before corrective forces come into play and the system will overshoot and may then tend to become oscillatory (cf. blood concentration in freshwater elasmobranchs, Chap. II, p.52).

These principles are well illustrated in the vertebrates, but curiously little is known of the homeostatic mechanisms of other animals, although it is obvious that elaborate control systems do exist in invertebrates. For example, the rate of salt uptake in *Carcinus* and *Nereis* is clearly dependent either on the blood concentration, or less probably, on the concentration gradient across the body wall (Chap. IV, p.135 *et seq.*). The rate of salt uptake in *Astacus* is also dependent on the concentration of the body fluids but the system is much stiffer than in *Nereis* because a very small change in blood concentration produces a large change in the rate of uptake (Chap, V, p.193). In contrast, the variation of rate of uptake with external concentration is probably not controlled by any servo-system, but is an inherent property of the transport system (Chap. I, p.34). The change in function of *Eriocheir* renal organs from magnesium excretion in sea water, to magnesium conservation in fresh water (Scholles, 1933) and the ability of *Aedes detritus* to conserve potassium in potassium-free solutions, and sodium in sodium-free solutions (Chap. II, p.88) must also imply elaborate control systems. However, practically nothing is known of the link between the level of the body fluids and the transport systems. By analogy with the vertebrates, we may guess that some of the mechanisms are hormonal, but with the exceptions of one or two crustaceans and insects (see below), experimental demonstrations of water and salt balance hormones in invertebrates are lacking.

The kinetics of salt exchanges are often very rapid; for instance, the teleost fish, *Blennius*, living in intertidal pools, can change from sodium uptake to sodium excretion within minutes of transfer from fresh water to sea water (C. R. House, pers. comm.) and similar times are required for the change in function in the brackish water prawn, *Palaemonetes varians* (Potts and Parry, pers. comm.). In the euryhaline teleost, *Platichthys flesus*, the speed of the functional change depends on whether the fish has been long in fresh water. After only ½ an hour in fresh water, the initiation of sodium exchange is immediate, but after longer periods in fresh water, the change in function takes place more slowly (Motais, 1961 b).

Vertebrates

Introduction

The principles governing the control of water and salt excretion in tetrapods are fairly well understood, and something is known of their control of water and salt uptake. On the other hand, the control of water and salt balance in fishes is still largely unknown.

In tetrapods, the excretion of both water and salt is under hormonal control but the link between the level of the blood concentration and the release of the hormones is complicated. In all tetrapods, water excretion is controlled by antidiuretic hormones liberated in the pituitaries, and the excretion of salt is controlled by another hormone, aldosterone, produced by the adrenal glands. The liberation of aldosterone favours the retention of sodium. The two systems of water and salt control are most conveniently considered separately, but in practice the two systems interact. The excretion or retention of water alters the salt concentration of the blood and hence affects salt secretion and vice versa. The interrelationships of the pituitary hormones are still obscure. These hormones include a group of closely related octopolypeptides which produce a variety of physiological effects. Different classes of vertebrates possess slightly different hormones and some differences even occur within the classes; the effects of injecting pituitary extracts from one vertebrate into another are therefore peculiarly difficult to interpret.

Water Balance

The pituitary hormones are produced in the hypothalamus, but are liberated from the posterior lobe of the pituitary or neurohypophysis. The presence of the hormones reduces urine flow by causing vasoconstriction of the arterioles supplying the glomeruli, and thus reducing the filtration rate, and/or by increasing the permeability of the collecting tubules. An increase in permeability allows a greater resorption of water from the hypo-osmotic urine into the blood in the amphibians and the reptiles. In the birds and mammals this increase facilitates an increased resorption from the urine into the loop of Henle. In general, hypophysectomy results in an excessive urine flow and a concomitant salt loss, known as diabetes insipidus.

The liberation of the hormones is under the control of cells in the supraoptic nucleus of the hypothalamus, which in turn, are activated by osmoreceptors somewhere nearby in the hypothalamus (Verney, 1947). An increase in the osmotic pressure of the blood stimulates the osmoreceptors and leads to the secretion of the hormones from the neurohypophysis. A 1% increase in the concentration of the blood may lead to a 90% reduction in urine flow. The system is therefore very stiff. Urine flow is curtailed within minutes of a rise in blood concentration, but it can increase again equally quickly when the blood concentration falls, because the hormone is destroyed very rapidly by both liver and kidney, and some is excreted. The rate of hormone liberation is proportional to the increase in blood concentration above normal and the secretory system does not fatigue, both necessary attributes of a successful control system (Verney, 1947). There is some evidence that the antidiuretic hormones may also be liberated in response to a decrease in blood volume as well as to an increase in blood concentration (Heller, 1956, p.26).

Many of the vertebrate pituitary hormones have been analysed and synthesised. The hormones differ in different ver-

TABLE IX.1. THE STRUCTURE OF SOME NEUROHYPOPHYSIAL HORMONES

Hormone	Structure	Occurrence
Arginine vasopressin	CyS-Tyr-Phe-GlnNH$_2$-AspNH$_2$-CyS NH$_2$Gly-Arg-Pro	Most mammals
Lysine vasopressin	CyS-Tyr-Phe-GlnNH$_2$-AspNH$_2$-CyS NH$_2$Gly-Lys-Pro	Pigs
Arginine vasotocin	CyS-Tyr-Ileu-GlnNH$_2$-AspNH$_2$-CyS NH$_2$Gly-Arg-Pro	Birds, reptiles, amphibians and fishes*
Oxytocin	CyS-Tyr-Ileu-GlnNH$_2$-AspNH$_2$-CyS NH$_2$Gly-Leu-Pro	All vertebrates and tunicates

* Katoozannis and Vigneaud, 1958.

tebrates and the same hormone may produce quite different effects in different animals. A list of some of the hormones is given in Table IX.1; it can be seen that they all have the same basic structure, but differ in one place in the ring and another in the side chain.

In most mammals, the antidiuretic factor is arginine vasopressin which causes an increase in the permeability of the collecting tubules, allowing increased water resorption and decrease in urine volume, and an increase in urine concentration. Ginetzinsky (1958) has suggested that the antidiuretic hormone acts by causing the liberation of hyaluronidase from the cells of the collecting tubules, thus loosening the intracellular cement and aiding water resorption, but Leaf (1960) has shown recently that although the antidiuretic hormone affects the permeability of frog skin, hyaluronidase does not. The hormone appears to act by dilating the pores in the membrane lining the collecting ducts. The hormone can exert its effect without any alteration of renal blood flow or of sodium excretion (Selkurt, 1954), but some additional sodium is usually swept out during diuresis. The antidiuretic hormone usually causes some degree of vasoconstriction, but a reduction in glomerular filtration is not an important means of water conservation in the mammals, although it is important in some other vertebrates. The pig is peculiar in possessing lysine vasopressin in place of the more usual mammalian arginine vasopressin (Sawyer, Munsick and van Dyke, 1960). The concentration of the antidiuretic hormone in the blood of the kangaroo rat, *Dipodomys*, is very high and the rate of urine flow is very small. If the animal is given a water load, the urine flow is not much affected (Schmidt-Nielsen, 1960 a). Whether this is due to the chronically high level of the hormone in the blood, or to some other factor, is not known. There is evidence that alcohol inhibits the release of the antidiuretic hormone (Strauss, Rourke, Rosenbaum and Nelson, 1949). A high intake of alcohol may therefore cause dehydration and the development of a chronic thirst.

In those birds, turtles, toads and frogs which have been examined, the antidiuretic hormone is arginine vasotocin (Table IX.1) (Heller and Pickering, 1960; Munsick, Sawyer and van Dyke, 1960). In birds and reptiles, its function is analogous to that of the mammalian hormone: it reduces water excretion by increasing the permeability of the collecting tubules, so allowing increased tubular resorption. In the amphibians, its effects are more extensive, since it not only allows increased tubular resorption which may vary from 1% to 74% of the filtrate in the frog (Sawyer, 1951), but it also increases the permeability of the bladder, favouring further water resorption there (Ewer, 1952; Leaf, 1960; Sawyer, 1960). In most amphibians, it also increases the permeability of the skin, allowing both increased water and salt uptake there (Andersen and Ussing, 1957; Sawyer, 1960). In all cases, the effect is probably produced by a dilation of the pores through which the water and ion movements take place. The increased permeability of the skin might allow an increased rate of salt uptake as a secondary effect, but there is some evidence that amphibian (and fish) neurohypophysial extracts contain a hormone distinct from the antidiuretic hormone which stimulates salt transport across the skin. This "natriferic" principle seems to be distinct from both oxytocin and arginine vasotocin (Leaf and Renshaw, 1957; Morel, Maetz, Archer, Chauvet and Lenci, 1961; Maetz and Juien, 1961), but its activity is much less than that of oxytocin (Heller, Pickering, Maetz and Morel, 1961).

In some vertebrates, neurohypophysial hormones also conserve water by causing a contraction of the afferent arterioles, thus reducing filtration. In the frog, this is brought about by the action of oxytocin (pitocin) (Sawyer, 1951).

The amphibians vary considerably in their response to antidiuretic hormones. The permanently aquatic toad, *Xenopus*, is not sensitive to antidiuretic hormones in any respect, while the semi-terrestrial toads are more sensitive to the vasoconstriction effect than are the aquatic frogs. This illustrates well how animals adapt to hormones, as well as how the hormones are adapted to the animal's requirements. Little is known about the control of water balance in the Urodeles: *Necturus* and *Ambystoma* both show an increased retention of water after injections of antidiuretic hormones, although it is not known whether this is due to renal or extrarenal effects.

Less is known about the control of water balance in the fishes. Both teleost and elasmobranch pituitary extracts contain substances which have an antidiuretic effect in tetrapods, but extracts of fish and tetrapod pituitaries, or of purified or synthetic antidiuretic hormones, have not been shown to produce clear effects in the fish. There are two possible explanations for this: first, almost any experimental treatment of fish is liable to produce acute diuresis and this may mask any physiological diuretic effect; and secondly, most of the experiments have been made on freshwater fish which, like *Xenopus*, probably are not sensitive to antidiuretic hormones, as such a sensitivity would have no survival value(Boyd and Dingwall, 1939). On the other hand, it is surprising that no antidiuretic response to injections of fish pituitary were found in fresh-run salmon kept in hyperosmotic solutions (Fontaine, 1956, p.71), and that hypophysectomy had no effect on the salinity tolerance of brackish water *Fundulus* (Matthews, 1933; Pickford, 1953). However, there is some evidence that the pituitary is involved in water balance in fish. Burden (1956) found that hypophysectomised *Fundulus* could not survive in fresh water, although the absence of a possible antidiuretic hormone should not be a disadvantage in fresh water. In the rainbow trout, after transfer to sea water from fresh, mammalian hormone ("pitressin"*) can induce antidiuresis even during the spawning period. In the absence of pitressin, the spawning fish continues to produce a large volume of urine after transfer to sea water. (Holmes, pers. comm.). Transfer of fish to very concentrated salt solutions (5–10% NaCl) has been shown to affect the histological picture of the secretory cells

---

* Mammalian pituitary extract (Parke Davis).

in the pituitary. In two marine teleosts, *Callionymus lyra* and *Ammodytes lanceolatus*, the cells of the preoptic nucleus lost their secretory products within a few minutes of transfer to salt solutions, while a hypo-osmotic medium ($\frac{1}{4}$ sea water) was associated with an accumulation of secretory products within the cells (Arvy and Gabe, 1954). In the absence of a clear demonstration of the effects of the pituitary in fish, attempts have been made to implicate the thyroid and the gonads in water balance. Changes occur in these glands during the migrations of anadromous and catadromous fishes, but these changes are not necessarily related to water balance. (For recent reviews, see Baggerman, 1958; Hoar, 1958; Pickford, 1958).

Salt Excretion

The adrenal gland produces several steroid hormones, including a number which affect salt balance, such as desoxycorticosterone and progesterone, but the most important for salt balance in the kidney is aldosterone, which has a far greater effect, weight for weight, than any other steroid. On the other hand, cortisol and desoxycorticosterone are more effective than aldosterone in stimulating the secretion of the duck nasal gland (Scothorne, unpub.). Experiments involving the injections of mixed cortical hormones into animals are difficult to interpret.

In the absence of aldosterone, large quantities of sodium are excreted by the kidney in mammals, and survival is only possible if a 1% sodium chloride solution is available in place of drinking water. A deficiency of aldosterone produces the syndrome known as Addison's disease. The hormone stimulates sodium resorption in the distal convoluted tubule, partly in exchange for potassium. After adrenalectomy, blood sodium falls and blood potassium rises. Reptiles and amphibians show similar changes after adrenalectomy (Jones, 1956, pp. 113, 114). Adrenalectomy also produces a substantial increase in the concentration of sodium in the muscle of mammals (Conway and

Hingerty, 1946), amphibians (Jones, 1956, p.112) and teleosts (Jones, 1956 p.111). Only a part of the increase is due to the change in blood composition; the rest must be attributed to a direct effect of the hormone on ion balance in the cells (Conway, 1956 b, p.14). Adrenal hormones in mammals also facilitate the resorption of sodium and chloride from sweat and saliva (Robinson, Kincaid and Rhany, 1950; Frawley and Fanham, 1951).

Further effects of aldosterone on salt transport in vertebrates include the facilitation of active transport across the toad bladder (Crabbé, 1961 a), stimulation of sodium transport in the loop of Henle (Crabbé, 1961 b), facilitated secretion of sodium chloride by the avian nasal gland (Holmes, W. N., Phillips and Butler, 1961), and increased sodium resorption in the gut.

In fish, the homologues of the tetrapod adrenal are the elasmobranch interrenal, and the teleost anterior interrenal. Interrenalectomy in the skate produces a rise in blood potassium, but also a slight rise in blood sodium (Hartman, Lewis, Brownell, Angerer and Sheldon, 1944). Interrenalectomy is not practicable in the teleosts, but stimulation of the interrenals in the brown trout by adrenocorticotropic hormone produces a rise in blood potassium and a fall in blood sodium (Spalding, reported in Jones, 1956, p.111). The effects of corticosteroid hormones injected into fish are contradictory. In the rainbow trout in fresh water, cortical hormones both depress sodium uptake (Sexton, 1955; Holmes, W.N., 1959) and increase sodium loss (Holmes, 1959) through the gills. In some euryhaline and marine teleosts, injection of the hormones did not alter sodium and potassium balance in plasma and muscle (Edelman, Young and Harris, 1960).

The liberation of aldosterone from the adrenals is only partly under the control of the pituitary which produces an adrenocorticotropic hormone and hypophysectomised mammals can still increase aldosterone secretion in response to a rise in serum sodium. Although massive doses of the adrenocorticotropic hormone bring about the release of aldosterone, small doses may have no effect (Mulrow and Ganany, 1961). The mechanism of control of aldosterone secretion is still obscure. There is evidence that angiotensin can stimulate the release of aldosterone (Mulrow and Ganany 1961, 1962) in hypophysectomised dogs (see below). A recent view is that an aldosterone stimulating hormone is also produced in the pineal region (Farrell, Pratt and Mellinger, 1962).

Two other hormone systems are involved in the control of water and electrolytes in the vertebrates. The parathyroids in the tetrapods produce a hormone which regulates the level of calcium and phosphate in the blood. Its secretion appears to be controlled directly by the level of calcium in the plasma. A reduction in the concentration of calcium in the plasma stimulates the production of the hormone, which increases the calcium retention in several ways. It increases calcium resorption in the kidney, thus reducing calcium excretion; it facilitates calcium uptake from the gut; and it promotes the destruction of bone by the osteoclasts, mobilising some of the large calcium reserves. At the same time, the parathyroid hormone stimulates the excretion of phosphate in the urine, and as the phosphate excreted exceeds that liberated from the bone, it reduces its concentration in the blood.

The level of calcium and phosphate in the blood is also influenced by the level of Vitamin D in the diet. The presence of calcium-D favours the retention of both calcium and phosphate, while the parathyroid hormone favours the retention of calcium but the excretion of phosphate. The level of phosphate in the plasma depends on the interaction of these two factors. When Vitamin D is deficient in the diet, plasma phosphate remains low and bone formation is reduced, even though the blood calcium may be high (rickets). (For a recent review of the hormone, Rasmussen, 1961).

The homologues of the parathyroids in the fishes are the ultimobranchial glands, but evidence for their function is slight. When the teleost, *Astyanax*, was kept in the dark, the ultimobranchial glands hypertrophied and there was excessive calcification of the skeleton (Rasquin and Rosenbloom, 1954).

The juxtaglomerular apparatus in the kidney appears to act as a volume receptor. When the blood pressure in the mammalian kidney declines, it liberates a hormone, renin, which reacts with other subtances in the blood to form an octopolypeptide, angiotensin. This causes the blood pressure to increase locally, thus compensating for the original decline. Such a system must counteract the vasoconstriction effects of the antidiuretic hormone. It is also probable that angiotensin stimulates the release of aldosterone, and this would help to maintain the blood volume.

The Control of Water and Salt Uptake

In the tetrapods water uptake as well as water excretion is controlled. When a land animal is deprived of water, a desire or reflex for drinking is created. This is initiated by osmoreceptors in the hypothalamus, which may be identical with those which control the release of the antidiuretic hormone. The drinking of a hyperosmotic salt solution merely increases the thirst reflex. In addition to hypothalamic receptors, there is evidence that dehydration of the mucous membranes in the mouth can also help to initiate drinking. When a dog or a rat with a water deficit of 0.5–5% is allowed access to water, it drinks within about 10 minutes sufficient water to cover the deficit and to produce an excess of 0.5–1%. Absorption of the water from the gut takes considerably longer than 10 minutes, so the drinking reflex is cut off before the blood concentration has been restored to normal, but when sufficient water has already been drunk. How this accurate control is brought about is unknown. In man and some other mammals, drinking continues at a lower rate for some time, until the deficit is cleared.

In the amphibians, the release of antidiuretic hormone increases water uptake through the skin. Salt uptake through the skin is under hormonal control by the pituitary natriferin and the adrenal aldosterone, as well as by the antidiuretic hormone controlling the permeability. Higher tetrapods must rely on salt in the diet, but it is probable that some control system exists; for example, sodium deficient sheep show increased preference for saline water, although most tetrapods show some preference for saline water this even when in salt balance (Denton and Sabine, 1961).

Invertebrates

A few demonstrations have been made of water and salt balance hormones in invertebrates, but these are limited to the crustaceans and insects. In the freshwater crayfish *Cambarus* and the brackish water crab *Carcinus*, the uptake of water which normally accompanies moulting appears to be controlled by a hormone produced by the sinus gland in the eye-stalk. Removal of the eye-stalks induces moulting and abnormal water uptake during the premoult period. This water uptake may be reduced by the implantation of sinus glands, or by the injection of sinus gland extracts. It seems probable that this diuretic hormone is distinct from the moult inhibiting hormone. The calcium content of the blood is also under the influence of eye-stalk hormones. (Scudamore, 1947; Carlisle, 1956, 1957).

Diuretic hormones have been demonstrated in the beetle, *Anisotarsus cupripennis*, and in the bug, *Rhodnius prolixus*. The beetle larva lives in a moist environment, and if its neck is ligatured, the water content increases continuously. Injection of brain extracts restores the water balance by facilitating water excretion. Similarly, decapitated 5th. stage instars of *Rhodnius* retain abnormal amounts of water after a meal. If isolated malpighian tubes are suspended in a drop of serum, they produce little urine, but the addition of blood from freshly fed larvae, causes an increase in the rate of secretion. The addition of breis of various tissues shows that the ganglion of the mesothorax is the most potent for diuretic activity (Nunez, 1956, 1961; Maddrell, 1962). The relationship of the two insect diuretic hormones is not known. Water balance hormones in both vertebrates and invertebrates have been reviewed recently by Jenkin (1962) (Chap. V).

REFERENCES

ACRIVO, C. (1938) Beobachtungen über die Morphologie und Struktur der Kiemenlamellen der Ganoiden.
Bull. Soc. St. Cluj, **9** pp.9–31.

ADOLPH, E. F. (1927) The excretion of water by the kidneys of frogs.
Amer. J. Physiol. **81** pp.315–324.

ADOLPH, E. F. (1932) The vapour tension relations of frogs.
Biol. Bull. Woods Hole **62** pp.112–125.

ADOLPH, E. F. (1933) Exchanges of water in the frog.
Biol. Rev. **8** pp. 224–240.

ADOLPH, E. F. (1936) Differential permeability to water and osmotic changes in the marine worm, *Phascolosoma*.
J. cell. comp. Physiol. **9** pp.117–135.

ADOLPH, E. F. (1943) *Physiological Regulations*
Jacques Cattell Press, Lancaster Pa., U.S.A., 502 pp.

ADOLPH, E. F. (1947) *The Physiology of Man in the Desert.*
Interscience Publishers, New York.

ALBRECTSON, S. R. and THAYSEN, J. H. (1955) The excretion of urea by human parotid gland.
Scand. J. clin. lab. Invest. **7** pp.231–238.

ALEXANDER, D. P. and NIXON, D. A. (1961) Foetal kidney.
Brit. Med. Bull. **17.** pp.112–116.

ALLEN K. (1961) The effect of salinity on the amino acid concentration in *Rangia cuneata* (Pelcypoda).
Biol Bull. Woods Hole **121** pp.419–424.

ANDERSEN, B. and USSING, H. H. (1957) Solvent drag on non-electrolytes during osmotic flow through isolated toad skin and its response to antidiuretic hormone.
Acta physiol scand. **39** pp.228–239.

ANDERSON, D. W. and FELLERS, C. R. (1952) The occurrence of trimethylamine and trimethylamine oxide in fresh water fishes.
Food Research **17** pp.472–474.

ANDRÉE, G. (1958 a) Über die Natur des Transkapularen der Linse.
Arch. f. Physiol. **267** pp.109–116.

ANDRÉE, G. (1958 b) Der Na-und Cl-Gehalt der Froschlinse.
Arch. f. Physiol. **267** pp.117–119.

ARVY, L. and GABE, M. (1954) Modification du système hypothalamo-hypophysaire chez *Callionymus lyra* L., et *Ammodytes lanceolatus* Les., au cours des variations de l'équilibre osmotique.
C. R. Ass. Anat. **41** pp.843–944.

AUDIO, M. (1958) Sodium and chloride spaces and water content of tendon in normal and depleted rats.
Amer. J. Physiol. **195** pp.702–704.

AURICCHIO, G. and BARANY, E. H. (1959) Role of osmotic water transport in secretion of aqueous humour.
Acta physiol. scand. **45** pp.190–210.

BACKMANN, E. L. and RUNNSTRÖM, J. (1912) Der osmotische Druck während der Embryonalentwicklung von *Rana temporaria.*
Pflüg. Arch. ges. Physiol. **148** pp.287–345.

BAGGERMAN, B. (1958) The role of external factors and hormones in migration of sticklebacks and juvenile salmon.
In: *Comparative Endocrinology,* ed. Gorbman, pp. 24–37, Wiley and Sons, New York, 1958. 746 pp.

BAHL, K. N. (1945) Studies on the structure, development and physiology of the nephridia of Oligochaeta VI. The physiology of excretion.
Quart. J. micr. Sci. **85** pp.343–387.

BAHL, K. N. (1947) Excretion in the Oligochaeta.
Biol. Rev. **22** pp.109–147.

BAILLIEN, M. and SCHOFFENIELS, E. (1961) Origin of the potential difference in the intestinal epithelium of the turtle.
Nature Lond. **190** pp.1107–1108.

BALSS, H. (1944) Decapoda. In: *Bronn's Tierreich,* Bd. 5, Abt. 1, Bch 7. Lfg. 4, 5 pp.562–591.
Akad. Verlagsges., Leipzig.

BARNES, H. (1954) Some tables for the ionic composition of sea water.
J. exp. Biol. **31** pp.582–588.

BARTHOLOMEW, G. A. and DAWSON, W. R. (1954) Body temperature and water requirements in the mourning dove, *Zenaidura macroura marginella.*
Ecology **35** pp.181–187.

BATEMAN, J. B. and KEYS, A. (1932) Chloride and vapour pressure relations in the secretory activity of the gills of the eel.
J. Physiol. **75** pp.226–240.

BAYLIS, L. E. (1959) *The Principles of General Physiology,* Vol. 1
Longmans, London. 520 pp.

BEADLE, L. C. (1931) The effect of salinity changes on the water content and respiration of marine invertebrates.
J. exp. Biol. **8** pp.211–227.

BEADLE, L. C. (1934) Osmotic regulation in *Gunda ulvae.*
J. exp. Biol. **11** pp.382–396.

BEADLE, L. C. (1937) Adaptation to changes of salinity in the polychaetes. I. Control of body volume and of body fluid concentration in *Nereis diversicolor.*
J. exp. Biol. **14** pp.56–70.

24*

BEADLE, L. C. (1939) Regulation of the haemolymph in the saline water mosquito larva, *Aedes detritus*.
J. exp. Biol. **16** pp.346–62.

BEADLE, L. C. (1943) Osmotic regulation and the fauna of inland waters.
Biol. Rev. **18** pp.172–183.

BEADLE, L. C. and CRAGG, J. B. (1940) Studies on the adaptation to salinity of *Gammarus* spp. 1. Regulation of blood and tissues and the problem of adaptation to fresh water.
J. exp. Biol. **17** pp.153–163.

BEAMENT, J. W. L. (1945) The cuticular lipoids of insects.
J. exp. Biol. **21** pp.115–131.

BEAMENT, J. W. L. (1954) Water transport in insects.
Symp. Soc. Exp. Biol. **8** pp.94–117.

BECKER, E. L., BIRD, R., KELLY, J. W., SCHILLING, S. S. and YOUNG, N. (1958) Physiology of marine teleosts. I. Ionic composition of the tissue.
Physiol. Zoöl. **31** pp.224–231.

BEKESY, G. von (1952) Direct current resting potentials inside the cochlear partition.
J. Acoust. Soc. Amer. **24** pp.72–76.

BELIAEV, G. M. (1951) Die osmotische Konzentration des Innenmediums der wasserlebenden Wirbellosen in Medien von verschiedenem Salz-gehalt.
Akad. d. Wiss. d. UDSSR, Arb. d. hydrobiol. Ges., Okologie u. Physiologie der wasserlebenden Organismen. **3** pp.92–139 (in Russian, cited in Remane and Schlieper, 1958)

BELIAEV, G. M. and TSCHUGUNOVA, M. N. (1952) Die physiologischen Unterschiede zwischen den Mytili *(Mytilus)* der Barentsee und der Ostsee.
Vortr. d. Akad. d. Wiss. d. UDSSR. Okologie **85** pp.223–236 (in Russian, cited in Remane and Schlieper, 1958).

BENTLEY, P. J. (1958 a) Loss of sodium from the skin of the dehydrated toad, *Bufo marinus*.
Nature Lond. **182** p.1810.

BENTLEY, P. J. (1958 b) The effects of neurohypophysial extracts on water transfer across the wall of the isolated urinary bladder of the toad, *Bufo marinus*.
J. Endocrin. **17** pp.201–209.

BENTLEY, P. J. (1959) Studies on the water and electrolyte metabolism of the lizard, *Trachysaurus rugosus* (Gray).
J. Physiol. **145** pp.37–47.
Protoplasma **6** pp.1–50.

BENTLEY P. J. and BLUMER, W. F. C. (1962) Uptake of water by the lizard, *Moloch horridus*.
Nature Lond. **194** pp.699–700.

BENTLEY, P. J., LEE, A. K. and MAIN, A. R. (1958) Comparison of dehydration and hydration of two genera of frogs *(Helicoporus* and *Neobatrachus)* that live in areas of varying aridity.
J. exp. Biol. **35** pp.677–684.

BERGER, E. (1931) Über die Anpassung eines Süsswasser- und eines Brachwasserkrebses an Medien von verschiedenem Salzehalt.
Pflüg. Arch. ges. Physiol. **228** pp.790–807.

BERLINER, R. W., KENNEDY, T. J. and HILTON, J. G. (1950) Renal mechanisms for excretion of potassium.
Amer. J. Physiol. **162** pp.348–367.

BERLINER, R. W., LEVINSKY, M. G., DAVIDSON, O. G. and EDEN, M. (1960) Dilution and concentration of the urine and the action of the antidiuretic hormone.
Am. J. Med. **24** pp.730–744.

BERNSTEIN, R. E. (1954) Potassium and sodium balance in mammalian red cells.
Science **120** pp.459–460.

BERTALANFFY, L. von (1950) The theory of open systems in physics and biology.
Science **111** pp.23–29.

BETHE, A. (1929) Ionendurchlässigkeit der Körperoberfläche von wirbellosen Tieren des Meeres als Ursache der Giftigkeit von Seewasser abnormer Zusammensetzung.
Pflüg. Arch. ges. Physiol. **221** pp.344–362.

BETHE, A. (1930) The permeability of the surface of marine animals.
J. gen. Physiol. **13** pp.433–444.

BETHE, A. (1934) Die Salz- und Wasserpermeabilität der Körperoberflächen verschiedener Seetiere in ihrem gegenseitigen Verhältnis.
Pflüg. Arch. ges. Physiol. **234** pp.629–644.

BETHE, A. and BERGER, E. (1931) Variationem in Mineralbestand verschiedener Blutarten.
Pflüg. Arch. ges. Physiol. **227** pp.571–584.

BETHE, A., HOLST, E. von and HUF, E. (1935) Die Bedeutung des mechanischen Innendrucks für die Anpassung gepanzerter Seetiere an Änderungen des Osmotischen Aussendrucks.
Pflüg. Arch. ges. Physiol. **235** pp.330–344.

BEVELANDER, G. (1935) Comparative study of the branchial epithelium in fishes with special reference to extrarenal excretion.
J. Morph. **57** pp.335–348.

BIALASCEWICZ, K. (1927) Contributions à l'étude de la composition minérale des cellule oeufs.
Pubbl. Staz. zool. Napoli **8** pp.355–369.

BIALASCEWICZ, K. (1929) Recherches sur repartition des electrolytes dans le protoplasme des cellules ovulaires.
Protoplasma 6 pp. 1–50.

BIALASCEWICZ, K. (1933) Contribution a l'étude de la composition minérale des liquides nourriciers chez les animaux marins.
Arch. int. Physiol. 36 pp.41–53.

BINYON J. (1962) Ionic regulation and mode of adjustment to reduced salinity of the starfish, *Asterias rubens* L.
J. mar. biol. Ass. U. K. 42 pp.49–64.

BLACK, V. S. (1957) Excretion and osmoregulation.
In: *The Physiology of Fishes*, I, ed. Brown. Academic Press, New York, 1957. 447 pp.

BOCK, K. G. and SCHLIEPER, C. (1953) Einfluss des Salzgehaltes im Meerwasser auf den Grundumsatz des Seesternes *Asterias rubens* L.
Keiler Meeresforsch. 9 (2) pp.201–212.

BOGERT, C. M. and COWLES, R. B. (1947) Moisture loss in relation to habitat selection in some Floridian reptiles.
Amer. Mus. Novit. No. 1358 pp.1–34.

BONÉ, G.–J. (1944) Le rapport sodium/potassium dans la liquide coelomique des insectes. 1. Ses relations avec le régime alimentaire.
Ann. Soc. zool. Belg. 75 pp.123–132.

BOTAZZI, F. (1897) La pression osmotique du sang des animaux marins.
Arch. ital. Biol. 28 pp.61–76.

BOTAZZI, F. (1906) Sulla regulazione della pressione osmotica negli organismi animali. Pressione osmotica e conduttivita elettrica dei liquidi animali.
Arch. fisiol. 1 pp. 416–446; 3 pp.547–556.

BOTAZZI, F. (1908) Osmotischer Druck und elektrische Leitfähigkeit der Flüssigkeiten der einzelligen, pflanzlichen und tierischen Organismen.
Ergebn. Physiol. 7 pp.161–402.

BOTZLER, E. and LEVINE, D. (1958) Permeability of smooth muscle.
Amer. J. Physiol. 195 pp.4–49.

BOUXIN, H. (1931) Influence des variations rapides de la salinité sur la consommation d'oxygène chez *Mytilus edulis*, var. *galloprovincialis* (LMK).
Bull. de l'Inst. Ocèanogr. No. 569 pp.1–11.

BOYD, E. M. and DINGWALL, M. (1939) The effect of pituitary (posterior lobe) extract on the body water of fish and reptiles.
J. Physiol. 95 pp.501–507.

BOYLE, P. J. and CONWAY, E. J. (1941) Potassium accumulation in muscle and associated changes.
J. Physiol. 100 pp.1–63.

BRASILOW, S. W. and COOKE, R. E. (1959) Role of parotid ducts in secretion of hypotonic saliva.
Amer. J. Physiol. 196 pp.831–834.

BRO-RASMUSSEN, E., KILLMANS, S. and THAYSEN, J. H. (1956) The composition of pancreatic juice as compared to sweat and parotid saliva.
Acta physiol. scand. **37** pp.97–113.

BRULL, L. and CUYPERS, Y. (1954 a) Quelques characteristiques biologiques de *Lophius piscatorius* L.
Arch. int. Physiol. **62** pp.70–75.

BRULL, L. and CUYPERS, Y. (1954 b) Blood perfusion of the kidney of *Lophius piscatorius* L. II. Influence of perfusion pressure on urine volume.
J. mar. biol. Ass. U. K. **33** pp.733–738.

BRULL, L. and NIZET, E. (1953) Blood and urine constituents of *Lophius piscatorius* L.
J. Mar. Biol. Ass. U. K. **32** pp.321–328.

BRULL, L., NIZET, E. and VERNEY, E. B. (1953) Blood perfusion of the kidney of *Lophius piscatorius* L.
J. Mar. Biol. Ass. U. K. **32** pp.329–36.

BRYAN, G. W. (1960 a) Sodium regulation in the crayfish *Astacus fluviatilis*. I. The normal animal.
J. exp. Biol. **37** pp.83–99.

BRYAN, G. W. (1960 b) Sodium regulation in the crayfish *Astacus fluviatilis*. II. Experiments with sodium depleted animals.
J. exp. Biol. **37** pp.100–112.

BRYAN, G. W. (1960 c) Sodium regulation in the crayfish *Astacus fluviatilis*. III. Experiments with NaCl-loaded animals.
J. exp. Biol. **37** pp.113–128.

BRYAN G. W. (1961) The accumulation of radioactive caesium in crabs.
J. mar. biol. Ass. U. K. **41** : pp.551–576.

BURDEN, C. E. (1956) The failure of hypophysectomised *Fundulus heteroclitus* to survive in fresh water.
Biol. Bull. Woods Hole **110** pp.8–28.

BURGEN, A. S. V., TERROUX, K. G. and DONGER, E. (1959) The sites of transfer of sodium, potassium and iodide in the parotid duct system of the dog.
Can. J. Biochem. Physiol. **37** pp.359–370.

BURGER, J. W. (1957) The general form of excretion in the lobster, *Homarus*.
Biol. Bull. Woods Hole **133** pp.207–223.

BURGER, J. W. and HESS, W. N. (1960) Function of the rectal gland in spiny dogfish.
Science **131** pp.670–671.

BURGER, J. W. and SMYTHE, MAC C. (1953) The general form of circulation in the lobster, *Homarus*.
J. cell. comp. Physiol. **42** pp.369–383.

BURIAN, R. (1910) Funktion der Nierenglomeruli und Ultrafiltration.
Pflüg. Arch. ges. Physiol. **136** pp.741–760.

BURTON, A. C. (1939) The properties of the steady state compared to those of equilibrium as shown by characteristic biological behaviour.
J. cell. comp. Physiol. **14** pp.327–349.

BUSNEL, R. G., DRILHON, A. and RAFFY, A. (1946) Recherches sur la physiologie des Salmonides.
Bull. Inst. oceanogr. Monaco No. **893** pp.45–67.

BUXTON, P. A. (1923) *Animal Life in Deserts,*
Arnold and Co., London. 176 pp.

CALDWELL, P. C. (1960) Some aspects of the part played by phosphate compounds in the regulation of certain inorganic ions in cells.
In: *Regulation of the Inorganic Ion Content of Cells.*
ed. G. E. W. Wolstenholme and C. M. O. O'Connor, pp.69–76.
Churchill, London.

CALDWELL, P. C. and KEYNES, R. D. (1957) The utilisation of phosphate bond energy for sodium extrusion from giant axons.
J. Physiol. **137.** 12P–13P.

CALDWELL, P. C., HODGKIN, A. L., KEYNES, R. D. and SHAW, T. I. (1960) The effects of injecting energy rich phosphate compounds on the active transport of ions into the giant axons of *Loligo.*
J. Physiol. **152** pp.561–590.

CAREY, M. J. and CONWAY, E. J. (1954) Comparison of various media for immersing frog sartorii at room temperatures, and evidence for the regional distribution of fibre sodium.
J. Physiol. **125** pp.232–250.

CARLISLE, D. B. 1956 On the hormonal control of water balance in *Carcinus. Publ. Staz. zool Napoli* **27** pp. 227–231.

CARLISLE, D. B. 1957 On the hormonal inhibition of moulting in decapod Crustacea. II. The terminal anecdysis in crabs.
J. Mar. Biol. Ass. U. K. **36** pp.291–307.

CARR, C. W. and WOODS, K. R. (1955) Studies on the binding of small ions in protein solutions with the use of membrane electrodes. V. The binding of magnesium ions in solutions of various proteins.
Arch. Biochem. Biophys. **55** pp.1–8.

CARTER, L. (1957) Ionic regulation in the ciliate, *Spirostomum ambiguum.*
J. exp. Biol. **34** pp.71–84.

CHEW, R. M. (1961 a) Water metabolism of desert vertebrates.
Biol. Rev. **36** pp.1–31.

CHEW R. M. (1961 b) Evaporative water loss of small vertebrates with an infrared analyser.
Science **133** pp.384–385.

CLARKE, R. W. (1934) The xylose clearance of *Myoxocephalus octodecimo spinosus* under normal and diuretic conditions.
J. cell. comp. Physiol. **5** pp.73–82.

CLARKE, R. W. (1936) Experimental production of diuresis in the dogfish
Bull. Mt. Des. Isl. biol. Lab. pp.25–26.

COLE, W. H. (1940) Ionic analysis of the blood of marine animals.
J. gen. Physiol. 23 pp.575–84.

CONWAY, E. J. (1943) The chemical evolution of the ocean.
Proc. Roy. Irish Acad. B 48 pp.161–212.

CONWAY, E. J. (1945) The physiological significance of the inorganic levels
in the internal medium of animals.
Biol. Rev. 20 pp.56–72.

CONWAY, E. J. (1950) Idiomolar values in mammalian skeletal muscle.
Irish J. Med. Soc. No. 294 pp.216–224.

CONWAY, E. J. (1953) The Biochemistry of Gastric Acid Secretion.
Thomas, Springfield, U.S.A. 185 pp.

CONWAY, E. J. (1956 a) A general cation carrier in the yeast cell wall.
Nature Lond. 178 pp.1043–1044.

CONWAY, E. J. (1956 b) Fundamental problems in the hormonal control
of water and salt electrolyte metabolism.
In: The Hormonal Control of Water and Salt-electrolyte Metabolism in
Vertebrates. Memoirs of the Society of Experimental Endocrinology.
No. 5 Part II. ed. I. Chester Jones and P. Eckstein, pp.3–22.
Cambridge Univ. Press.

CONWAY, E. J. (1958) The redox pump theory and present evidence.
In: The Method of Isotopic Tracers Applied to the Study of Active Transport.
ed. J. Coursaget, pp.1–27.
Pergamon Press, London.

CONWAY, E. J. (1960 a) Critical energy barriers to active transport in muscle
and the redox pump theory.
In: Regulation of the Inorganic Ion Content of Cells.
ed. G.E.W. Wolstenholme and C. M. O'Connor, pp.2–14.
Churchill, London.

CONWAY, E. J. (1960 b) Principles underlying the exchange of sodium and
potassium ions across cell membranes.
J. gen. Physiol. 43 Suppl. I. pp.17–41.

CONWAY, E. J. and HINGERTY, D. (1946) The influence of adrenalectomy
on muscle constituents.
Biochem. J. 40 pp.561–8.

CONWAY, E. J. and McCORMACK, J. (1953) The total intracellular concentration of mammalian tissues compared with that of the extracellular
fluid.
J. Physiol. 120 pp.1–14.

COOPERSTEIN, I. L., CHALFIN, D. and HOGBEN, C. A. M. (1957) Ionic
transfer across the isolated large bullfrog intestine.
Fed. Proc. 16 pp.24–25.

COPELAND, D. E. (1950) Adaptive behaviour of the chloride cell in the gill of *Fundulus heteroclitus*.
J. Morph. **87** pp.369–379.

COULSON, R. A. and HERNANDEZ, T. (1955) Renal excretion of carbon dioxide and ammonia by the alligator.
Proc. Soc. exp. Biol. N. Y. **88** pp.682–686.

COWEY C. B. (1961) The non-protein nitrogenous constituents of the tissues of the freshwater crayfish, *Astacus pallipes* Lereboullet.
Comp. Biochem. Physiol. **2** : pp.173–180.

COWEY C. B., DAISLEY K. and PARRY, G. (1962) Studies on free and protein-bound amino acids and some B vitamins in the tissues of the Atlantic *Salmo salar*, during spawning migration.
Comp. Biochem. Physiol. **1** pp.29–38.

CRABBÉ J. (1961 a) Stimulation of active sodium transport across the isolated toad bladder after injection of aldosterone to the animal.
Endocrinol. **69** : pp.673–682.

CRABBÉ J. (1961 b) Stimulation by aldosterone of sodium transport in the loop of Henle.
Nature Lond. **191** : p.817.

CRANE, E. E. and DAVIES, R. E. (1951) Chemical and energy relations for the stomach.
Biochem. J. **49** pp.169–175.

CREESE, R. (1954) Measurement of cation fluxes in rat diaphragm.
Proc. Roy. Soc. B **142** pp.497–513.

CROGHAN, P. C. (1958 a) The osmotic and ionic regulation of *Artemia salina* L.
J. exp. Biol. **35** pp.219–233.

CROGHAN, P. C. (1958 b) The mechanism of osmotic regulation in *Artemia salina* L.: the physiology of the branchiae.
J. exp. Biol. **35** pp.234–242.

CROGHAN, P. C. (1958 c) The mechanism of osmotic regulation in *Artemia salina* L.: the physiology of the gut.
J. exp. Biol. **35** pp.243–249.

CROGHAN, P. C. (1958 d) Ionic fluxes in *Artemia salina* L.
J. exp. Biol. **35** pp.425–436.

CROGHAN, P. C. (1959) The interstitial soil-water and the evolution of terrestrial arthropods.
Proc. Roy. Phys. Soc. Edin. **27** pp.103–104.

CROGHAN, P. C. (1961) Competition and mechanism of osmotic adaptation.
Symp. soc. exp. Biol. **15** pp.156–166.

DAHL, E. (1956) Ecological salinity boundaries in poikilohaline waters.
Oikos **7** pp.1–23.

DAINTY, J. and KRNJEVIC, K. (1955) The rate of exchange of ^{24}Na in cat nerves.
J. Physiol. **128** pp.489–503.

DAKIN, W. J. (1911) Notes on the biology of fish eggs and larvae.
Int. Rev. Hydrobiol. **3** pp.487–495.

DAKIN, W. J. and EDMONDS, E. (1931) The regulation of the salt contents of the blood of aquatic animals and the problem of the permeability of the bounding membranes of aquatic invertebrates.
Aust. J. exp. Biol. med. Sci. **8** pp.169–87.

DANIEL, E. F. and ROBINSON, K. (1960) The secretion of sodium and uptake of potassium by isolated uterine segments made sodium-rich.
J. Physiol. **154** pp.421–444.

DANIEL, E. E. and SINGH, H. (1958) Electrical properties of the smooth muscle cell membrane.
Canad. J. Biochem. **36** pp.959–975.

DANIELLI, J. F. and PANTIN, C.F.A.(1950) Alkaline phosphatase in protonephridia of terrestrial nemertines and planarians.
Quart. J. micr. Sci. **91** pp.209–214.

DARROW, D. C., HARRISON, H. E. and TAFFEL, M. (1939) Tissue electrolyte in adrenal insufficiency.
J. biol. Chem. **130** pp.487–502.

DAVENPORT, H. W. (1939) Gastric carbonic anhydrase.
J. Physiol. **97** pp.32–43.

DAVIES, F., DAVIES, R. E., FRANCIS, E and WHITTAM, R. (1952) The sodium and potassium content of cardiac and other tissues of the ox.
J. Physiol. **118** pp.276–281.

DAVIES, R. E. (1948) Hydrochloric acid production by the isolated gastric mucosa.
Biochem. J. **42** pp.609–618.

DAVIES, R. E. (1951) Hydrochloric acid production by the stomach.
Biol. Rev. **26** pp.87–120.

DAVIS, C. C. (1953) Concerning the flotation mechanism of *Noctiluca*.
Ecology **34** pp.189–192.

DAVSON, H. (1956) *Physiology of the Ocular and Cerebrospinal Fluids.*
Churchill London. 378 pp.

DAVSON, H., DUKE-ELDER, W. S. and MAURICE, D. M. (1949) Changes in ionic distribution following dialysis of aqueous humour against plasma.
J. Physiol. **109** pp.32–40.

DAVSON, H., MATCHETT, P. A. and ROBERTS, J. R. E. (1952) Comparative studies of the distribution of chloride between aqueous humour and plasma.
J. Physiol. **116** 47P.

DAVSON, H. and PURVIS, C. (1954) Cryoscopic apparatus for studies on aqueous humour and cerebrospinal fluid.
J. Physiol. **124** pp.12–13.

DAWSON, A. B. (1951) Functional and degenerate or rudimentary glomeruli in the kidney of two species of Australian frogs (*Cyclorana*) (*Chiroleptis*).
Anat. Rec. **109** pp.417–424.

DAWSON, W. R. (1954) Temperature regulation and water requirements of the brown and Albert Towhees, *Pipilo fiscus* and *Pipilo Alberti.*
Univ. Calif. Publ. Zool. **59** pp.81–124.

DEHNEL, P. A. (1960) Effect of temperature and salinity on the oxygen consumption of two intertidal crabs.
Biol. Bull. Woods Hole **118** pp.215–249.

DEHNEL, P. A. 1962 Aspects of osmoregulation in two species of intersidal crabs.
Biol. Bull. Woods Hole **122** pp.208–227.

DEKHUYZEN, M. C. (1904) Ergebnisse von osmotischen Studien namentlich bei Knochenfischen.
Bergens Mus. Aarb. No. **8**.

DELAUNAY, H. (1931) Excretion azotée des Invertebrés.
Biol. Rev. **6** pp.265–301.

DEMPSEY, E. F., CARROLL, E. L., ALBRIGHT, F. and HENNEMAN, P. H. (1958) Factors affecting faecal electrolyte excretion.
Metabolism **7** pp.108–118.

DENTON D. A., & SABINE J. R. (1961) The selective appetite for sodium by sodium deficient sheep.
J. Physiol. **157** pp.97–116.

DENTON, E. J. (1960) The buoyancy of marine animals.
Sci. Amer. **203** No. I. pp.118–128.

DENTON, E. J., SHAW, T. I. and GILPIN-BROWN, J. B. (1958) Bathyscaphoid squid.
Nature Lond. **182** pp.1810–1811.

DICK, D. A. T. (1959) Osmotic properties of living cells.
Int. Rev. Cytol. **8** pp.388–448.

DICKERSON, J. W. T. and WIDDOWSON, E. M. (1960) Chemical changes in skeletal muscle during development.
Biochem. J. **74** pp.247–257.

DITTMAR, W. (1884) Report on researches into the composition of ocean water collected by H.M.S. *Challenger.*
Challenger Rep. Physics and Chem. **1** pp.1–251.

DIXON, J. M. (1958) Investigation of urinary water resorption in the cloaca and rectum of the hen.
Poult. Sci. **37** pp.410–414.

DOYLE, W. L. and GORECKI, D. (1961) The so-called chloride cell of the fish gill.
Physiol. Zool **34** pp.81–85.

DRESEL, E. B. and MOYLE, V. (1950) Nitrogenous excretion in amphipods and isopods.
J. exp. Biol. **27** pp.210–225.

DRILHON, A. (1934) Sur le milieu intérieur des Léidpoptéres.
C. R. Soc. Biol. Paris **115** pp.1194–1195.

DUCHATEAU, G., FLORKIN, M. and JEUNIAUX, C. (1959) Composante aminoacide des tissus chez les Crustacés. I. Composante aminoacide des muscles de *Carcinus maenas* L. lors du passage de l'eau de mer a l'eau saumatre et au cours de la mue.
Arch. int. Physiol. **67** pp.489–500.

DUCHATEAU, G., FLORKIN, M. and LECLERQ, J. (1953) Concentrations des bases fixes et types de composition de la base totale de l'hémolymphe des insects.
Arch. int. Physiol. **61** pp.518–549.

DUCHATEAU-BOSSON G., FLORKIN M., and JEUNIAUX C.(1961) Rôle de la variation de la composante amino-acide intracellulaire dans l'euryhalinité d'*Arenicola marina* L.
Arch. int. Physiol. Biochim, **69**. pp.97–116.

DUMONT, P. (1957) Inhibition a l'aide de certains antibiotiques du transport actif des ions sodium au travers les branchies isolées du crabe *Eriocheir*.
Arch. int. Pharmacodyn. **114** pp.334–343.

DURBIN, R. P., CURRAN, P. F. and SOLOMON, A. K. (1958) Ion and water transport in stomach and intestine.
Adv. biol. and med. Phys. **6** pp.1–36.

DUVAL, M. (1925) Recherches physico-chemique et physiologiques sur le milieu intérieur des animaux aquatiques. Modifications sous l'influence du milieu extérieur.
Ann. Inst. oceanogr. **2** pp.232–407.

DUVAL, M. and PORTIER, P. (1927) Carbon dioxide content of invertebrate blood.
C. R. Acad. Sci., Paris **184** pp.1594–1596.

EDELMAN I. S. YOUNG H. L. and HARRIS J. B. (1960) Effects of corticosteroids on electrolyte metabolism during osmoregulation in teleosts.
Am. J. Physiol. **199** pp.666–670.

EDNEY, E. B. (1947) Laboratory studies on the bionomics of the rat flea, *Xenopsylla brasiliensis* Baker and *X. cheopis* Roths. II. Water relations during the cocoon period.
Bull. ent. Res. **38** pp.263–280.

EDNEY, E. B. (1957) *The Water Relations of Terrestrial Arthropods.*
Cambridge Univ. Press, Cambridge. 109 pp.

EDWARDS, J. G. (1928) Studies on glomerular and aglomerular kidneys. I. Anatomical.
Amer. J. Anat. **42** pp.75–108.

EDWARDS, J. G. (1935) The epithelium of the renal tubule in bony fish.
Anat. Rec. **63** pp.263–279.

EICHELBERGER, L. and BIBLER, W. G. (1940) Water and electrolytes in kidneys.
J. biol. Chem. **132** pp.645–656.

EICHELBERGER, L. and BROWN, J. D. (1945) The fat, water, chloride, total nitrogen and collagen nitrogen content in the tendons of the dog.
J. biol. Chem. **158** pp.283–289.

EICHELBERGER, L., FETCHER, E. S., GEILING, E. M. K. and VOS, B. J. (1940) The composition of dolphin milk.
J. biol. Chem. **134** pp.171–176.

EICHELBERGER, L. and MACLEAN, F. C. (1942) The distribution of calcium and magnesium between the cells and extracellular fluids of skeletal muscle and liver in dogs.
J. biol. Chem. **142** pp.467–476.

ELIASSEN, E. (1953) The energy metabolism of *Artemia salina* in relation to body size, seasonal rhythms and different salinities.
Natur vitensk bekke No. **11** pp.3–17.

ELLIS, W. G. (1937) The water and electrolyte exchange of *Nereis diversicolor* (Muller).
J. exp. Biol. **14** pp.340–350.

ENAMI, M. (1959) The morphology and functional significance of the caudal neurosecretory system of fishes.
In: *Comparative Endocrinology,* ed. Gorbman.
John Wiley and Sons. New York, 746 pp.

ENGBAEK, L. and HOSHIKO, T. (1957) Electrical potential gradients through frog skin.
Acta physiol. scand. **39** pp.348–355.

EPSTEIN, E. and HAGEN, C. E. (1952) A kinetic study of the absorption of alkali cations by barley rooss.
Plant Physiol **27**: pp.457–474.

ERULKAR, S. D. and MAREN, T. H. (1961) Carbonic anhydrase and the inner ear.
Nature Lond. **189** pp.459–460.

EWER, F. (1952) The effects of pituitrin on fluid distribution in *Bufo regularis* Reuss.
J. exp. Biol. **29** pp.173–177.

FANGE, R., SCHMIDT-NIELSEN, K. and OSAKI, H. (1958) The salt gland of the herring gull.
Biol. Bull. Woods Hole **115** pp.162–171.

FARRELL, G., PRATT A. D., and MELLINGER J. F. (1962) Adrenocortico-
tropin, a diencephalic factor specific for aldosterone secretion.
In: *The Human Adrenal Cortex*. ed. Currie A. R., Symington T., and
Grant, J. K., pp.196–202.
E. S. Livingstone Ltd., Edinburgh and London.

FETCHER, E. S. (1939) The water balance in marine mammals.
Quart. Rev. Biol. **14** pp.451–459.

FETCHER, E. S. and FETCHER, W. F. (1942) Experiments on osmotic
regulation of dolphins.
J. cell. comp. Physiol. **19** pp.123–130.

FLEMING W. R., SCHEFFEL K. G., and LINTON J. R. (1962) Studies on the
gill cholinesterase activity of several cyprinodont fishes.
Comp. Biochem. Physiol. **6**: pp.205–213.

FLEMISTER, L. J. (1958) Salt and water anatomy, constancy and regulation
in related crabs from marine and terrestrial habitats.
Biol. Bull. Woods Hole **115** pp.180–200.

FLEMISTER, L. J. and FLEMISTER, S. C. (1951) Chloride ion regulation and
oxygen consumption in the crab, *Ocypode albicans* (Bosq).
Biol. Bull. Woods Hole **101** pp.259–273.

FLEMISTER, S. C. (1959) Histophysiology of gill and kidney of the crab
Ocypode albicans.
Biol. Bull. Woods Hole **116** pp.37–48.

FLORKIN, M. (1949) *Biochemical Evolution*, trans. Morgulis.
Academic Press, New York. 157 pp.

FLORKIN, M. and DUCHÂTEAU, G. (1943) Les formes de systeme enzym-
atique de l'uricolyse et l'evolution du catabolisme purique chez les
animaux.
Arch. int. Physiol. **53** pp.267–307.

FLORKIN, M. and DUCHÂTEAU, G. (1948) Sur l'osmoregulation de l'Anodonte. (*Anodonta cygnaea* L.)
Physiol. comp. **1** pp.29–45.

FLORKIN, M. and DUCHÂTEAU, G. (1950) Concentrations cellulaire et
plasmatique de potassium, de calcium, et de magnesium chez une serie
d'animaux dulcicoles.
C. R. Soc. Biol. Paris **144** pp.1132–1133.

FONTAINE, M. (1956) The hormonal control of water and salt-electrolyte
metabolism in fish.
In: *The Hormonal Control of Water and Salt-electrolyte Metabolism in Vertebrates*.
Memoirs of the Society of Experimental Endocrinology No. **5**. Part II.
ed. I. Chester Jones and P. Eckstein. pp.65–81.
Cambridge Univ. Press.

FORSTER, R. P. (1948) The use of thin kidney slices and isolated renal tubules for direct study of cellular transport kinetics.
Science **108** pp.65–67.

FORSTER, R. P. (1953) A comparative study of renal function in marine teleosts.
J. cell. comp. Physiol. **42** pp.487–509.

FORSTER, R. P. and BERGLUND, F. (1953) Total electrolyte distribution in blood and urine of the aglomerular teleost, *Lophius piscatorius.*
Anat. Rec. **117** pp.591–592.

FORSTER, R. P., SPERBER, I. and TAGGART, J. V. (1954) Transport of phenolphthalein dyes in isolated tubules of the flounder or in kidney slices of the dogfish. Competitive phenomena.
J. cell. comp. Physiol. **44** pp.315–318.

FORSTER, R. P. and TAGGART, J. V. (1950) The use of isolated renal tubules for examination of metabolic processes associated with active cellular transport.
J. cell. comp. Physiol. **36** pp.251–270.

FOX, H. M. (1952) Anal and oral intake of water by Crustacea.
J. exp. Biol. **29** pp. 583–599.

FOX, H. M. and BALDES, E. J. (1935) The vapour pressure of the blood of arthropods from swift and still fresh waters.
J. exp. Biol. **12** pp.174–178.

FRAWLEY, T. F. and FANHAM, P. H. (1951) The salivary Na/K ratio and adrenal salt-regulatory factors. Prolonged salt retention with desoxycorticosterone trimethylacetate.
J. clin. Endocrin. **11** pp.772–773.

FREDERICQ, H., BACQ, Z. H. and FLORKIN, M. (1957) Étude par le radiocalcium de l'état physicochimique du calcium sanguin absorbe a partin du milieu exterieur chez l'anodonte.
Arch. int. Physiol. **59** pp.139–140.

FRETTER, V. (1955) Uptake of radioactive sodium (Na^{24}) by *Nereis diversicolor* Mueller and *Perinereis cultrifera* Grube.
J. mar. biol. Ass. U. K. **34** pp.151–160.

FREY-WYSSLING, A. (1948) *Submicroscopic Morphology of Protoplasm and its Derivatives.*
Elsevier Publ. Co., New York. 255 pp.

FRITSCHE, H. (1916) Studien über die Schwankungen des osmotischen Druckes der Körperflüssigkeiten bei *Daphnia magna.*
Int. Rev. Hydrobiol. **8** pp.22–80; 125–203.

FRY, F. E. J. (1957) The aquatic respiration of fish. In: *The Physiology of Fishes* I. ed. Brown. M. E., pp.1–64. Academic Press, New York and London. 447 pp.

GETMAN, H. C. (1950) Adaptive changes in the chloride cells of *Anguilla rostrata*.
Biol. Bull. Woods Hole 99 pp.439–445.

GIARDINI, A. and ROBERTS, J. R. E. (1950) Concentration of glucose and total chloride in tears.
Brit. J. Ophthal. 34 pp.737–743.

GIEBISCH, G. (1960) Measurements of electrical potential differences on single nephrons of the perfused *Necturus* kidney.
J. gen. Physiol. 44 pp.659–678.

GILBERT, A. B. (1959 a) The composition of the blood of the shore crab, *Carcinus maenas* Pennant, in relation to sex and body size. I. Blood conductivity and freezing-point depression.
J. exp. Biol. 36 pp.113–119.

GILBERT, A. B. (1959 b) The composition of the blood of the shore crab, *Carcinus maenas* Pennant, in relation to sex and body size. II. Blood chloride and sulphate.
J. exp. Biol. 36 pp.356–362.

GILBERT, A. B. (1959 c) The composition of the blood of the shore crab, *Carcinus maenas* Pennant, in relation to sex and body size. III. Blood non-protein nitrogen.
J. exp. Biol. 36 pp.495–500.

GILBERT, D. L. (1960) Magnesium equilibrium in muscle.
J. gen. Physiol. 43 pp.1103–1118.

GILBERT, D. L. and FENN, W. O. (1956) Calcium equilibria in muscle.
J. gen. Physiol. 40 pp.393–408.

GILCHRIST, B. M. (1956) The oxygen consumption of *Artemia salina* (L.) in different salinities.
Hydrobiologia 8 pp.54–63.

GINETZINSKY, A. G. (1958) Role of hyaluronidase in the reabsorption of water in renal tubules.
Nature Lond. 182 pp.1218–1219.

GLYNN, I. M. (1957) The action of the cardiac glycosides on sodium and potassium movements in human red cells.
J. Physiol. 136 pp.148–173.

GLYNN, I. M. (1959) The sodium potassium exchange pump. In: *The Method of Isotopic Tracers applied to the Study of Active Ion Transport*, pp. 46–42, ed. J. Coursaget. Pergamon Press, London. 196 pp.

GOETHARD, W. C. and HENSIUS, H. W. (1892) Report on *Noctiluca* (in Dutch).
Nederlandische Staatscourant (cited in Krogh, 1939).

GOODRICH, E. S. (1946) Nephridia and genital ducts since 1895.
Quart. J. micr. Sci. 86 pp.113–393.

25

GORDON, M. S. (1959 a) Ionic regulation in the brown trout (*Salmo trutta* L.)
J. exp. Biol. **36** pp.227–252.

GORDON, M. S. (1959 b) Osmotic and ionic regulation in Scottish brown
trout and sea trout (*Salmo trutta* L.).
J. exp. Biol. **36** pp.253–260.

Gordon, M. S. (1962) Osmotic regulation in the green toad *(Bufo viridis)*.
J. exp. Biol. **39** pp.261–270.

GORDON, M. S., AMDUR, B. H. and SCHOLANDER, P. F. (1959) Further
observations on supercooling and osmoregulation in Arctic fishes.
1st. Internat. Oceanog. Congress pp. 234–236.

GORDON, M. S., SCHMIDT-NIELSEN, K, and KELLY, H. M. (1961) Osmotic
regulation in the crab-eating frog *(Rana cancrivora)*.
J. exp. Biol. **38** pp.659–678.

GOTTSCHALK, C. N. (1960) Osmotic concentration and dilution in the
mammalian nephron.
Circulation **21** pp.861–868.

GRAETZ, E. (1931) Versuch einer exakten analyse der zur osmoregulation
benötigten Kräfte in ihrer Beziehung zum Gesamtstoffwechsel von
Süsswasserstichlungen in hypo- und hypertonischen Medium.
Zool. J. **49** pp.37–58.

GRAFFLIN, A. L. (1931) Urine flow and diuresis in marine teleosts.
Amer. J. Physiol. **97** pp. 602–610.

GRASSÉ, P. P. (1958) *Traité de Zoologie*, Agnathes et Poissons XIII. 924 pp.
Masson et Cie, Paris.

GRAY, I. E. (1954) Comparative study of the gill area of marine fishes.
Biol. Bull. Woods Hole **107** pp.219–225.

GRAY, J. (1928) The role of water in the evolution of terrestrial vertebrates.
J. exp. Biol. **6** pp.26–31.

GRAY, J. (1932) The osmotic properties of the eggs of the trout (*Salmo
fario*).
J. exp. Biol. **9** pp.277–299.

GREEN, J. W., HARSCH, M., BARR, L. and PROSSER, C. L. (1959) The
regulation of water and salt by the fiddler crabs, *Uca pugnax* and
Uca pugilator.
Biol. Bull. Woods Hole **116** pp.76–87.

GREGERSON, M. I. and INGALLS, E. N. (1931) The influence of the rate
of secretion on the concentrations of sodium and potassium in the
dog's submaxillary saliva.
Amer. J. Physiol. **98** pp.441–446.

GROSS, W. J. (1955) Aspects of osmotic regulation in crabs showing terrestrial habit.
Amer. Nat. **89** pp.205–222.

GROSS, W. J. (1957) An analysis of the response to osmotic stress in selected decapod crustaceans.
Biol. Bull. Woods Hole **112** pp.43–62.

GUDIKSEN, E. (1943) Investigations on the electrolyte content of gastric juice.
Acta. physiol. scand. **5** pp.39–54.

HARDING, J. P. (1953) The first known example of a terrestrial ostracod *Mesocypris terrestris* sp. nov.
Ann. Natal Mus. **12** pp.359–365.

HARDISTY, M. W. (1956) Some aspects of osmotic regulation in lampreys.
J. exp. Biol. **33** pp. 431–447.

HARGITAY, B., KUHN, W. and WIRZ, H. (1951) Ein Modellversuch zum Problem der Harnkonzentrierung.
Helv. physiol acta. **9** pp.26–27.

HARRIS, E. J. (1950) The transfer of sodium and potassium between the muscles and the surrounding medium. 2. The sodium flux.
Trans. Faraday Soc. **46** pp.872–882.

HARRIS, E. J. (1960) *Transport and Accumulation in Biological Systems*, 2nd ed. Butterworths, London. 291 pp.

HARRIS, E. J. and MAIZELS, M. (1951) The permeability of human erythrocytes to sodium.
J. Physiol. **113** pp.506–524.

HARRIS, E. J. and MAIZELS, M. (1952) The distribution of ions in suspensions of human erythrocytes.
J. Physiol. **118** pp.40–53.

HARRIS E. J., and R. A. SJODIN (1961) Kinetics of exchange and net movements of frog muscle potassium.
J. Physiol. **155** pp.221–245

HARRISON, F. M. (1962) Some excretory processes in the abalone, *Haliotis rufescens*.
J. exp. Biol. **39** pp.179–192.

HARTMAN, F. A., LEWIS, L. A., BROWNELL, K. A., ANGERER, C. A. and SHELDON, F. F. (1944) Effect of interrenalectomy on some blood constituents in the skate.
Physiol. Zool. **17** pp.228–238.

HAYES, F. R. (1949) The growth, general chemistry and temperature relations of salmonid eggs.
Quart. Rev. Biol. **24** pp.281–308.

HAYES, F. R., DARCY, D. A. and SULLIVAN, C. M. (1946) Changes in the inorganic constituents of developing salmon eggs.
J. biol. Chem. **163** pp.42–51.

25*

HAYES, F. R. and PELLUET, D. (1947) The inorganic constitution of molluscan blood and muscle.
J. mar. biol. Ass. U. K. **26** pp.580–589.

HAYMAN, J. M. (1927) Estimation of afferent arteriole and glomerular pressure in frog kidney.
Amer. J. Physiol. **79** pp.389–409.

HELLER, H. (1956) The hormonal control of water and salt-electrolyte metabolism with special reference to the higher vertebrates.
In: *The Hormonal Control of Water and Salt-electrolyte Metabolism in Vertebrates.*
Memoirs of the Society of Experimental Endocrinology No. **5** Part. II.
ed. I. Chester Jones and P. Eckstein. Cambridge Univ. Press. pp. 25–36.

HELLER, H. and PICKERING, B. T. (1960) Identification of a new hypophysial hormone.
J. Physiol. **152**. 56P.

HELLER, H., PICKERING, B. T., MAETZ, J. and MOREL, F. (1961) Pharmacological characterization of the oxytocic peptides in the pituitary of a marine teleost fish *(Pollachius virens).*
Nature Lond. **191** pp.670–671.

HENRIQUES B. L. (1961) Acinar and duct transport sites for Na^+ and K^+ in dog submaxillary gland.
Am. J. Physiol. **201** pp.935–938.

HERFS, A. (1922) Die pulsierende Vakuole der Protozoen, ein Schutzorgan gegen Aussüssung. Studien über Anpassung der Organismen an das Leben im Süsswasser.
Arch. Protistenk. **44** pp.227–260.

HERMAN, R. T., WILSON, T. H. and KAZYAK, L. (1957) Electrolyte migrations across the wall of the guinea pig gall bladder.
J. cell. comp. Physiol. **51** pp.133–144.

HEUTS, M. J. (1943) Studies oven de osmoregulatie van het bloed bij enkele crustaceen *Asellus aquaticus* (Sars), *Gammarus pulex* (L.), en *Gammarus duebeni.*
Meded. vlaansche. Acad. Kl. Wet. **5** No. **2.**

HEVESEY, G., HOFER, E. and KROGH, A. (1935) The permeability of the skin of frogs to water as determined by D_2O and H_2O.
Skand. Arch. Physiol. **72** pp.199–214.

HICKMAN, C. P. (1959) The osmoregulatory role of the thyroid gland in the starry flounder, *Platichthys stellatus.*
Canad. J. Zool. **37** pp.997–1060.

HINKE, J. A. M. (1961) The measurement of Na and K activities in the squid axon by means of cation selective glass microelectrodes.
J. Physiol. **156** pp.314–335.

HIRSCHOWITZ, B. I., STRATEN, D. H. P., LONDON, J. A. and POLLARD, H. M. (1957) Basal secretion and plasma and urinary pepsinogen.
J. clin. Invest. **36** pp.1171–1182.

HOAR, W. S. (1958) Endocrine factors in the ecological adaptation of fishes In: *Comparative Endocrinology.* ed. Gorbman, pp.1–23. Wiley and Sons New York, 1958. 746 pp.

HODGKIN, A. L. (1956) Ionic movement and electrical activity in giant nerve fibres.
Proc. roy. Soc. B **148** pp.1–37.

HODGKIN, A. L. and KEYNES, R. D. (1955 a) Active transport of cations in the giant axons from *Sepia* and *Loligo.*
J. Physiol. **128** pp.28–60.

HODGKIN, A. L. and KEYNES, R. D. (1955 b) Potassium permeability of nerve.
J. Physiol. **128** pp.61–88.

HOGBEN, C. A. M. (1955) Active transport of chloride by isolated frog gastric epithelium.
Amer. J. Physiol. **180** pp.641–649.

HOKIN, L. E. and HOKIN, M. R. (1959) Evidence for phosphatidic acid as the sodium carrier.
Nature Lond. **184** pp.1068–1069.

HOKIN, M. R. and HOKIN, L. E. (1961) Further evidence for phosphatidic acid as the sodium carrier.
Nature Lond. **190** pp.1016–1017.

HOLLIDAY, F. G. T. and BLAXTER, J. H. S. (1960) The effects of salinity on the developing eggs and larvae of the herring.
J. mar. biol. Ass. U. K. **39** pp.591–603.

HOLLIDAY, F. G. T. and BLAXTER, J. H. S. (1961) The effects of salinity on the herring after metamorphosis.
J. mar. biol. Ass. U. K. **41** pp.37–48.

HOLLIDAY, F. G. T. and PARRY, G. (1962) Acidophil cells in the gills and psaudobranch of teleosts.
Nature Lond. **195** p.192.

HOLMAN, M. E. (1957) The effect of changes in sodium chloride concentration on smooth muscle of the guinea pig's *Taenia coli.*
J. Physiol. **136** pp.569–584.

HOLMES, R. M. (1960) Kidney function in the rainbow trout.
Ann. Rep. Challenger, Soc. **3** XIII.

HOLMES W. N. (1959) Studies on the hormonal control of sodium metabolism in the rainbow trout *(Salmo gairdneri).*
Acta endocrinol. **31** pp.587–602.

HOLMES, W. N., PHILLIPS, J. G., and BUTLER, A. G. The effect of adreno-cortical steroids on the renal and extra-renal response of the domestic duck *(Anas platyrhynchus)* after hypertonic saline loading. *Endocrinol.* **69** pp.483–495.

HOUSTON, A. H. (1959) Osmoregulatory adaptation of steelhead trout *(Salmo gairdneri* Richardson) to sea water. *Can. J. Zool.* **37** pp.729–748.

HOYLE, G. (1953) Potassium ions and insect nerve and muscle. *J. exp. Biol.* **30** pp.121–135.

HOYLE, G. (1954) Changes in the blood otassium concentration of the African migratory locust *(Locusta migratoria migratoroides* R. and F.), during food deprivation, and the effect on the muscular activity. *J. exp. Biol.* **31** pp.261–270.

HUF, E. (1934) Über den Einfluss der narkose auf den Wasserhaushalt bei Süsswassertieren. *Pflug. Arch. ges. Physiol.* **235** pp.29–40.

HUF, E. (1936) Der Einfluss des mechanischen Innendrucks auf die Flüssig-keitsausscheidung bei gepanzerten Süsswasser- und Meereskrebsen. *Pflüg. Arch. ges. Physiol.* **237** pp.240–250.

HUTCHINSON, G. E. (1944) Conway on sea water. A critique. *Amer. J. Sci.* **242** pp.272–280.

IIDA, T. T. and IWATA, K. S. (1943) Cell sap of *Noctiluca.* *J. Fac. Sci. Imp. Univ. Tokyo Sec. IV., Zool.* **6** (1) pp. 175–178.

INGRAHAM, R. C. and VISSCHER, M. B. (1936) The production of chloride-free solutions by the action of the interstitial epithelium. *Amer. J. Physiol.* **114** pp.676–687.

IRVING, L., FISCHER, K. C. and McINTOSH, F. C. (1935) The water balance of a marine mammal, the seal. *J. cell. comp. Physiol.* **6** pp.387–391.

JENKIN. P. M. (1962) *Animal Hormones. Part I: Kinetic and Metabolic Hormones.* Pergamon Press, Oxford and London. 310 pp.

JEUNIAUX, C., DUCHATEAU–BOSSON, G. and FLORKIN, M. (1961) Free amino acids in the intracellular osmoregulation of euryhaline marine worms. *Biochem. J.* **79** 24 P.

JEUNIAUX C., DUCHATEAU–BOSSON G. and FLORKIN M. (1961) Variation of component amino acids of the tissues and euryhalinity of *Perinereis cultrifera* GR, and *Nereis diversicolor* (O. F. Mueller). *J. Biochem. Tokyo* **49** pp.427–531.

JONES, I. C. (1956) The role of the adrenal cortex in the control of water and salt electrolyte metabolism in vertebrates. In: *The Hormonal Control of Water and Salt-electrolyte Metabolism in Vertebrates.*

Memoirs of the Society of Experimental Endocrinology No. 5. Part II. ed. I. C. Jones and P. Eckstein. Cambridge Univ. Press. pp.102–120.

JONES, L. L. (1941) Osmotic pressure relations of nine species of crabs of the Pacific coast of N. America.
J. cell. comp. Physiol. 18 pp.79–92.

JØRGENSEN, C. B. and DALES, R. P. (1957) The regulation of volume and osmotic regulation in some Nereid polychaetes.
Physiol. comp. 4 pp.357–374.

JØRGENSEN, C. B., LEVI, H. and USSING, H. H. (1946) On the influence of the neurohypophysial principles on the sodium metabolism of the Axolotl (*Ambystoma mexicanum*).
Acta physiol. scand. 12 pp.350–371.

JØRGENSEN, C. B., LEVI, H. and ZERAHN, K. (1954) On active uptake of sodium and chloride ions in Anurans.
Acta physiol. scand. 30 pp.178–190.

JØRGENSEN, C. B., WINGSTRAND, K. G. and ROSENKILDE, P. (1956) Neurohypophysis and water metabolism in the toad, *Bufo bufo* (L.)
Endocrinol. 59 pp.601–610.

JULLIEN, A., VIELLE-CESSAY, CH., ACOLAT, L., RIPPLINGER, J. and JOLY, M. (1955) La teneur en ions Na, K, et Ca de l'hemolymphe determine au photometre à flamme et ses rapports avec la composition de solutions artificielles optes à assurer une activité de longue durée au coeur isolé chez les Helicides.
C. R. Soc. Biol. Paris, 149 pp.723–726.

JURGENS, O. (1935) Die Wechselbeziehungen von Blutkreislauf, Atmung, und Osmoregulation bei Polychaeten (*Nereis diversicolor* Mull).
Zool. Jb. Physiol. 55 pp.1–46.

KALASHNIKOV, G. N. and SKADOVSKII, S. N. (1948) Ecological and physiological study of sevriuga during the period of reproduction under natural and experimental conditions.
Zool. Zh. 27 pp.513–524.

KAMEMOTO, F. I. SPALDING A. E. and KEISTER, S. M. 1962 Ionic balance in the blood and coelomic fluid of earthworms.
Biol. Bull. Woods Hole. 122 pp.228–231.

KARPEVICK, A. F. (1958) Survival, reproduction and respiration of *Mesomysis kowalewskyi* (*Paramysis lacustris kowalewskyi*) in brackish water of the U.S.S.R.
Zool. Zh. 37 pp.1121–1135.

KATOOZANNIS, P. G. and VIGNEAUD, DU V. (1958) Arginine vasotocin, a synthetic analogue of the posterior pituitary hormones containing the ring of oxytocin and the side chain of vasopressin.
J. biol. Chem. 233 pp.1352–1354.

KAY, R. N. B. (1960) The rate of flow and composition of various salivary secretions in sheep and calves.
J. Physiol. **150** pp.515–537.

KEDEM, O. and KATCHALSKY, A. (1958) Thermodynamic analysis of the permeability of biological membranes to non-electrolytes.
Biochem. et biophys. Acta. **27** pp.229–246.

KEDEM O. and KATCHALSKY, A. (1961) A physical interpretation of the phenomenological coefficient of membrane permealibity.
J. gen. Physiol. **45** 143–179.

KEMPTON, R. T. (1953) Studies on elasmobranch kidney. II. Reabsorption of urea by the smooth dogfish *Mustelis canis.*
Biol. Bull. Woods Hole. **104** pp.45–56.

KEPCS, I. D., LORD, G. A., FRENCH, E. E. and VANDERLINDER, R. J. (1956) External pancreatic secretion.
Gastroenteologia, Basel. **31** pp.190–197.

KERMACK, W. H., LEES, H. and WOOD, J. D. (1955) Some non-protein constituents of the tissues of the lobster.
Biochem. J. **60** pp.424–428.

KEYNES, R. D. (1954) The ionic fluxes in frog muscle.
Proc. roy. Soc. B **142** pp.359–382.

KEYS, A. B. (1931) Chloride and water secretion and absorption by the gills of the eel.
Z. vergl. Physiol. **15** pp.364–388.

KEYS, A. B. and WILLMER, E. N. (1932) "Cloride secreting cells" in the gills of fishes, with special reference to the common eel.
J. Physiol. **76** pp.368–381.

KILL F., and AUKLAND K. (1960) Renal tubular localisation of water and sodium resorption in antidiuresis and water diuresis.
Scand. J. Clin. Lab. Invest. **12** pp.277–289.

KINNE, O. and ROTTHAUWE, H. W. (1952) Biologische Beobachtungen und Untersuchungen über die Blutkonzentration an *Heteropanope tridentatus* Maitland (Dekapoda).
Kieler Meeresforsch. **8** pp.212–217.

KINSEY, V. E. (1960) Ion movement in the eye.
Circulation. **21** pp.968–987.

KIRSCHER, L. B. (1955 a) On the mechanism of active sodium transport across frog skin.
J. cell. comp. Physiol. **45** pp.61–87.

KIRSCHNER, L. B. (1955 b) On the mechanism of active sodium transport across frog skin.
J. cell. comp. Physiol. **45** pp.513–530.

KITCHENER, J. A. (1957) *Ion Exchange Resins.*
Methuen, London. 109 pp.

KITCHING, J. A. (1934) The physiology of contractile vacuoles. II. The control of body volume in marine Peritricha.
J. exp. Biol. **13** pp.11–27.

KITCHING, J. A. (1938) The physiology of contractile vacuoles. III. The water balance of freshwater Peritricha.
J. exp. Biol. **15** pp.143–151.

KITCHING, J. A. (1939) The physiology of contractile vacuoles. IV. A note on the sources of the water evacuated and on the function of the contractile vacuoles in marine Protozoa.
J. exp. Biol. **16** pp.34–37.

KITCHING, J. A. (1954) The physiology of contractile vacuoles. X. The effects of high hydrostatic pressure on the contractile vacuole of a suctorian.
J. exp. Biol. **31** pp.68–75.

KITCHING, J. A. (1956) Contractile vacuoles in Protozoa.
Protoplasmatologia, Bd. III, Cytoplasma-Organellen. D. Vacuom 3, Special Vacuoles.

KOCH, A. R., BRAZEAU, P. and GILMAN, A. (1956) The role of renal tubular secretion in potassium homeostasis.
Amer. J. Physiol. **186** pp.350–356.

KOCH, H. J. and EVANS, J. (1956) On the absorption of sodium from dilute solutions by the crab *Eriocheir sinensis* M. (Edw.).
Mededel. Kon. Vl. Acad. Kl. Wet. **18** Nr. 7 pp.1–15.

KOCH, H.J., EVANS, J. and SCHICKS, E. (1953) Inhibitions à l'aide de colorantes basiques du transport actif de matières minérales par les branchies isolées du Crabe *Eriocheir sinensis* M. Edw.
Arch. int. Physiol. **61** pp.476–484.

KOCH, H. J., EVANS, J. and SCHICKS, E. (1954) The active absorption of ions by the isolated gills of the crab, *Eriocheir sinensis*. (M. Edw.)
Mededel. Kon. Vl. Acad. Kl. Wet. **16** Nr. 5 pp.1–16.

KOEFOED-JOHNSEN, V.. LEVI H, and USSING H. H. (1952) The mode of passage of chloride ions through the isolated frog skin.
Acta Physiol. Skand. **25** pp.150–163.

KOEFOED-JOHNSEN, V. and USSING, H. H. (1953) The contributions of diffusion and flow to the passage of D_2O through living membranes.
Acta physiol. scand. **28** pp.60–76.

KOEFOED-JOHNSEN, V. and USSING, H. H. (1958) The nature of the frog skin potential.
Acta physiol. scand. **42** pp.298–308.

KOEHRING, V. (1930) The neutral red reaction.
J. Morph. **49** pp.45–138.

KOIDSUMI, K. (1935) Experimentelle Studien über die Transpiration und den Wärmehaushalt bei Insekten.
Mem. Fac. Sci. Agric. Tohoku. **12** pp.1–179 ; 281–380.

KOIZUMI, T. (1932) Studies on the exchange and equilibrium of water and elecrolytes in a holothurian *Caudina chilensis* (J. Müller). I.
Sci. Rep. Tohoku Univ. IV. **7** pp.259–311.

KOIZUMI, T. (1935 a) On the velocity of permeation of K^+, Na^+, Ca^{++} and Mg^{++} through the isolated body wall of *Caudina*.
Sci. Rep. Tohoku Univ. IV. **10** pp.269–275.

KOIZUMI, T. (1935 b) On the inorganic composition of the corpuscles of the body fluid.
Sci. Rep. Tohoku Univ. IV. **10** pp.277–280.

KOIZUMI, T. (1935 c) On the inorganic composition of the longitudinal muscles and the body wall without longitudinal muscles.
Sci. Rep. Tohoku Univ. IV. **10** pp.281–286.

KOIZUMI, T. and HOSOI, K. (1936) Electrolytes in medusae.
Sci. Rep. Tohoku Univ. IV. **10** pp.709–719.

KON, S. K. and COWIE, A. T. (1961) Milk: The Mammary Gland and its Secretion. Academic Press, New York and London.

KORR, I. (1939) The osmotic function of chicken kidney.
J. cell. comp. Physiol. **13** pp.175–193.

KRNJEVIC, K. (1955) The distribution of sodium and potassium in cat nerves.
J. Physiol. **128** pp. 473–488.

KROGH, A. (1937 a) Osmotic regulation in the frog (*Rana esculenta*) by active absorption of chloride ions.
Skand. Arch. Physiol. **76** pp.60–73.

KROGH, A. (1937 b) Osmotic regulation in freshwater fishes by active absorption of chloride ions.
Z. vergl. Physiol. **24** pp.656–666.

KROGH, A. (1938) The active absorption of ions in some freshwater animals.
Z. vergl. Physiol. **25** pp.235–250.

KROGH, A. (1939) *Osmotic Regulation in Aquatic Animals.*
Cambridge Univ. Press. 242 pp.

KROGH, A., SCHMIDT-NIELSEN, K. and ZEUTHEN, E. (1938) The osmotic behaviour of frogs' eggs and young tadpoles.
Z. vergl. Physiol. **26** pp.230–238.

KROGH, A. and USSING, H. H. (1937) A note on the permeability of trout eggs to D_2O and H_2O.
J. exp. Biol. **14** pp.35–37.

KROMHAUT, G. A. (1943) A comparison of freshwater, brackish water and marine specimens of *Gyratrix hermaphroditus*.
J. Morph. **72** pp.167–177.

KROHØFFER, P. (1946) Inulin as an indicator for the extracellular space.
Acta physiol. scand. **11** pp.16–36.

KUENEN, D. J. (1939) Systematical and physiological notes on the brine
shrimp, *Artemia*.
Arch. neerland. Zool. **3** pp.365–449.

LARSEN, N. A., MUNCK, O. and THAYSEN, J. H. (1961) Oxygen consumption and sodium resorption in the kidney.
Acta. physiol. scand. **51** pp.371–384.

LASSITER, W. E., GOTTSCHALK, C. W. and MYLLE, M. (1961) Micropuncture
study of net trans-tubular movement of water and urea in non-diuretic
mammalian kidney.
Am. J. Physiol. **200** pp.1139–1147.

LEAF, A. (1960) Some actions of neurohypophysial hormones on a living
membrane.
J. gen. Physiol. **43** Suppl. pp.175–189.

LEAF, A. and RENSHAW, A. (1956) A test of the redox hypothesis of active
ion transport.
Nature Lond. **178** pp.156–157.

LEAF, A. and RENSHAW, A. (1957) Ion transport and respiration of isolated
frog skin.
Biochem. J. **65** pp.82–90.

LEES, A. D. (1946) The water balance in *Ixodes nicinus* L. and certain other
species of ticks.
Parasitology. **37** pp.1–20.

LEVENBOOK, L. (1958) (Ed.) *Biochemistry of Insects*.
Fourth Internat. Congr. Biochem. Sympos. XII. Pergamon Press.
252 pp.

LEVI, H. and USSING, H. H. (1948) The exchange of sodium and chloride
ions across the fibre membrane of the isolated frog sartorius.
Acta physiol. scand. **16** pp.232–249.

LEWIS, P. R. (1952) The free amino-acids of invertebrate nerve.
Biochem. J. **52** pp.330–338.

LIENEMANN, L. J. (1938) The green glands as mechanisms for osmotic
and ionic regulation in the crayfish, *Cambarus*.
J. cell. comp. Physiol. **11** pp.149–161.

LIFSON, N., VARCO, R. L. and VISSCHER, M. B. (1941) Relationship between osmotic activity and sodium content of gastric juice.
Proc. Soc. exp. Biol. N. Y. **47** pp.422–425.

LILLY, S. (1955) Osmotic and ionic regulation in *Hydra*.
J. exp. Biol. **32** pp.423–439.

LING, E. R., KON, S. K. and PORTER, J. W. G. (1961) The composition of milk and the nutritive value of its components. In: *Milk: The Mammary Gland and its Secretion.* ed. Kon and Cowie, Academic Press, New York and London, 1961.

LIU, C. K. (1942) Osmoregulation and chloride secreting cells in the paradise fish *Macropodium opercularis.* *Sinensia.* **13** pp.17–20.

LIU, C. K. (1944) Sodium sulphate as an agent causing the development of chloride secreting cells in *Macropus.* *Nature Lond.* **153** p.252.

LOBECK, C. C. (1958) Studies on chloride of bone in cat and rat. *Proc. Soc. exp. Biol. N. Y.* **98** pp.856–860.

LOCKWOOD, A. P. M. (1959 a) Composition of the haemolymph of *Petrobius maritimus* Leach. *Nature Lond.* **184** pp.370–371.

LOCKWOOD, A. P. M. (1959 b) The osmotic and ionic regulation of *Asellus aquaticus* (L.). *J. exp. Biol.* **36** pp.546–555.

LOCKWOOD, A. P. M. (1960) Some effects of temperature and concentration of the medium on the ionic regulation of the isopod *Asellus aquaticus* (L.). *J. exp. Biol.* **37** pp.614–630.

LOCKWOOD, A. P. M. (1961) Osmoregulation in gammarids. *J. exp. Biol.* **38** pp.647–658.

LOCKWOOD, A. P. M. and CROGHAN, P. (1959) Composition of th haemolymph of *Petrobius maritimus* Leach. *Nature Lond.* **184** pp.370–371.

LOFTS, B. (1956) The effect of salinity changes on the respiration rate of prawn, *Palaemonetes varians* (Leach). *J. exp. Biol.* **33** pp.730–736.

LØVTRUP, S. and PIGON, A. (1951) Diffusion and active transport in the amoeba *Chaos chaos* L. *C. R. Lab. Carlsberg.* Ser. chim. **28** pp.1–36.

LÖWENSTEIN, O. (1935) The respiratory rate of *Gammarus chevreuxii* in relation to difference in salinity. *J. exp. Biol.* **12** pp.217–221.

LUMBYE, J. (1958) The oxygen consumption of *Theodoxus fluviatilis* L. and *Potamopyrgus jenkinsi* (Smith) in brackish and fresh water. *Hydrobiologia.* **10** pp.245–262.

LUNDBERG, A. (1958) Electrophysiology of salivary glands. *Physiol. Revs.* **38** pp.21–40.

LUNDEGARDH, H. (1954) Anion respiration.
In: Soc. exp. Biol. Symposium No. 8: *Active Transport and Secretion.*
Camb. Univ. Press. pp.262–296.

LYMAN, J. and FLEMING, R. H. (1940) Composition of sea water.
J. mar. Res. 3 pp.134–46.

MACALLUM, A. B. (1903) On the inorganic composition of the Medusae
Aurelia flavidula and *Cyanea arctica.*
J. Physiol. 29 pp.213–41.

MACALLUM, A. B. (1926) The palaeochemistry of body fluids and tissues.
Physiol. Rev. 6 pp.316–55.

MACAN, T. T. and WORTHINGTON, E. B. (1951) *Life in Lakes and Rivers.*
Collins, London. 272 pp.

MACFARLAND, L. Z. (1959) Captive marine birds possessing a functional
lateral nasal gland (salt gland).
Nature Lond. 184 pp.2030–2031.

MACIE, I. G. (1949) Composition of human colostrum and milk.
Amer. J. Dis. Child. 78 pp.589–603.

MADDRELL, S. H. P. (1962) A diuretic hormone in *Rhodnius prolixus* Stal.
Nature, Lond. 194 pp.605–606.

MAETZ, J. (1953) L'anhydrase carbonique dans deux teleosteens voisins.
C. R. Soc. Biol., Paris. 147 pp.204–206.

MAETZ, J. and JUIEN, M. (1961) Action of neurohypophysial hormones
on the sodium fluxes of a freshwater teleost.
Nature Lond. 189 pp.152–153.

MAFFLY, R. H. and LEAF, A. (1959) Potential of water in mammalian tissues.
J. gen. Physiol. 42 pp.1257–1275.

MALOEUF, N. S. R. (1938) Studies on the respiration (and osmoregulation)
of animals.
Z. vergl. Physiol. 25 pp.1–42.

MALUF, N. S. R. (1939) On the anatomy of the kidney of the crayfish and
on the absorption of chloride from fresh water by this animal.
Zool. Jb. 59 pp.515–534.

MALUF, N. S. R. (1941 a) Experimental cytological evidence for an outward
secretion of water by the nephridial tubules of the crayfish.
Biol. Bull. Woods Hole. 81 pp.127–133.

MALUF, N. S. R. (1941 b) Secretion of inulin, xylose and dyes and its bear-
ing on the manner of urine formation in the kidney of the crayfish.
Biol. Bull. Woods Hole. 81 pp.235–260.

MANERY, J. F. (1939) Electrolytes in squid blood and muscle.
J. cell. comp. Physiol. 14 pp.365–369.

MANERY J. F. (1954) Water and electrolyte metabolism.
Physiol. Revs. 34 pp.334–417.

MANERY, J. F. and BALE, W. F. (1941) The penetration of radioactive sodium and phosphorus into the extra- and intracellular phases of tissues.
Amer. J. Physiol. **132** pp.215–231.

MANERY, J. F. and IRVING, L. (1935) Water changes in trout eggs at the time of laying.
J. cell. comp. Physiol. **5** pp.457–464.

MARSHALL, E. K. (1930) A comparison of the function of the glomerular and aglomerular kidney.
Amer. J. Physiol. **94** pp.1–10.

MARSHALL, E. K. (1934) Comparative physiology of the vertebrate kidney.
Physiol. Rev. **14** pp.133–159.

MARSHALL, E. K. and GRAFFLIN, A. L. (1932) The function of the proximal convoluted segment of the renal tubule.
J. cell. comp. Physiol. **1** pp.161–176.

MARTIN, A. W. (1957) Recent advances in knowledge of invertebrate renal function.
In: *Recent Advances in Invertebrate Physiology.* ed. B. Scheer, pp. 247–276. Univ. Oregon, Eugene, Oregon, U.S.A.

MARTIN, A. W., HARRISON, F. M., HUSTON, M. J. and STEWART D. M. (1958) The blood volumes of some representative molluscs.
J. exp. Biol. **35** pp.260–279.

MARTIN, A. W., STEWART, D. M. and HARRISON, F. M. (1954) Kidney function in the giant African snail.
J. cell. comp. Physiol. **44** pp.345–346.

MATTHEWS, S. A. (1933) Color changes in *Fundulus* after hypophysectomy.
Biol. Bull. Woods Hole. **64** pp.315–320.

MEDWEDEWA, N. B. (1927) Über den Osmotischen Druck der Hämolymphe von *Artemia salina.*
Z. vergl. Physiol. **5** pp.547–554.

MELLANBY, K. (1932) The effect of atmospheric humidity on the metabolism of the fasting meal worm (*Tenebrio molitor* L. Coleoptera).
Proc. roy. Soc. B. **111** pp.376–390.

MERCER, E. H. (1959) An electron microscope study of *Amoeba proteus.*
Proc. roy. Soc. B. **150** pp.216–232.

MEYER, D. K. (1951) The sodium flux through the gills of the goldfish.
Amer. J. Physiol. **165** pp.580–595.

MILNE, A. (1940) Some ecological aspects of the intertidal area of the estuary of the Aberdeenshire Dee.
Trans. roy. Soc. Edin. **50** pp.107–140.

MOLLITOR, A. (1937) Beiträge zur Untersuchung des Exkretsstoffwechsels und der Exkretion von *Eriocheir sinensis.*
Zool. Jb. **57** pp.323–354.

MOREL, F., MAETZ, J., ARCHER, R., CHAUVET, J. and LENCI, M. T. (1961)
A "natriferic" principle other than arginine-vasoctocin in the frog
neurohypophysis.
Nature Lond. 190 pp.828–829.

MORRIS, R. (1956) The osmoregulatory ability of the lampern (*Lampetra
fluviatilis*) in sea water during the course of its spawning migration.
J. exp. Biol. 33 pp.235–248.

MORRIS, R. (1957) Some aspects of the structure and cytology of the gills
of *Lampetra fluviatilis* L.
Quart. J. micr. Sci. 98 pp.473–485.

MORRIS, R. (1958) The mechanism of marine osmoregulation in the lampern
(*Lampetra fluviatilis*) and the causes of its breakdown during the spawn-
ing migration.
J. exp. Biol. 35 pp.649–665.

MORRIS, R. (1960) General problems of osmoregulation with special
reference to cyclostomes.
Symp. zool. soc. London 1 pp.1–16.

MOTAIS R. (1961 a) Sodium exchange in a euryhaline teleost, *Platichthys
flesus flesus.*
Endocrinol. 70 pp.724–726

MOTAIS, (1961 b) Kinetics of sodium exchange in a euryhaline teleost *(Platichthys flesus)* during successive passages from sea water, fresh water
and to sea water, as a function of the period of stay in fresh water.
C. R. Acad. Sci. Paris 235: pp.2609–2611.

MOYLE, V. (1948) Nitrogenous excretion in chelonian reptiles.
Biochem. J. 44 pp.581–584.

MULLINS, L. J. (1950) Osmotic regulation in fish as studied with radio-
isotopes.
Acta physiol. scand. 21 pp.303–314.

MULROW P. and GANANY W. F. (1961) Stimulation of aldosterone secretion by angiotensin II.
Yale J. Biol. Med. 33 pp.386–395.

MULROW P. and GANANY W. F. (1962) Role of the kidney in adrenocortical response to haemorrhage in hypophysectomised dogs.
Endocrinol. 70 pp.182–188.

MUNSICK, R. A., SAWYER, W. H. and VAN DYKE, H. B. (1960) Avian
neurohypophysial hormone and tentative identification.
Endocrinol. 66 pp.860–871.

MURRAY, R. W. and POTTS, W. T. W. (1961) The composition of the endolymph, perilymph and other body fluids of elasmobranchs.
Comp. Biochem. Physiol. 2 pp.65–75.

NAGEL, H. (1934) Die Aufgabe der Extkretionsorgane und der Kiemen bei der Osmoregulation von *Carcinus maenas*.
Z. *vergl. Physiol.* **21** pp.468–491.

NANNINGA L. B. (1961) Calculation of free magnesium, calcium and potassium in muscle.
Biochem. Biophys. Acta **54** pp.338–344.

NEEDHAM, J. (1931) *Chemical Embryology*.
Cambridge Univ. Press. 2021 pp.3 vols.

NEEDHAM, J. (1950) *Biochemistry and Morphogenesis*.
Cambridge Univ. Press. 787 pp.

NEEDHAM, J. and NEEDHAM, D. (1930) Nitrogen excretion in selachian ontogeny.
J. *exp. Biol.* **7** pp.7-18.

NEMENZ, H. (1960 a) Experimente zur Ionenregulation der Larve von *Ephydra cinerea* Jones (Dipt.).
Sitzungsberichten der Österr. Akad. Wiss. Mothen-naturw. Kl. Abt. 1 **169** pp.1–41.

NEMENZ, H. (1960 b) On the osmotic regulation of the larvae of *Ephydra cinerea*.
J. *Insect. Physiol.* **4** pp.38–44.

NEMENZ, H. (1960 c) Beiträge zur Kenntnis der Biologie von *Ephydra cinerea* Jones (Dipt.).
Zool. Anz. **165** pp.218–226.

NORRIS, E. R. and BENOIT, G. J. (1945) Studies on trimethylamine oxide. I. Occurrence of trimethylamine oxide in marine organisms.
J. *biol. Chem.* **158** pp.433–448.

NUMANOI, H. (1934) Calcium in the blood of *Ligia exotica* during non-moulting and moulting phases.
J. *Fac. Sci. Tohoku Univ. IV.* **3** pp.351–358.

NUNEZ, J. A. (1956) Untersuchungen über die Regelung des Wasserhaushaltes bei *Anisotarsus cupripennis* Gesm.
Z. *vergl. Physiol.* **38** pp.341–354.

NUNEZ, J. A. (1962) Regulation of water economy in *Rhodnius prolixus*.
Nature London. **194** p.704.

ÖBRINK, K. J. (1956) Water permeability of the isolated stomach of the mouse.
Acta physiol. scand. **36** pp.229–244.

ODDO, A M. and ESPOSITO, M. (1951) Changes in the potassium content of sea urchin eggs on fertilisation.
J. *gen. Physiol.* **34** p.285–293.

OKA A. (1922) Vertrocknung und Wiederbelebung bei einer Süsswasser Hirudinee.
Zool. Anz. **54** pp.92–94.

PANIKKAR, N. K. (1941) Osmoregulation in some Palaemonid prawns.
J. mar. biol. Ass. U. K. **25** pp.317–359.

PANIKKAR, N. K. (1950) Physiological aspects of adaptation to estuarine
conditions.
Proc. Indo-Pacific Fish Council. **2** pp.168–175.

PANTIN, C. F. A. (1931 a) The adaptation of *Gunda ulvae* to salinity. I. The
environment.
J. exp. Biol. **8** pp.63–72.

PANTIN, C. F. A. (1931 b) The adaptation of *Gunda ulvae* to salinity. III. The
electrolyte exchange.
J. exp. Biol. **8** pp.82–94.

PANTIN, C. F. A. (1931 c) The origin of the composition of the body fluids
of animals.
Biol. Rev. **6** pp.459–82.

PANTIN, C. F. A. (1947) The nephridia of *Geonemertes dendyi.*
Quart. J. micr. Sci. **88** pp.15–25.

PARRY, D. A. (1954) On the drinking of soil capillary water by spiders.
J. exp. Biol. **31** pp.218–227.

PARRY, G. (1953) Osmotic and ionic regulation in the isopod crustacean
Ligia oceanica L.
J. exp. Biol. **30** pp.567–574.

PARRY, G. (1954) Ionic regulation in the Palaemonid prawn, *Leander serratus*
(Pennant).
J. exp. Biol. **31** pp.601–613.

PARRY, G. (1955) Urine production by the antennal glands of *Palaemonetes
varians* (Leach).
J. exp. Biol. **32** pp.408–422.

PARRY, G. (1957) Osmoregulation in some freshwater prawns.
J. exp. Biol. **34** pp.417–423.

PARRY, G. (1961 a) Osmotic and ionic changes in the blood and muscle
migrating salmonids.
J. exp. Biol. **38** pp.411–428

PARRY, G. (1961 b) Osmoregulation in the freshwater prawn, *Palaemonetes
antennarius.*
Mem. inst. Ital. Idrobiol. **13** pp.139–149.

PARRY, G. and HOLLIDAY, F. G. T. (1960) An experimental analysis of
the function of the pseudobranch in teleosts.
J. exp. Biol. **37** pp.344–354.

PARRY, G., HOLLIDAY, F. G. T. and BLAXTER, J. H. S. (1959) Chloride
secretory cells in the gills of teleosts.
Nature Lond. **183** pp.1248–1249.

PARSONS, O. S. and WINGATE, D. L. (1958) Fluid measurement across the wall of the small intestine in vitro.
Biochim. Biophys. Acta. **30** pp.666–667.

PATTERSON, W. B. and STETTON, D. W. (1949) A study of gastric hydrochloric acid formation.
Science. **109** pp.256–258.

PAUL, D. H. (1960) The effect of calcium on rat diaphragm muscle fibres.
J. Physiol. **152** pp.57–58.

PAULSON, T. L. and BARTHOLOMEW, G. A. (1962) Salt balance in the Savannah sparrow.
Physiol. Zool. **35** pp.109–119.

PETERS, H. (1935) Über den Einfluss des Salzgehaltes im Aussenmedium auf den Bau und die Funktion der Exkretionsorgane dekapoder Crustaceen.
Z. Morph. Okol. Tiere. **30** pp.355–381.

PETTENGILL, O. (1947) Phosphatase activity in the chloride cells of the gill of *Fundulus heteroclitus.*
Biol. Bull. Woods Hole. **93** pp.224–225.

PETTENGILL, O. and COPELAND, D. E. (1948) Alkaline phosphatase activity in the chloride cell of *Fundulus heteroclitus* and its relation to osmotic work.
J. exp. Zool. **108** pp.235–242.

PHILLIPS, A. M. and BROCKWAY, D. R. (1958) The inorganic constituents of brown trout blood.
Prog. Fish. Cult. **20** pp.58–61.

PICKEN, L. E. R. (1936) The mechanism of urine formation in invertebrates. I. Excretion mechanism in certain Arthropoda.
J. exp. Biol. **13** pp.309–328.

PICKEN, L. E. R. (1937) The mechanism of urine formation in invertebrates. II. Mollusca.
J. exp. Biol. **14** pp.20–37.

PICKFORD, G. E. (1953) Disturbances of mineral metabolism and osmo-regulation in hypophysectomised *Fundulus.*
Anat. Rec. **115** p. 409.

PICKFORD, G. E. (1958) The nature and physiology of the pituitary hormones of fishes.
In: *Comparative Endocrinology.* ed. Gorbman, pp.404–420.
Wiley and Sons, New York.

PICKFORD, G. E. and ATZ, J. (1957) *The Physiology of the Pituitary Gland of Fishes.*
New York, New York Zool. Soc. **613** pp.

PIEH, S. (1936) Über die Beziehungen zwischen Atmung, Osmoregulation und Hydration der Gewebe bei euryhalinen Meeresevertebraten. *Zool. Jb. Abt. Allg. Zool. u. Physiol.* **56** pp.130–158.

PILGRIM, R. L. C. (1953 a) Osmotic relations in molluscan contractile tissues I. *J. exp. Biol.* **30** pp.297–317.

PILGRIM, R. L. C. (1953 b) Osmotic relations in molluscan contractile tissues II. *J. exp. Biol.* **30** pp.318–330.

PITTS, R. F. (1934) Urinary composition in marine fish. *J. cell. comp. Physiol.* **4** pp.389–395.

Plymouth Marine Fauna. (1931) Plymouth, Mar. Biol. Ass., 2nd. Edition. 371 pp.

PODOLSKY, R. J. (1959) The influence of hydrostatic pressure on ion-solvent interaction and its application to the study of biological ion specificity. *Proc. 1st. Nat. Biophysics. Sym.* pp.95–96. Yale Univ. Press.

PORTIER, P. (1910) Pression osmotiques des liquides des oiseaux et mammifères marins. *J. Physiol. Path. gén.* **12** pp.202–208.

POTTS, W. T. W. (1954 a) The inorganic composition of the blood of *Mytilus edulis* and *Anodonta cygnaea.* *J. exp. Biol.* **31** pp.376–385.

POTTS, W. T. W. (1954 b) The rate of urine formation in *Anodonta cygnaea.* *J. exp. Biol.* **31** pp.614–617.

POTTS, W. T. W. (1954 c) The energetics of osmotic regulation in brackish- and fresh water animals. *J. exp. Biol.* **31** pp.618–630.

POTTS, W. T. W. (1958) The inorganic and amino acid composition of some lamellibranch muscles. *J. exp. Biol.* **35** pp.749–764.

POTTS, W. T. W. (1959) The sodium fluxes in the muscle fibres of a marine and a freshwater lamellibranch. *J. exp. Biol.* **36** pp.676–689.

PRESCOTT, D. M. and ZEUTHEN, E. (1953) Water diffusion and water filtration across cell surfaces. *Acta physiol. scand.* **28** pp.77–94.

PROSSER, C. L., GREEN, J., JAHN, and WOLF, A. V. (1950) *Comparative Animal Physiology.* W. B. Saunders and Co., Philadelphia and London. 888 pp.

PROSSER, C. L., GREEN, J. and CHOW, T. J. (1955) Ionic and osmotic concentrations in blood and urine of *Pachygrapsus crassipes* acclimated to different salinities. *Biol. Bull. Woods Hole.* **109** pp.99–107.

26*

PROSSER, C. L. and SPERELAKIS, N. (1958) Transmission in ganglion free circular muscle from the cat intestine.
Amer. J. Physiol. **187** pp.536–545.

PUMPHREY, R. J. (1931) The potential difference across the surface bounding the unfertilised egg of the brown trout.
Proc. roy. Soc. B. **108** pp.511–521.

RAFFY, A. (1933) Recherches sur le métabolisme respiratoire des poikilothermes aquatiques.
Ann. Inst. Oceanogr. Monaco. **13** pp.259–393.

RAFFY, A. and FONTAINE, M. (1930) De l'influence des variations de salinité sur la respiration des civelles.
C. R. soc. Biol. Paris. **104** pp.466–468.

RAMSAY, J. A. (1935) The evaporation of water from the cockroach.
J. exp. Biol. **12** pp.373–383.

RAMSAY, J. A. (1949 a) The osmotic relations of the earthworm.
J. exp. Biol. **26** pp.46–56.

RAMSAY, J. A. (1949 b) The site of formation of hypotonic urine in the nephridium of the earthworm, *Lumbricus*.
J. exp. Biol. **26** pp.65–75.

RAMSAY, J. A. (195 0) Osmotic regulation in mosquito larvae.
J. exp. Biol. **27** pp.145–157.

RAMSAY, J. A. (1951) Osmotic regulation in mosquito larvae; the role of the malpighian tubules.
J. exp. Biol. **28** pp.62–73.

RAMSAY, J. A. (1953 a) Exchanges of sodium and potassium in mosquito larvae.
J. exp. Biol. **30** pp.79–89.

RAMSAY, J. A. (1953 b) Active transport of potassium by the malpighian tubules of insects.
J. exp. Biol. **30** pp.358–369.

RAMSAY, J. A. (1954 a) Active transport of water by the malpighian tubules of the stick insect *Dixippus morosus* (Orthoptera, Phasmidae).
J. exp. Biol. **31** pp.104–113.

RAMSAY, J. A. (1954 b) Movements of water and electrolytes in invertebrates.
Soc. Exp. Biol. Symposia **8** *Active Tranport and Secretion.* pp.1–15.

RAMSAY, J. A. (1955 a) The excretory system of the stick insect.
J. exp. Biol. **32** pp.183–199.

RAMSAY, J. A. (1955 b) The excretion of sodium potassium and water by the malpighian tubules of the stick insect *Dixippus morosus* (Orthoptera, Phasmidae).
J. exp. Biol. **32** pp.200–216.

RAMSAY, J. A. (1956) Excretion by the malpighian tubules of the stick insect *Dixippus morosus* (Orthoptera, Phasmidae): calcium, magnesium chloride, phosphate and hydrogen ions.
J. exp. Biol. **33** pp.697–708.

RAMSAY J. A. and RIEGEL J. A. (1961) Excretion of inulin by malpighian tubules.
Nature Lond. **191** p.1115.

RAO, K. P. (1958) Oxygen consumption as a function of size and salinity in *Metapenaeus monoceros* Fab. from marine and brackish water environments.
J. exp. Biol. **35** pp.307–313.

RASMONT, R., VANDERMEERSCHE, G. and CASTIAUX, P. (1958) Ultrastructure of the coxal glands of the scorpion.
Nature Lond. **182** pp.328–329.

RASMUSSEN, H. (1961) The parathyroid hormone.
Amer. Sci. No. 4. **204** pp.56–67.

RASQUIN, P. and ROSENBLOOM, L. (1954) Endocrine imbalance and tissue hyperplasia in teleosts maintained in darkness.
Bull. Amer. Mus. nat. Hist. **104** pp.359–426.

REHM, W. S. (1945) The effect of electric current on the gastric secretion and potential.
Amer. J. Physiol. **144** pp.115–125.

REHM, W. S., HOKIN, L. E., GRAFFENRIED, T. P., BAJANDAS, F. J. and COY, F. E. (1951) Relationship between potential difference of the resting and secretory stomach.
Amer. J. Physiol. **164** pp.187–201.

REMANE, A. (1934) Die Brackwasserfauna.
Verh. dt. Sch. zool. Ges.

REMANE, A. (1941) Einführung in die zoologische Ökologie der Nord- und Ostsee.
In: *Tierwelt der Nord- und Ostsee*, I pp.1–238.

REMANE, A. and SCHLIEPER, C. (1958) Die Biologie des Brackwassers.
In: *Die Binnengewässer von Prof. Dr. August Thienemann.* Band XXII. E. Schweizerbartsche Verlagsbuchhandlung, Stuttgart.

RHODES, E. L. and VANATTA, J. C. (1958) Determinations of ether soluble sodium and potassium in the rat kidney.
Fed. Proc. **17** p.132.

RICHARDS, A. N. (1935) Urine formation in the amphibian kidney.
Harvey Lect. pp.93–118.

RIEGEL, J. A. (1961) The influence of water loading on certain functional aspects of the crayfish antennal gland.
J. exp. Biol. **38** pp.291–300.

RIEGEL, J. A. and KIRSCHNER, L. B. (1960) The excretion of inulin and glucose by the crayfish antennal gland.
Biol. Bull. Woods Hole. **118** pp.296–307.

RIEGEL, J. A. and LOCKWOOD, A. P. M. (1961) The role of the antennal gland in the osmotic and ionic regulation of *Carcinus maenas.*
J. exp. Biol. **38** pp.491–499.

ROBERTSON, J. D. (1939) The inorganic composition of the body fluids of three invertebrates.
J. exp. Biol. **16** pp. 387–397.

ROBERTSON, J. D. (1949) Ionic regulation in some marine invertebrates.
J. exp. Biol. **26** pp. 182–200.

ROBERTSON, J. D. (1953) Further studies on ionic regulation in marine invertebrates.
J. exp. Biol. **30** pp.277–296.

ROBERTSON, J. D. (1954) The chemical composition of the blood of some aquatic chordates, including members of the Tunicata, Cyclostomata and Osteichthyes.
J. exp. Biol. **31** pp.424–442.

ROBERTSON, J. D. (1957 a) The habitat of the early vertebrates.
Biol. Rev. **32** pp.156–187.

ROBERTSON, J. D. (1957 b) Osmotic and ionic regulation in aquatic invertebrates. pp.229–246.
In: *Recent Advances in Invertebrate Physiology.* ed B. T. Scheer, University of Oregon, Eugene, Oregon, U.S.A.

ROBERTSON, J. D. (1960) Ionic regulation in the crab, *Carcinus maenas,* (L.) in relation to the moulting cycle.
Comp. Biochem. Physiol. **1** pp.183–212.

ROBERTSON, J. D. (1961) Studies on the chemical composition of muscle tissues 11. Abdominal flexor muscle of the lobster *Nephrops norvegicus L.*
J. exp. Biol. **38** pp.707–728.

ROBERTSON, R. N., WILKINS, M. J. and HOPE, A. B. (1955) Plant mitochondria and salt accumulations.
Nature Lond. **175** pp.640–641.

ROBINSON, J. R. (1960) The metabolism of intracellular water.
Physiol. Rev. **40** pp.112–149.

ROBINSON, S., KINCAID, K. K. and RHANY, R. K. (1950) Effects of desoxy-corticosterone acetate on acclimatisation of man to heat.
J. appl. Physiol. **2** pp.399–406.

ROCH, F. (1924) Experimentelle Untersuchungen an *Cordylophora caspia* (Pallas) (= *lacustris* Allman) über die Abhängigheit ihrer geographischen

Verbreitung und ihrer Wuchsformen von den physikalisch-chemischen Bedingungen des umgebenden Mediums.
Z. Morph. Ökol. Tiere. **2** pp.350–426.

ROMER, A. S. and GROVE, B. H. (1935) Environment of early vertebrates.
Amer. Midland Naturalist. **16** pp.805–856.

ROSS, D. B. (1960) Influence of sodium on the transport of magnesium across the intestinal wall of the rat, *in vitro*.
Nature Lond. **189** pp.840–831.

ROSS, D. M. and PANTIN, C. F. A. (1940) Factors influencing facilitation in Actinozoa. The action of certain ions.
J. exp. Biol. **17** pp.61–73.

ROTHSCHILD, LORD and BARNES, H. (1953) The inorganic constituents of the sea-urchin egg.
J. exp. Biol. **30** pp.534–544.

ROUSCHAL, W. (1940) Osmotische Werte wirbelloser Landtiere und ihre ökologische Bedeutung.
Z. wiss. Zool. **153** pp.196–218.

RUBEY, W. W. (1951) Geological history of sea water.
Bull. geol. Soc. Amer. **62** pp.1112–1147.

SAWYER, M. (1955) In: Black 1957: Chap. IV Excretion and Osmoregulation, *The Physiology of Fishes*, ed. M. E. Brown.
Academic Press, New York & London. pp.447.

SAWYER, W. H. (1951) Effects of pituitary extracts on urine formation and glomerular circulation in the frog.
Amer. J. Physiol. **164** pp.457–466.

SAWYER, W. H. (1956) The hormonal control of water and salt-electrolyte metabolism with special reference to the amphibians.
In: *The Hormonal Control of Water and Salt-electrolyte Metabolism in Vertebrates*. Memoirs of the Society of Experimental Endocrinology No **5**. Part II. ed. I. Chester Jones and P. Eckstein. Cambridge Univ. Press. pp.44–56.

SAWYER, W. H. (1960) Increased water permeability of the bullfrog (*Rana catesbiana*) bladder *in vitro* in response to synthetic oxytocin and arginine vasotocin and to neurohypophysial extracts from non-mammalian vertebrates.
J. Endocrinology. **66** pp.112–120.

SAWYER, W. H., MUNSICK, R. A. and VAN DYKE, H. B. (1960) Pharmacological characteristics of neurohypophysial hormones from a marsupial (*Didelphys virginiana*) and a monotreme (*Tachyglossus* (Echidna) *aculeatus*).
Endocrinology. **67** pp.137–138.

SCHLIEPER, C. (1929) Über die Einwirkung niederer Salzkonzentrationen auf Marine Organismen.
Z. vergl. Physiol. **9** pp.478–514.

SCHLIEPER, C. (1933 a) Über die osmoregulatorische Funktion der Aalkiemen.
Z. vergl. Physiol. **18** pp.682–695.

SCHLIEPER, C. (1933 b) Über die Permeabilität der Aalkiemen I, Die Wasser-durchlässigkeit und der angebliche Wassertransport der Aalkiemen bei hypertonischem Aussenmedium.
Z. vergl. Physiol. **19** pp.68–83.

SCHMIDT-NIELSEN, B. and SCHMIDT-NIELSEN, K. (1951) A complete account of the water metabolism of kangaroo rats and an experimental verification.
J. cell. comp. Physiol. **38** pp.165–181.

SCHMIDT-NIELSEN B., SCHMIDT-NIELSEN, K., HAUPT, T. R. and JARNUM, S. A. (1957) Urea excretion in the camel.
Amer. J. Physiol. **188** pp.477–484.

SCHMIDT-NIELSEN, B., O'DELL, R. and OSAKI, H. (1961) Interdependence of urea and electrolytes in production of a concentration urine.
Amer. J. Physiol. **200** pp.1115–1132.

SCHMIDT-NIELSEN, K. (1959) The physiology of the camel.
Scientific American **201** No. 6 pp. 140–151.

SCHMIDT-NIELSEN, K. (1960 a) Salt Glands.
Scientific American. **200** No. 1 pp.109–119.

SCHMIDT-NIELSEN, K. (1960 b) The salt secreting gland of marine birds.
Circulation **21** pp.1027–1037.

SCHMIDT-NIELSEN, K. and FÄNGE, R. (1958) Salt glands in the marine reptiles.
Nature Lond. **182** pp.783–785.

SCHMIDT-NIELSEN, K., SCHMIDT-NIELSEN, B. and SCHNEIDERMAN, H. (1948) Salt excretion in desert rodents.
Amer. J. Physiol. **154** pp.163–166.

SCHMIDT-NIELSEN, K. and SLADEN, W. J. L. (1958) Nasal salt secretion in the Humboldt penguin.
Nature Lond. **181** pp.1217–1218.

SCHNEYER, C. A. and SCHNEYER, L. H. (1961) Secretion by salivary glands deficient in acini.
Amer. J. Physiol. **201** pp.938–942.

SCHNEYER, L. H. (1956) Source of resting total mixed saliva in man.
J. appl. Physiol. **9** pp.79–81.

SCHOFFENIELS, E. (1951) Distribution du calcium diffusible et non diffusible dans le plasma sanguin de l'Anodonte determinée par ultrafiltration a haute pression.
Arch. int. Physiol. **59** pp.49–52.

SCHOFFENIELS, E. (1960 a) Origine des acides aminés intervenant dans la regulation de la pression osmotique intracellulaire de *Eriocheir sinensis* Milne-Edw.
Arch. int. Physiol. **68** pp.696–698.

SCHOFFENIELS, E. (1960 b) Les bases physiques et chimiques des potentials bioélectriques chez *Electrophorus electricus.*
Arch. int. Physiol. **68** pp.1–151.

SCHOLANDER, P. F., VAN DAM L., KANWISHER, J. W., HAMMEL, H. T. and GORDON, M. S. (1957) Supercooling and osmoregulation in fishes
J. cell. comp. Physiol. **49** pp.5–24.

SCHOLLES, W. (1953) Über die Mineralregulation Wasserlebender Evertebraten.
Z. vergl. Physiol. **19** pp.522–554.

SCHWABE, E. (1953) Über die Osmoregulation verschiedener Krebse (Malacostracen).
Z. vergl. Physiol. **19** pp.183–236.

SCHWARTZ, I.L. and THAYSEN, J. H. (1956) Excretion of sodium and potassium in human sweat.
J. clin. Invest. **35** pp.114–120.

SCHWARTZ, I. L., THAYSEN, J. H. and DALE, V. P. (1953) Urea excretion in human sweat as a tracer for movement of water within the secretory gland.
J. exp. Med. **97** pp.429–437.

SCOTHORNE, R. J. (1958) Histochemical study of the nasal (supra-orbital) gland of the duck.
Nature Lond. **182** p.732.

SCOTHORNE, R. J. (1959 a) On the response of the duck and the pigeon to intravenous hypertonic saline solution.
Quart J. exp. Physiol. **44** pp.200–207.

SCOTHORNE, R. J. (1959 b) The nasal glands of birds. A histological and histochemical study of the inactive gland of the domestic duck.
J. Anat. **93** pp.246–256.

SCUDAMORE, H. H. (1947) The influence of the sinus gland on moulting and associated changes in the crayfish.
Physiol. Zool. **20** pp.187–208.

SECK, CH. (1958) Untersuchungen zur Frage der Ionenregulation bei in Brackwasser lebenden Evertebraten.
Kieler Meeresforsch. **13** pp.220–243.

SELKURT, E. E. (1954) Sodium excretion by the mammalian kidney.
Physiol. Rev. **34** pp.287–333.

SEXTON, A. W. (1955) Factors influencing the uptake of sodium against a diffusion gradient in the goldfish gill.
Ph. D. Dissertation, Univ. of Missouri. Diss. Abstr. **15** pp.2270–2271.

SEXTON, A. W. and MEYER, D. K. (1955) Effects of potassium, lithium and magnesium ions on sodium transport through the gills of the goldfish *Fed. Proc.* **14** p. 137.

SHAW, J. (1955 a) The permeability and structure of the cuticle of the aquatic larva of *Sialis lutaria*.
J. exp. Biol. **32** pp.330–352.

SHAW, J. (1955 b) Ionic regulation and water balance in the aquatic larva of *Sialis lutaria*.
J. exp. Biol. **32** pp.352–382.

SHAW, J. (1955 c) Ionic regulation in the muscle fibres of *Carcinus maenas*. I. The electrolyte composition of single fibres.
J. exp. Biol. **32** pp.383–396.

SHAW, J. (1955 d) Ionic regulation in the muscle fibres of *Carcinus maenas*. II. The effect of reduced blood concentration.
J. exp. Biol. **32** pp.664–680.

SHAW, J. (1958 a) Osmoregulation in the muscle fibres of *Carcinus*.
J. exp. Biol. **35** pp.920–929.

SHAW, J. (1958 b) Further studies on ionic regulation in the muscle fibres of *Carcinus maenas*.
J. exp. Biol. **35** pp.902–919.

SHAW, J. (1959 a) The absorption of sodium ions by the crayfish, *Astacus pallipes*. Lereboullet. I. The effect of external and internal sodium concentrations.
J. exp. Biol. **36** pp.126–144.

SHAW, J. (1959 b) Solute and water balance in the muscle fibres of the East African freshwater crab, *Potamon niloticus* (M. Edw.).
J. exp. Biol. **36** pp.145–156.

SHAW, J. (1959 c) Salt and water balance in the East African freshwater crab *Potamon niloticus* (M. Edw.)
J. exp. Biol. **36** pp.157–176.

SHAW, J. (1960 a) The absorption of sodium ions by the crayfish, *Astacus pallipes* Lereboullet. II. The effect of the external anion.
J. exp. Biol. **37** pp.534–547.

SHAW, J. (1960 b) The absorption of sodium ions by the crayfish, *Astacus pallipes* Lereboullet. III. The effect of other cations in the external solution.
J. exp. Biol. **37** pp.548–556.

SHAW, J. (1960 c) The absorption of chloride ions by the crayfish, *Astacus pallipes* Lereboullet.
J. exp. Biol. **37** pp.557–572.

SHAW, J. (1961 a) Studies on the ionic regulation in *Carcinus maenas* L. I. Sodium balance.
J. exp. Biol. **38** pp.135–153.

SHAW, J. (1961 b) Sodium balance in *Eriocheir sinensis* M–Edw. The adaptation of the Crustacea to fresh water.
J. exp. Biol. **38** pp.154–162.

SHAW, J. and SUTCLIFFE, D. (1961) Studies on sodium balance in *Gammarus duebeni Lilljeborg* and *G. pulex pulex* (L).
J. exp. Biol. **38** pp.1–16.

SHOUP, C. S. (1932) Salinity of the medium and its effects on respiration in the sea anemone.
Ecology. **8** pp.81–85.

SIMPSON, J. W., ALLEN, K. and AWAPARA, J. (1959) Free amino acids in some aquatic invertebrates.
Biol. Bull. Woods Hole **117** pp.371–381.

SMITH, C. A., LOWRY, O. H. and WU, M. L. (1954) The electrolytes of the labyrinthine fluids.
Laryngoscope, St. Louis. **64** pp.141–153.

SMITH, H. W. (1929 a) The composition of the body fluids of elasmobranchs.
J. biol. Chem. **81** pp.407–419.

SMITH, H. W. (1929 b) The excretion of ammonia and urea by the gills of fish.
J. biol. Chem. **81** pp. 727–742.

SMITH, H. W. (1930 a) Metabolism of the lung-fish, *Protopterus aethiopius.*
J. biol. Chem. **88** pp.97–130.

SMITH, H. W. (1930 b) The absorption and excretion of water and salts by marine teleosts.
Amer. J. Physiol. **93** pp.480–505.

SMITH, H. W. (1931 a) The absorption and excretion of water and salts by the elasmobranch fishes. I. Fresh water elasmobranchs.
Amer. J. Physiol. **98** pp.279–295.

SMITH, H. W. (1931 b) The absorption and excretion of water and salts by the elasmobranch fishes. II. Marine elasmobranchs.
Amer. J. Physiol. **98** pp.269–310.

SMITH, H. W. (1932) Water regulation and its evolution in fishes.
Quart. Rev. Biol. **7** pp.1–26.

SMITH, H. W. (1936 a) The retention and physiological role of urea in the Elasmobranchii.
Biol. Rev. **11** pp.49–82.

SMITH, H. W. (1936 b) The composition of seal urine.
J. cell. comp. Physiol. **7** pp.465–74.

SMITH, H. W. (1951) *The Kidney: Structure and function in health and disease.* Oxford Univ. Press. 1049 pp.

SMITH, H. W. (1953) *From Fish to Philosopher.*
Little and Brown, Boston, U.S.A. pp.

SMITH, H. W. (1956) *Principles of Renal Physiology.*
Oxford Univ. Press. 237 pp.

SMOCZKIEWICZOWA, A. (1959) Sodium, potassium and chloride ion contents and protein fractions in the fluids of chick embryos.
Nature Lond. **183** pp.1260–1261.

SOLOMON, A. K. (1959) Equivalent pore dimensions in cellular membranes.
Proc. Ist. Nat. Biophysics. Sym. pp.95–96. Yale Univ. Press.

SOLOMON, A. K., LIONETTI, N. and CUMAN, P. F. (1956) Possible cation carrier substances in blood.
Nature Lond. **178** pp.582–583.

SPENCER, J. O. and EDNEY, E. B. (1954) The absorption of water by woodlice.
J. exp. Biol. **31** pp.491–496.

SPERBER, I. (1944) Studies on the mammalian kidney.
Zoo. Bidrag. Uppsala. **22** pp.249–431.

STEINBACH, H. B. (1937) Potassium in frog skin.
J. cell. comp. Physiol. **10** pp.51–60.

STEINBACH, H. B. (1940 a) The distribution of electrolytes in *Phascolosoma* muscle.
Biol. Bull. Woods Hole. **78** pp.444–453.

STEINBACH, H. B. (1940 b) The distribution of electrolytes in *Thyone* muscle.
J. cell. comp. Physiol. **15** pp.1–9.

STOBBART, R. H. (1959) Studies on the exchange and regulation of sodium in the larvae of *Aedes aegypti* (L.). I. The steady state exchange.
J. exp. Biol. **36** pp.641–653.

STOBBART, R. H. (1960) Studies on the exchange and regulation of sodium in the larva of *Aedes aegypti* (L.). II. The net transport and the fluxes associated with it.
J. exp. Biol. **37** pp.594–608.

STRAUSS, M. B., ROURKE, G. M. T., ROSENBAUM, J. D. and NELSON, W. P. (1949) Alcohol and homeostasis in uncompensated diuresis induced by whiskey.
J. clin. Invest. **28** pp.813–814.

SUDZUKI, M. (1924) Untersuchungen über Cetacea VIII. Über das Blut.
Tohuku J. exp. Med. **5** pp.419–427.

SUOMALAINEN, P. (1956) Sauerstuffverbrauch finnischer *Gammarus*-Arten.
Verh. int. Ver. Limnol. Helsinki.

SUTCLIFFE, D. W. (1960) Osmotic regulation in the larvae of some euryhaline Diptera.
Nature Lond. **187** pp.331–332.

SUTCLIFFE D. W. (1961 a) Studies on salt and water balance in caddis larvae (Trichoptera). I. Osmotic and ionic regulation of body fluids in *Limnephilus affinis* Curtis.
J. exp. Biol. **38** pp.501–520.

SUTCLIFFE, D. W. (1961 b) Studies on salt water balance in caddis larvae (Trichoptera). II. Osmotic and ionic regulation of body fluids in *Limnephilus stigma* Curtis and *Anabolia nervosa* Leach.
J. exp. Biol. **38** pp.521–530.

SVETLOV, P. (1928) Entwicklungsphysiologische Beobachtungen an Forelleneiern.
Zeit. wiss. Biol. Abt. D. **114** pp.771–785.

TAGGART, J. V. and FORSTER, R. P. (1950) Renal tubular transport: Effect of 2–4 dinitrophenol and related compounds of phenol red transport in the isolated tubules of the flounder.
Amer. J. Physiol. **161** pp.167–172.

TEORELL, T. (1939) On the permeability of the stomach mucosa for acids and some other substances.
J. gen. Physiol. **23** pp.263–274.

TEORELL, T. (1940) On the primary acidity of the gastric juice.
J. Physiol. **97** pp.308–315.

TEORELL, T. (1947) Electrolyte diffusion in relation to acidity regulation of the gastric juice.
Gastroenterologia, Basel. **9** pp.425–443.

THAYSEN, J. H., LARSEN, N. A. and MUNCK, O. (1961) Sodium transport and oxygen consumption in the mammalian kidney.
Nature Lond. **190** pp.919–921.

THAYSEN, J. H. and THORN, N. A. S. (1954) Excretion of urea, sodium, potassium and chloride in human tears.
Amer. J. Physiol. **178** pp.160–164.

THAYSEN, J. H., THORN, N. A. S. and SCHWARTZ, I. L. (1954) Excretion of sodium, potassium, chloride and carbon dioxide in human parotid saliva.
Amer. J. Physiol. **178** pp.155–159.

THIENEMANN, A. (1928) *Mysis relicta* in sauerstoffarmen Tiefenwasser der Ostsee und das Problem der Atmung in Salzwasser und Süsswasser.
Zool. Jb. Abt. Zool. u. Physiol. **45** pp.371–384.

THORSON, T. B. (1955) The relationship of water economy to terrestrialism in amphibians.
Ecology. **36** pp.100–116.

THORSON, T. B. (1956) Adjustment of water loss in response to desiccation in amphibians.
Copeia pp.230–237.

THORSON, T. B. (1958) Measurement of the fluid compartment of four species of marine chondrichthyes.
Physiol. Zool. **31** pp.16–23.

THORSON, T. B. (1961) The partitioning of body water in Osteichthyes: phylogenetic and ecological implications in aquatic vertebrates.
Biol. Bull. Woods Hole **120** pp.238–254.

THORSON, T. B. and SVIKLA, A. (1943) Correlation of the habitats of amphibians with their ability to survive the loss of body water.
Ecology. **24** pp.374–381.

THREADGOLD, L. T. and HOUSTON, A. H. (1961) An electron microscope study of the "chloride secretory cell" of *Salmo salar* L., with special reference to plasma electrolyte regulation.
Nature Lond. **190** pp.612–614.

TOBIAS, J. M. (1948 a) Potassium, sodium, and water exchange of irritable tissues and haemolymph of an omnivorous insect, *Periplaneta americana.*
J. cell. comp. Physiol. **31** pp.125–142.

TOBIAS, J. M. (1948 b) The high potassium and low sodium in the body fluid and tissues of the phytophagous insect the silk worm, *Bombyx mori* and the change before pupation.
J. cell. comp. Physiol. **31** pp.143–148.

TREHERNE, J. E. (1954) Exchange of labelled Na in the larvae of *Aedes aegypti* (L.).
J. exp. Biol. **31** pp.386–404.

TREHERNE J. E. (1961) The movements of sodium ions in the isolated abdominal nerve of the cockroach, *Periplaneta americana.*
J. exp. Biol. **38** pp.629–636.

TREHERNE, J. E. (1962 a) Distribution of water and inorganic ions in the central nervous system of an insect *(Periplaneta americana* L).
Nature Lond **193** pp.750–752.

TREHERNE, J. E. (1962 b) The distribution and exchange of some ions and molecules in the central nervous system of *Periplaneta americana* L.
J. exp. Biol. **39** pp.193–218.

TROLLE, C. (1937) A study of insensible perspiration in man and its nature
Skand. Arch. Physiol. **76** pp.225–246.

DE TURVILLE, C. M. (1961) Terrestrial accretion from solar wind.
Nature Lond. **190** pp.156.

ULLRICH, K. J., DRENKAHN, F. O. and JARAUSCH, K. H. (1955) Untersuchungen zum Problem der Harnkonzentrierung und -verdünnung.
Pflüg. Arch. ges. Physiol. **261** pp.62–77.

UREY, H. C. (1952) *The Planets: Their Origin and Development.*
Oxford Univ. Press, London. 245 pp.

USSING, H. H. (1947) Interpretation of the exchange of radio-sodium in isolated muscle.
Nature Lond. **160** p.262.

Ussing, H. H. (1958) Active and passive transport across epithelial membranes. In: *The Method of Isotopic Tracers as Applied to the Study of Active Ion Transport*. ed. J. Coursaget, pp.139–154.
Pergamon Press, London and Oxford.

Ussing, H. H. (1960) Frog skin potential.
J. gen. Physiol. **43** Suppl. pp.135–147.

Ussing, H. H. and Andersen, B. (1955) The relation between solvent drag and active transport of ions.
Proc. 3rd. Internat. Congr. Brussels. 1956 pp.434–440.

Ussing, H. H. and Zerahn, K. (1951) Active transport of sodium as the source of electric current in the short-circuited isolated frog skin.
Acta. physiol. scand. **23** pp.110–127.

Van Asperen, K. and Van Esch, I. (1956) The chemical composition of the haemolymph in *Periplaneta* with special reference to the mineral constituents.
Arch. Neerland. Zool. **11** pp.342–360.

Van Oosten, J. (1957) The skin and scales.
In: *The Physiology of Fishes*, I. ed. M. E. Brown, pp.207–244.
Academic Press, New York and London. 447 pp.

Velankar N. K. and Govindan, T. K. (1960) Trimethylamine content of marine prawns occurring in the backwaters and the sea of Cochin.
Proc. Ind. Acad. Sci. B. **52** pp.111–115.

Verney, E. B. (1947) The antidiuretic hormone and factors which determine its release.
Proc. roy. Soc. B. **135** pp.27–106.

Vickers, T. (1961) A study of the so-called 'Chloride Secretory' cells of the gills of teleosts.
Q. J. micr. Sci. **102** pp.507–518.

Visscher, M. B., Roepke, R. R. and Lifson, N. (1945) Osmotic and electrolyte concentration relationships during the absorption of autogenous serum from ileal segments.
Amer. J. Physiol. **144** pp.457–463.

Walker, A. M. and Hudson, C. L. (1937) Resorption of glucose from the renal tubule in Amphibia and the action of phlorizin on it.
Amer. J. Physiol. **118** pp.130–141.

Walker, A. M., Hudson, C. L., Findlay, T. and Richards, A. N. (1937) Total molecular concentration and chloride concentration of fluid from different segments of the renal tubule of Amphibia.
Amer. J. Physiol. **118** pp.121–129.

Waterman, T. H. (1960) General crustacean biology. In: *The Physiology of Crustacea*. I. ed. Waterman.
Academic Press, New York and London. 670 pp.

WEATHERBY, J. H. (1929) Excretion of nitrogenous substances in the Protozoa.
Physiol. Zool. **2** pp.375–394.

WEBB, D. A. (1939) Observations on the blood of certain ascidians with special reference to the biochemistry of vanadium.
J. exp. Biol. **16** pp. 499–523.

WEBB, D. A. (1940) Ionic regulation in *Carcinus maenas*.
Proc. roy. Soc. B. **129** pp.107–136.

WELLS, G. P. and LEDINGHAM, I. C. (1940) Physiological effects of a hypotonic environment. I. The action of hypotonic salines on isolated rhythmic preparations from polychaete worms (*Arenicola marina, Nereis diversicolor, Perinereis cultrifera*).
J. exp. Biol. **17** pp. 337–363.

WESTFALL, B. B., FINDLAY, T. and RICHARDS, A. N. (1934) Quantitative studies on the composition of glomerular urine of frogs and Necturi.
J. biol. Chem. **107** pp.661–672.

WHEELER, H. O., RAMOS, O. L. and WHITLOCK, R. T. (1960) Electrolyte excretion in bile.
Circulation. **21** pp.988–996.

WHITTAM, R. (1961) Active cation transport as a pace-maker of respiration.
Nature Lond. **191** pp.603–604.

WHITTAM, R. and DAVIES, R. E. (1954) Relations between metabolism and rate of turnover of sodium and potassium in guinea pig kidney cortex slices.
Biochem J. **56** pp.445–453.

WHITTEMBURY, G., SUGINO, N. and SOLOMON, A. K. (1960) Effect of adrenocortical hormone and calcium on the equivalent pore radius of kidney slices from *Necturus*.
Nature Lond. **189** pp.699–701.

WIDDOWSON, E. M. and McCANCE, R. A. (1956) Effect of development on the composition of the serum and extracellular fluid.
Clin. Sci. **15** pp.360–365.

WIGGLESWORTH, V. B. (1931) Excretion in *Rhodinus* (Hempitera).
J. exp. Biol. **8** pp.411–451.

WIGGLESWORTH, V. B. (1932) Function of the rectal glands.
Quart J. micr. Sci. **75** pp.131–150.

WIGGLESWORTH, V. B. (1938) The regulation of osmotic pressure and chloride concentration in the haemolymph of mosquito larvae.
J. exp. Biol. **15** pp.235–247.

WIGGLESWORTH, V. B. (1953) *Principles of Insect Physiology.*
5th Edition Methuen and Co., London. 546 pp.

WIKGREN, B. (1953) Osmotic regulation in some animals with special reference to temperature.
Acta. zool. Fenn. **71** pp.1–102.

WINKLER, H., THEIL, S. and GOETZE, E. (1962) Effect of the addition of sodium and potassium and of peritoneal dialysis with hypotonic solutions of sodium chloride on the sodium and potassium content of the maternal and foetal sera and the amniotia fluid of rats.
Natur Lond. **194** pp.779–780.

WIRZ, H. (1953) Der osmotische Druck des Blutes in den Nieren-papillae.
Helv. physiol. acta. **11** pp.20–29.

WIRZ, H. (1956) Der osmotische Druck in den corticalen Tubuli der Rattenniere.
Helv. physiol. acta. **14** pp.353–362.

WOLF, A. V. (1940) Paths of water exchange in the earthworm.
Physiol. Zoöl. **13** pp.294–308.

WOODHEAD, P. M. J. and WOODHEAD, A. D. (1959) The effects of low temperature on the physiology and distribution of the cod, *Gadus morhua* L., in the Barents Sea.
Proc. zool. Soc. London. **133** pp.181–199.

ZERAHN, K. (1956a) Oxygen consumption and active transport of sodium in the isolated and short-circuited frog skin.
Nature Lond. **177** pp.937–938.

ZERAHN, K. (1956b) Oxygen consumption and active sodium transport in the isolated short-circuited frog skin.
Acta physiol. scand. **36** pp.300–318.

AUTHOR INDEX

27*   405

28

SUBJECT INDEX